CALCIFIED TISSUE

STRUCTURAL, FUNCTIONAL AND METABOLIC ASPECTS

CALCIFIED TISSUE

Structural, Functional and Metabolic Aspects

Proceedings of the Eighth European Symposium on Calcified Tissues
28 March to 2 April 1971, Jerusalem, Israel

Edited by

J. MENCZEL, M.D.

Head, Department of Medicine, Shaare Zedek Hospital and Metabolic Unit for Bone Disease,
Hadassah University Hospital and Hebrew University–Hadassah Medical School, Jerusalem, Israel

and

A. HARELL, M.D.

Chairman, Department of Endocrinology and Director of Municipal Health Services,
Government–Municipal Medical Center, Ichilov Hospital and Head of Department of Endocrinology,
Faculty of Continuing Medical Education, Tel Aviv University, Tel Aviv, Israel

Academic Press   New York / London

CONTENTS

HORMONAL EFFECTS ON CALCIUM METABOLISM: CORTISONE, GROWTH HORMONE

CALCIUM TRANSPORT IN BIOLOGICAL SYSTEMS

BIOCHEMICAL AND BIOPHYSICAL ASPECTS OF CALCIFIED TISSUE

METABOLIC BONE DISEASES

HORMONAL EFFECTS ON CALCIUM METABOLISM: PARATHORMONE

HORMONAL REGULATION OF CYCLIC 3',5'-AMP IN SPECIFIC RECEPTOR TISSUES

BIOLOGICAL EFFECTS OF A SYNTHETIC N-TERMINAL TETRATRIACONTAPEPTIDE OF PARATHYROID HORMONE

G. D. AURBACH, R. MARCUS, J. HEERSCHE, S. MARX, H. NIALL, J. TREGEAR, H. T. KEUTMANN, L. J. DEFTOS and J. T. POTTS, Jr.

Section on Mineral Metabolism, NIAMD, National Institutes of Health, Bethesda, Maryland and Endocrine Unit, Massachusetts General Hospital, Boston, Massachusetts, USA

A large body of evidence gathered within the past three years indicates that the mechanism of action of parathyroid hormone is mediated by an increase in concentration of cyclic adenosine 3', 5'-monophosphate (3', 5'-AMP) in the kidney (1, 2) and bone (3), the two tissues recognized as the classical receptors for the action of the hormone. The effect of the hormone is brought about by direct activation of the enzyme adenyl cyclase in bone (4) and in the tubules of the renal cortex (5). One consequence of the increased concentration of cyclic AMP in the renal tubule is an increased rate of elaboration of cyclic 3', 5'-AMP into the urine.

Wells and Lloyd (6, 7), Rasmussen et al. (2, 8) and Russell (personal communication) have found that injections of either dibutyryl-cyclic-AMP or theophylline into parathyroid-ectomized rats mimic the physiologic actions of parathyroid hormone on blood calcium and urinary phosphate excretion. Vaes (9) and Raisz et al. (10) have also shown that dibutyryl-cyclic-AMP causes effects on bone *in vitro* that are similar to those produced by parathyroid hormone.

The amino acid sequence of bovine parathyroid hormone (Fig. 1) has recently been elucidated (11, 12). Earlier studies indicated that the active biologically important area of the molecule is contained within the first quarter to third of the polypeptide chain at the amino terminus. These findings suggested that it might be possible to synthesize a polypeptide representing an active fragment of the hormonal molecule. Synthesis of a peptide chain representing amino acids 1 to 34 at the amino terminus was accomplished by a solid phase

```
          5               10                15               20
H-Ala-Val-Ser-Glu-Ile-Gln-Phe-Met-His-Asn-Leu-Gly-Lys-His-Leu-Ser-Ser-Met-Glu-Arg-
          25              30                35               40
Val-Glu-Trp-Leu-Arg-Lys-Lys-Leu-Gln-Asp-Val-His-Asn-Phe-Val-Ala-Leu-Gly-Ala-Ser-
          45              50                55               60
Ile-Ala-Tyr-Arg-Asp-Gly-Ser-Ser-Gln-Arg-Pro-Arg-Lys-Lys-Glu-Asp-Asn-Val-Leu-Val-
          65              70                75               80
Glu-Ser-His-Gln-Lys-Ser-Leu-Gly-Glu-Ala-Asp-Lys-Ala-Asp-Val-Asp-Val-Leu-Ile-Lys-

Ala-Lys-Pro-Gln-OH
```

FIG. 1. Complete amino acid sequence of bovine parathyroid hormone.

method (13). The synthetic peptide shows qualitatively all of the known physiological effects of the native hormone. One mg of the synthetic product given i.v. to dogs caused a rise in blood calcium from 10.4 to 12.0 mg/100 ml. Bioassay *in vivo* with parathyroidectomized rats showed dose response curves parallel to that for the native molecule. Bioassay *in vitro*, based on activation of adenyl cyclase, indicated that the synthetic product was 25% as active as the native molecule on a molar basis and was twice as active as a corresponding fragment hydrolyzed from the native molecule. The synthetic product caused a rise in concentration of 3',5'-AMP in bone incubated *in vitro* and also induced a rapid increase in the rate of excretion of 3',5'-AMP as well as phosphate into the urine when given i.v. to a parathyroidectomized rat. Tests of immunological activity of the synthetic product and the natural fragments of corresponding size hydrolyzed from the native molecule showed identical response in the radioimmunoassay developed for parathyroid hormone. In the course of this work, a tridecapeptide representing amino acids 1 to 13 was also synthesized. This peptide was completely inactive biologically as well as immunologically.

These findings provide additional validation of the structure of the native hormone molecule at the amino terminus. Further, they indicate that the physiological effects of parathyroid hormone on both kidney and bone represent the action of the same limited region of the hormone molecule at the amino terminus. It is also implied that the receptor sites for the hormone in either tissue are very similar in nature.

REFERENCES

1. Melson GL, Chase LR and Aurbach GD. *Endocrinology* **86**: 511, 1970.
2. Rasmussen H and Tenenhouse A. *Proc Nat Acad Sci (USA)* **59**: 1364, 1968.
3. Chase LR and Aurbach GD. *J Biol Chem* **245**: 1520, 1970.
4. Chase LR, Fedak SA and Aurbach GD. *Endocrinology* **84**: 761, 1969.
5. Chase LR and Aurbach GD. *Science* **159**: 545, 1968.
6. Wells H and Lloyd W. *Endocrinology* **81**: 139, 1967.
7. Wells H and Lloyd W. *Endocrinology* **84**: 861, 1969.
8. Rasmussen H, Pechet M and Fast D. *J Clin Invest* **47**: 1843, 1968.
9. Vaes G. *Nature (London)* **219**: 939, 1968.
10. Raisz LG, Brand JS, Klein DC and Au WYW. in: Gual C and Ebling FJG (Eds), *Proc Third Int Cong Endocrinology.* Amsterdam, Excerpta Medica Foundation, 1969, p 696.
11. Niall H, Keutmann H, Sauer R, Hogan M, Dawson B, Aurbach G and Potts J Jr. *Hoppe Seyler Z Physiol Chem* (in press).
12. Brewer HB, Jr. *Proc Nat Acad Sci (USA)* (in press).
13. Potts JT Jr, Tregear GW, Keutmann HT, Niall HD, Sauer R, Deftos LJ, Dawson BF, Hogan ML and Aurbach, GD. *Proc Nat Acad Sci (USA)* (in press).

A PARATHYROID HORMONE-LIKE ACTION OF DIBUTYRYL CYCLIC AMP (DCA) ON EXPLANTED EMBRYONIC MOUSE RADIUS

II. The Effect of DCA and Parathyroid Hormone on the Linear Growth of the Radius

M. P. M. HERRMANN-ERLEE

Laboratory for Cell Biology and Histology, University of Leiden, The Netherlands

Recently it was found (1) that exogenous dibutyryl cyclic AMP (DCA) reproduced, to a greater or lesser extent, the morphological effects of parathyroid hormone (PTH) on 15-day-old embryonic mouse radii. In contrast to the action of PTH however, cultivation for

TABLE 1. *Effect of PTE and DCA on total length of cultivated embryonic mouse radii*

Substance	% increase	P
0.5 IU/ml PTE (5)	−8.5 ± 1.7	⟨ 0.001
0.15 mM DCA (11)	2.3 ± 1.7	ns
0.30 mM DCA (12)	1.8 ± 1.8	ns
0.60 mM DCA (10)	6.5 ± 1.8	⟨ 0.01

Values expressed as means ± SE. Number of determinations in parentheses. Cultivation period, 48 hr.

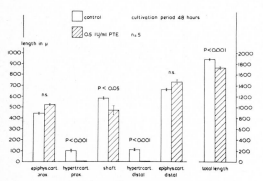

FIG. 1. The effect of PTE (0.5 IU/ml) on the linear growth of embryonic mouse radii.

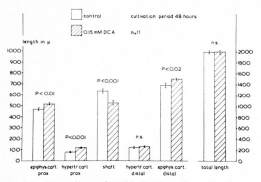

FIG. 2. The effect of DCA (0.15 mM) on the linear growth of embryonic mouse radii.

48 hr with DCA did not result in a shortening of the total length of the radius.

Table 1 shows that after cultivation with 0.15 and 0.30 mM DCA, no significant effect on the total length of the radii could be observed. To our surprise the total length even increased significantly when the radii were

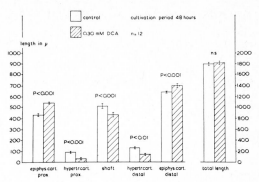

FIG. 3. The effect of DCA (0.30 mM) on the linear growth of embryonic mouse radii.

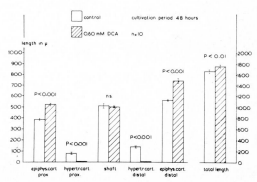

FIG. 4. The effect of DCA (0.60 mM) on the linear growth of embryonic mouse radii.

cultivated with 0.60 mM DCA. To study this obvious discrepancy between the effects of parathyroid extract (PTE) and DCA it was decided to measure the length of the shaft and the length of the epiphyseal and hypertrophic cartilage zones of both the proximal and distal epiphyses separately. The results of the measurements after application of PTE or DCA are shown in Fig. 1–4.

As a result it can be stated that the length of the shaft decreased after cultivation of the radii with 0.15 mM and 0.30 mM DCA (Fig. 2 and 3), as could also be shown for PTE (Fig. 1). This effect was not observed when the explants were cultivated with 0.60 mM DCA (Fig. 4). The length of the epiphyseal cartilage zones of both proximal and distal epiphyses, however, turned out to increase

11

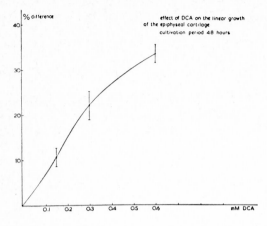

FIG. 5. The effect of different concentrations of DCA on the linear growth of the epiphyseal cartilage.

after cultivation of the radii with PTE and DCA. The combined values for the percentage increase in linear growth of the proximal and distal epiphyseal cartilage zones were plotted against the DCA concentrations in Fig. 5. The percentage increase in linear growth of this cartilage zone after cultivation of the radii with 0.15 IU/ml PTE amounted to 13.1 ± 3.3. A maximum value of 18.5 ± 2.5 was reached when higher PTE concentrations (2 and 10 IU/ml) were used (P. J. Gaillard, personal communication).

In contrast to the increase in length of the epiphyseal cartilage, the zone of hypertrophic cartilage cells completely disappeared with 0.5 IU/ml PTE and 0.60 mM DCA, remained partially with 0.30 mM DCA and was slightly increased with 0.15 mM DCA. From these and other results (Herrmann-Erlee, 1970) it became apparent that DCA has different effects on the different cell species composing the embryonic mouse radius. Since it is known that PTH increases the cyclic AMP content of embryonic bone cells (Chase and Aurbach, 1970; Herrmann-Erlee, 1970), it was interesting to know if PTE would also increase the cyclic AMP content of epiphyseal cartilage cells. In a preliminary experiment we were able to demonstrate that after an incubation period of 10 min at 37 C, IU/ml PTE caused a three- to 30-fold increase in the cyclic AMP content of epiphyseal cartilage cells derived from the radii, ulnae and humeri of 15-day-old mouse embryos. This finding would suggest that the action of PTE on epiphyseal cartilage cells, although quite different from that on the shaft, is also mediated by cyclic AMP.

REFERENCES

1. HERRMANN-ERLEE MPM. *Calcif Tissue Res* **4**: (suppl) 70, 1970.
2. CHASE LR and AURBACH GD. *J Biol Chem* **245**: 1,520, 1970.
3. HERRMANN-ERLEE MPM and KONIJN TM. *Nature (London)* **227**: 177, 1970.

MODE OF ACTION OF DIBUTYRYL CYCLIC AMP ON BONE

J. N. M. HEERSCHE and G. D. AURBACH

Section on Mineral Metabolism, NIAMD, National Institutes of Health, Bethesda, Maryland, USA

It has been established that adenosine $3',5'$-monophosphate ($3',5'$-AMP) is the intracellular mediator of the action of parathyroid hormone (PTH) on the receptor tissues, bone and kidney (1–3). The $N^6O^{2'}$-dibutyryl derivative of $3',5'$-AMP (DBcAMP) causes effects *in vivo* (4) or *in vitro* (5, 6) similar to those recognized as physiological responses to the hormone. DBcAMP is effective even when exogenous $3',5'$-AMP itself has little if any activity. It is generally assumed that DBcAMP is more active in those instances because it passes biological membranes more readily than 3′,5′-AMP and is more resistant to the action of 3′,5′-nucleotide phosphodiesterase. There is no experimental evidence for the first assumption, but it has been found (7, 8) that phosphodiesterase from liver or adipocytes does not degrade DBcAMP. Other observations (9) indicate that DBcAMP exerts its biological action in isolated adipocytes without undergoing hydrolysis of either butyryl group.

We have recently found that DBcAMP added *in vitro* causes a rise in concentration of 3′,5′-AMP in bone. Klein and Berg (10) found that DBcAMP inhibited cyclic nucleotide phosphodiesterase in the pineal. The work reported here indicates that the effects of DBcAMP on bone are effected through a rise in endogenous concentration of 3′,5′-AMP in the tissue consequent to inhibition of phosphodiesterase within the cell.

Calvaria from 18- to 20-day-old rat embryos were incubated for 15 min under conditions described previously (3) with 0.3 and 0.6 mM DBcAMP. The results show a three- to five-fold increase over control values in the concentration of 3′,5′-AMP in the tissue. Incubation with H³-DBcAMP [$N^6O^{2′}$-dibutyryl adenosine-H³ (G) 3′,5′-cyclic phosphate, New England Nuclear, lot no. 481-250, specific activity 3.5 c/mM] demonstrated no detectable hydrolysis of H³-DBcAMP to H³-3′,5′-AMP or H³-5′-AMP during the 15 min incubation. In addition, we investigated the possibility that DBcAMP was a substrate for phosphodiesterase. There was no significant breakdown of H³-DBcAMP after incubation for up to 30 min with phosphodiesterase purified from bovine heart, as described previously (11). Phosphodiesterase in fetal calvaria was assayed by the method reported

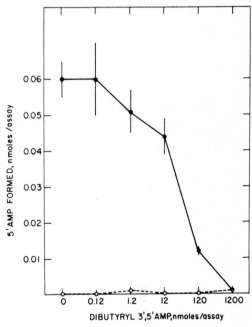

FIG. 2. Effect of DBcAMP on the formation of 5′-AMP in an assay mixture containing 0.06 nmole of 3′, 5′-AMP and varying amounts of DBcAMP. Total volume of the test mixture was 40 µl; thus 1 nmole of DBcAMP corresponds to 0.025 mM. Results are indicated as the mean ±SE, based on four determinations.¹ Control reactions (without phosphodiesterase are the mean of duplicate determinations. ●—●) complete test mixture; O—O: test mixture without: phosphodiesterase.

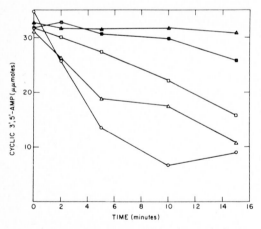

FIG. 1. Phosphodiesterase activity in crude homogenates from fetal rat calvaria. For control reactions the homogenate was boiled for 15 min prior to assay for phosphodiesterase. DBcAMP was added to the given concentration. ▲—▲ : + boiled enzyme; O—O: no additions; △—△ : DBcAMP 0.12 mM; □—□: DBcAMP 1.2 mM; ■—■: DBcAMP 12 mM. Results represent the mean of duplicate determinations. Each test mixture contained 200 µg of protein.

earlier (2), using H^3-cyclic AMP (Schwarz Bio-Research, specific activity 16.3 c/mM) as the substrate and measuring disappearance of radioactivity from solution after precipitation of the 5'-AMP formed with zinc sulfate and barium hydroxide. The results represented in Fig. 1 show that increasing concentrations of DBcAMP caused progressive inhibition of phosphodiesterase. DBcAMP also caused inhibition of the purified heart phosphodiesterase (Fig. 2). This was determined by using the assay method for 3',5'-AMP developed by Aurbach and Houston (9). In this assay 3',5'-AMP is converted by purified heart phosphodiesterase to 5'-AMP and the latter is detected by enzymatic conversion to ATP. The ATP formed is determined by a radioactive phosphate exchange reaction. As illustrated in Fig. 2, increased concentrations of DBcAMP reduced formation of 5'-AMP, indicating inhibition of phosphodiesterase by DBcAMP.

It is concluded that the biological action of DBcAMP on bone is effected by inhibiting intracellular phosphodiesterase activity and a consequent increase in concentration of endogenous 3',5'-AMP. The possibility that DBcAMP itself has an effect cannot be excluded.

REFERENCES

1. CHASE LR and AURBACH GD. *Science* **159**: 545, 1968.
2. CHASE LR, FEDAK SA and AURBACH GD. *Endocrinology* **84**: 761, 1969.
3. CHASE LR and AURBACH GD. *J Biol Chem* **245**: 1520, 1970.
4. WELLS H and LLOYD W. *Endocrinology* **84**: 861, 1969.
5. RAISZ LG, BRAND JS, KLEIN DC and AU, WYW. in: Gual C and Ebling FJG (Eds), *Proc Third Int Cong Endocrinology*, Amsterdam, Excerpta Medica Foundation, 1969, p. 696.
6. VAES G. *Nature (London)* **219**: 939, 1968.
7. MENAHAN LA, HEPP KD and WIELAND O. *Europ J Biochem* **8**: 435, 1969.
8. HEPP KD, MENAHAN LA, WIELAND O and WILLIAMS RB. *Biochim Biophys Acta* **184**: 554, 1969.
9. BLECHER M, RO'ANE JT and FLYNN PO. *J Biol Chem* **245**: 1867, 1970.
10. KLEIN DC and BERG JR. *Adv Biochem Psychopharm* **3**: 241, 1970.
11. AURBACH GD and HOUSTON BA. *J Biol Chem* **243**: 5935, 1968.

OSTEOPOROSIS AND PARATHYROID GLANDS

STUDIES ON THE VOLUME AND THE ACTIVITY OF THE PARATHYROID GLANDS IN DISUSE BONE ATROPHY IN ADULT RATS

J. A. SEVASTIK and S. MATTSSON

Orthopedic Clinic, Umeå University, Umeå, Sweden

The pathomechanism of bone atrophy by disuse is not yet understood. It has been reported recently that parathyroidectomized, thyroidectomized and thyroparathyroidectomized dogs do not develop signs of bone atrophy after immobilization of one hind leg by a hip spica cast for three and 12 weeks. This was considered an indication that both the parathyroid and the thyroid glands are necessary for the development of immobilization osteoporosis (1).

The reaction of the parathyroid glands to bone atrophy induced in rats by immobilization of one hind leg by a plaster cast or by resection of the sciatic nerve was studied. Earlier observations in this laboratory had shown that treatment of rats as indicated above results in characteristic skeletal changes

TABLE 1. *The initial and final body weight and the parathyroid volume of the rats immobilized by plaster cast*

	Initial body wt (g)	Final body wt (g)	Total parathyroid volume (mm³)	Parathyroid volume/100 g body wt
Control rats				
No.	6	6	6	6
Mean	567.0	542.0	0.458	0.085
SD	9.0	9.0	0.034	0.007
Treated rats				
No.	6	6	6	6
Mean	538.0	589.0	0.337	0.087
SD	12.0	6.0	0.029	0.081
p^a	> 0.05	< 0.001	> 0.05	> 0.05

[a] Comparison between treated and control rats by the "t" test for non-paired experiments.

TABLE 2. *The cell nuclei "hits," nuclear diameters (D_1 and D_2) and serum calcium values of the rats immobilized by plaster cast*

	Nuclei "hits"	D_1 (μ)	D_2 (μ)	Serum calcium (mEq/liter)
Control rats				
No.	6	6	6	6
Mean	7.4	5.16	3.12	4.6
SD	0.12	0.02	0.06	0.06
Treated rats				
No.	6	6	6	5
Mean	7.7	4.82	3.03	5.1
SD	0.13	0.03	0.07	0.14
p^a	> 0.05	< 0.001	> 0.05	< 0.05

[a] See footnote, Table 1.

of localized bone atrophy in the immobilized leg. These changes reached maximal development at the end of the 12th and 16th weeks of treatment respectively, with a tendency to decrease later (J. A. Sevastikoglou et al., unpublished data). The following experiments were conducted for the purpose of the present study:

a) In six rats the right hind leg was immobilized by a plaster cast for four and one-half months. Another six untreated rats were used as controls.

b) In 18 rats the sciatic nerve was resected at the level of the right hip joint under ether anesthesia. Groups of four to five animals were sacrificed one, four, 12 and 24 weeks after surgery. One intact rat was sacrificed at each of these time-intervals and was used as a control. All animals were adult, 1-year-old male Sprague-Dawley rats and they were maintained on a common laboratory ration containing 1.40% calcium, 1.20% phosphorus and adequate amounts of vitamin D.

For determinations of the volume and the activity of the parathyroid glands the methods described in detail elsewhere (2) were used; a) estimation of the volume of the glands by planimetry of projected serial sections of the specimens and computation of the data as total volume and volume/100 g body wt; b) counting of the cell nuclei "hits" in the

TABLE 3.   *The initial and final body weight and the parathyroid volume values of the rats treated by resection of the sciatic nerve*

	Initial body wt (g)	Final body wt (g)	Total parathyroid volume (mm³)	Parathyroid volume/100 g body wt
Control rats				
No.	4	4	4	4
Mean	632	584	0.627	0.109
SD	29	30	0.108	0.019
Treated rats				
1 week				
No.	5	5	5	5
Mean	623	585	0.371	0.062
SD	7	10	0.04	0.06
P	ns	ns	ns	ns
4 weeks				
No.	4	4	4	4
Mean	637	589	0.668	0.114
SD	13	16	0.07	0.12
P	ns	ns	ns	ns
12 weeks				
No.	5	5	5	5
Mean	572	511	0.267	0.053
SD	12	9	0.04	0.09
P	ns	ns	< 0.05	ns
16 weeks				
No.	4	4	4	4
Mean	611	561	1.163	0.021
SD	13	12	0.08	0.18
P	ns	ns	ns	ns

Wilcoxon Mann Whitneys' non-parametric test (4) has been used.

TABLE 4.   *The cell nuclei "hits," nuclear diameters (D_1 and D_2) and serum calcium values treated by resection of the sciatic nerve*

	Nuclear "hits"	D_1 (µ)	D_2 (µ)	Serum calcium (mEq/liter)
Control rats				
No.	4	4	4	4
Mean	9.84	5.50	3.54	4.8
SD	0.401	0.097	0.08	0.16
Treated rats				
1 week				
No.	5	5	5	5
Mean	10.47	5.25	3.56	5.2
SD	0.16	0.10	0.08	0.11
P	ns	ns	ns	ns
4 weeks				
No.	4	4	4	4
Mean	10.32	5.56	3.83	5.3
SD	0.10	0.04	0.08	0.05
P	ns	ns	ns	ns
12 weeks				
No.	5	5	5	4
Mean	9.64	4.83	3.03	4.8
SD	0.15	0.10	0.05	0.16
P	ns	ns	< 0.01	ns
16 weeks				
No.	4	4	4	3
Mean	8.15	5.86	3.78	4.8
SD	0.07	0.03	0.05	0.12
P	ns	ns	ns	ns

See footnote, Table 3.

histological sections of the glands; c) measuring of two perpendicular diameters (D_1 and D_2) of the cell nuclei; d) serum calcium determinations by flame photometry. It has been stated that such studies indicate the functional activity of the parathyroids (3).

The results are shown in Tables 1–4. It was found that the volume of the parathyroids was not changed after prolonged immobilization by either method of one hind leg of the rats, with the exception of a significantly lower total gland volume 12 weeks after resection of the sciatic nerve. The frequency of the cell nuclei and their size did not show significant changes, except in one case where the D_1 cell diameter was significantly lower in the treated than in the control rats (Table 2). The serum calcium level of the rats immobilized by a plaster cast was significantly higher than the corresponding value of the control animals, but there were no significant differences regarding the serum calcium level

of the denervated rats as compared to the controls.

These results indicate that inactivity of one leg of the adult rat, either by immobilization with a plaster cast or resection of the sciatic nerve, does not influence the volume or activity of the parathyroid gland. Some significant differences observed in this material point to inhibited activity of the glands during immobilization. These observations seem to indicate further that the extensive bone atrophy induced by these treatments is due to local factors and not to central influences through the parathyroids as suggested previously (1).

REFERENCES

1. BUCKHART JM and JOWSEY J. *Endocrinology* **81**: 1053, 1967.
2. LARSSON S-E and SEVASTIKOGLOU JA. In press.
3. ENGFELDT B. *Acta Endocr* (Kobenhavn) Suppl. **4**: 1950.
4. LINDGREN S. "Statistical theory." New York McMillan Co., 1966.

FETAL CALCEMIA AND FETAL PARATHYROIDS

J. M. GAREL

Laboratory of Comparative Physiology, Faculty of Sciences, Paris, France

Previous experiments have shown that in rat fetuses removal of the thyroid and parathyroids by decapitation induces slight hypocalcemia (1). Selective ablation of the parathyroids with some thyroid tissue decreased the fetal plasma calcium but after unilateral parathyroidectomy the fetal calcemia did not change (2).

The purpose of this investigation was to study the effect of parathyroid extract (PTE) on normal or decapitated fetuses at $21\frac{1}{2}$ days of gestation and the effect of antibovine PTH serum injection in normal fetuses of the same age.

Fetal decapitation was performed according to the method of Jost (3) on day $18\frac{1}{2}$ o gestation, under ether anesthesia. On day $21\frac{1}{2}$ of gestation two or three fetuses in one uterine horn were injected with hormone or antihormone, and the same number of fetuses in the opposite horn were injected with the vehicle. The fetuses were excised one by one from the well-ventilated living mother and blood samples were immediately obtained from the individual fetuses by puncture in the armpit.

A dimunition of fetal calcemia of the order of 8 mg/liter ($P < 0.001$) was produced by fetal decapitation (thyroidectomized and thyro-

TABLE 1. *Fetal plasma calcium valves (mg/liter) at 21½ days of gestation, normal or decapitated on day 18½. Effect of a s.c. PTE injection (five units USP)*

Delay after injections (time)		Plasma calcium (mg/liter)		
		Fetuses		
		Normal	Decapitated	Mothers
0		125 ± 1.2 (48)	117 ± 1.0 (99)	111 ± 0.9 (43)
4	Control injection	132 ± 1.4 (17)	121 ± 1.6 (16)	109 ± 0.8 (15)
to	PTE	144 ± 1.4 (16)	141 ± 2.3 (20)	
6 hr	△Ca	+ 12^a	+ 20^a	

Mean ± SE. Number of animals in parentheses. ^{a} $P < 0.001$.

TABLE 2. *Fetal plasma calcium values and fetal plasma inorganic phosphorus values after s.c. injection of 50 μ antibovine PTH serum*

Delay after injections (time)	Calcium in mg/liter				Inorganic phosphorus in mg/liter			
		Fetuses on day 21½ of gestation				Fetuses on day 21½ of gestation		
	Mothers	AntiPTH serum	Control serum	Difference	Mothers	AntiPTH serum	Control serum	Difference
0	105±2.0 (6)	123 ± 0.9 (25)			58±2.2 (5)	108 ± 0.8 (39)		
1 hr	108 (3)	128 ± 1.7 (11)	135 ± 1.4 (12)	−7^a	52 (2)	120 ± 2.2 (11)	102 ± 2.0 (12)	+18^b
2 hr	114 (3)	129 ± 1.8 (12)	139 ± 1.2 (12)	−10^b	80 (3)	118 ± 3.3 (12)	117 ± 3.9 (12)	+1^c
4 hr	105 (2)	126 ± 2.7 (6)	127 ± 3.9 (6)	−1^c	82 (2)	113 ± 2.0 (6)	116 ± 4.2 (6)	−3^c

Mean ± SE.   Number of animals in parentheses. ^{a} $P < 0.01$ ^{b} $P < 0.001$ ^{c} Not significant.

parathyroidectomized animals). Injection of five units of PTE in normal fetuses increased the fetal calcemia (ΔCa = +12 mg/liter). The same dose injected into decapitated fetuses raised the fetal calcemia by 20 mg/liter. This effect was more marked than in the normal fetus (Table 1). A similar reduction (−7 and −10 mg/liter) of the fetal calcemia resulted from injection of 50 μl antibovine PTH serum (pooled guinea pig antisera to partially purified parathyroid hormone). The fetal phosphatemia increased (+18 mg/liter after injection of this antiserum). These effects were faster than in adult rats (4) (Table 2).

These data provide evidence for a role of the fetal parathyroids in the control of fetal calcemia and phosphatemia.

PTH serum was kindly provided by Dr. G. Court, prepared at the Wellcome Research Laboratories in collaboration with Dr. J. L. H. O'Riordan of the Medical Research Council.

REFERENCES

1. PIC P, MANIEY J and JOST A. *CR Soc Biol* **159**: 1274, 1965.
2. PIC P. DSc Thesis, Paris, 1970.
3. JOST A. *CR Acad Sci [D] (Paris)* **225**: 322, 1947.
4. KOOH SW and FRASER D. in: Talmage RV and Belanger LF (Eds), "Parathyroid hormone and thyrocalcitonin." Amsterdam, Excerpta Medica Foundation, 1968, p 442.

A STUDY OF THE METABOLISM OF BONE IN A PERFUSION SYSTEM

THE RAPID EFFECT OF PARATHYROID HORMONE ON THE RATE OF LACTATE PRODUCTION

J. W. HEKKELMAN

Laboratory for Cell Biology and Histology, University of Leiden, Leiden, The Netherlands

In the course of an investigation into the regulation of enzyme activities present at the surface of bone cells the need was felt for a method to study these phenomena with intact living cells. A useful method (1) proved to be the incubation of bone tissue or cells in a continuously perfused vessel. The advantages of this method are obvious: a) the tissue is bathed in a medium of constant composition, irrespective of the incubation time; b) determination of surface bound enzyme activities and released metabolites can be performed directly and continuously; c) the time course of hormone induced metabolic phenomena is easily followed.

To study the sensitivity of embryonic rat calvaria to parathyroid hormone (PTH) in the perfusion system, the effect of parathyroid extract (PTE) on the rate of production of lactate was measured. The increase in lactate production is one of the best known and least controversial parameters (e.g. 2, 3) of the metabolic action of PTH. In addition, it is of great interest for our understanding of the interrelationships between the different PTH actions to obtain information concerning the lag time of the lactate response.

Materials and methods. Calvaria of 20-day-old rat fetuses were preincubated at 37 C for 1 hr in 15% human serum in Hank's salt solution after storage for 1 to 5 hr at 2 C. Immediately after preincubation two calvaria were placed in a basket rotating (60 rev/min) in an incubation vessel as will be described elsewhere. The vessel (contents 0.85 ml) was perfused (0.07 ml/min) with prewarmed and aerated Hank's salt solution of pH 8.2. After passage of the incubator, the medium was mixed with the reagents (0.10 ml/min; 0.02 M Tris, 0.02% albumin, 5 units/ml Worthington lactate dehydrogenase, 1 mM NAD$^+$, pH 7.0) and a glycine buffer (0.12 ml/min; 0.27 M glycine-NaOH, 0.08% Triton-X100, pH 9.7). The pumping velocities have to be determined for every series of experiments. The values given are averages to show the order of magnitude. The mixture was pumped (0.29 ml/min) through a coil with a passage time of 9 min in order to complete the oxidation of the lactate. Finely, the NADH formed was measured and recorded by a flow-through fluorometer (Technicon Fluorometer II). Before and after every experiment the instrument was calibrated with solutions containing respectively 0.04, 0.06, 0.08 and 0.10 µg/ml quinine sulfate in 0.1 N H_2SO_4. The lactate content of the medium was calculated from readings obtained by pumping solutions of known lactate concentrations through the system. The PTE (Eli Lilly), diluted with bidistilled water to a concentration of 40 units/ml, and the corresponding control solution, were pumped (0.014 ml/min) directly in the incubator vessel. At the start of the addition, 0.050 ml of the diluted extract or the control solution were pipetted into the incubation vessel in order to cause a sharp rise in hormone concentration. The additions were performed during a period of only 20 min because it had appeared that the hormone effect is irreversible within the time course of the experiments.

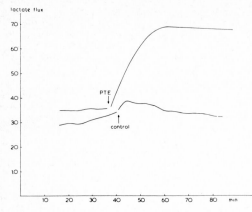

FIG. 1. Typical example of the lactate production by embryonic rat calvaria during incubation in a perfusion system. The lactate flux is expressed as nmole min^{-1} mg^{-1}.

Results. In Fig. 1 an example is given of a typical experiment. It appeared that the calvaria show a constant rate of lactate production which increases sharply after the addition of PTE (final concentration 8 IU/ml). The increase lasted for about 25 min when a constant flux again occurred. The lactate response appeared to start within a period of about 2 min. The values of the different parameters describing the hormonal effect on the lactate production are given in Table 1.

A further analysis of the start of the lactate response has resulted in the following preliminary data. The initial period of the effect as shown in Fig. 1 is in fact the result of two

factors: the increase of the lactate production due to the hormone and the subsequent increase of the lactate concentration in the incubation vessel dependent on its volume. The second factor can be visualized theoretically on the assumption that the effect of the hormone reaches its maximum immediately at the addition. In this case the increase in lactate flux as measured in the outflow of the incubator can be calculated according to:

$$F_t = F - (F-F_0)e^{-\frac{v}{V} \cdot t}$$

in which: F_0 is the initial constant lactate flux, F the constant maximal lactate flux after addition of the hormone, v the pumping velocity, V the volume of the incubation vessel and t the time. Substitution of the data given in Table 1 results in a graph almost identical with the experimental ones, as e.g. given in Fig. 1. On the supposition that this graph is linear for the first 10 min, it is possible to calculate the regression line and the initial slope. The values of this theoretical slope and the mean of the experimental ones are given in Table 2. It appeared that no significant difference exists which favors the view that the maximal hormone response occurs within a negligible period in the system used, probably a couple of seconds or less.

Discussion. Concerning the specificity of the observed phenoma it is of great impor-

TABLE 1. *Effect of PTE on the rate of lactate production by embryonic rat calvaria in a perfusion system*

	Control	PTE
Initial constant lactate flux nmole min^{-1} mg^{-1}	3.5 ± 0.2 (5)	3.9 ± 0.3 (5)
Constant lactate flux 20 to 30 min after additions nmole min^{-1} mg^{-1}	3.6 ± 0.2 (6)	7.7 ± 0.4 (3)
Percentage increase	3.5 ± 2.0 (5)	101.0 ± 16.0 (3)

Data are expressed as means $\pm$ SE. The number of experiments is given in parentheses. The results show an effect of the hormone on the flux of lactate which amounts to about 100% within a period of 20 to 30 min. A statistical analysis of the results appeared to be superfluous due to the magnitude of the effect.

TABLE 2. *The start of the increase in rate of lactate production by PTE*

	nmole min^{-2} mg^{-1}
Experimental initial slope	0.26 ± 0.05
Theoretical initial slope	0.21

The experimental slope is given as the mean ±SE of five experiments.

tance to extend this work by performing experiments with a range of lower concentrations of PTE and by the use of purified PTH.

Literature data (3) show that with the usual methods it is hardly possible to demonstrate the lactate response of PTE within a period of 30 min. The continuous perfusion technique used in the present work made it possible to demonstrate this effect within less than 2 min. This technique, however, is not suitable for investigations in the range of seconds or milliseconds. It would be very interesting to extend the study of the response time towards this range in order to obtain information concerning a possible relationship between the formation of cyclic AMP and the increased lactate production. A comparison of the present results with data in the literature concerning the effect of PTE on the concentration of cyclic AMP (4) suggests a difference in response time of maximally a few tens of seconds. A possible relation between the two phenomena is therefore probably a rather direct one, e.g. activation of an enzyme or transport system by phosphorylation. An indirect relation involving, for instance, protein synthesis is less probable.

The technical assistance of Mr. G. M. Bögemann is gratefully acknowledged.

Sponsored by the Institute of Radiopathology and Radiation Protection, Leiden.

REFERENCES

1. HEKKELMAN JW. *Calcif Tissue Res* **4** (Suppl): 73, 1970.
2. NEUMAN WF and DOWSE CM in: Greep RO and Talmage RV (Eds), "The parathyroids." Springfield Ill, CC Thomas 1961, p 310.
3. HEKKELMAN JW and HERRMANN-ERLEE MPM in: Talmage RV and Bélanger LF (Eds) "Parathyroid hormone and thyrocalcitonin." Amsterdam, Excepta Medica Foundation, 1968, p 273.
4. HERRMANN-ERLEE MPM and KONIJN TM *Nature (London)* **227**: 177, 1970.

SKELETAL UPTAKE OF H³-ESTRADIOL BY RATS PRIMED WITH NONRADIOACTIVE ESTROGEN AND PARATHYROID EXTRACT

J. J. B. ANDERSON and J. M. FLOECKHER

College of Veterinary Medicine, University of Illinois at Urbana-Champaign, Urbana, Illinois, USA

Several studies have indicated that estrogens may influence skeletal metabolism and, hence, calcium metabolism by inhibiting bone resorption or, alternatively, by stimulating bone accretion. Knowledge of the potentially significant role of estrogens on bone may not only be important to an understanding of postmenopausal osteoporosis, but may also be important in the elucidation of bovine parturient hypocalcemia for very different reasons. In the bovine syndrome it has been postulated that the surge in blood estrogen concentration just prior to paturition may inhibit the influence of parathyroid hormone at the level of bone, for it is now known from radioimmunoassay studies of Mayer and coworkers (1) that blood parathyroid hormone concentration is negatively correlated with blood calcium concentration in parturient cows.

21

TABLE 1.

Group	No. of rats	Treatment	Disintegration/min per mg wet femur wt $\pm$ SD	P
1	4	0.1 µg E_2 + 110 USP units PTE	2,230 $\pm$ 617	< 0.01
2	4	0.5 µg E_2 + 110 USP units PTE	2,208 $\pm$ 1,126	< 0.05
3	4	2.5 µg E_2 + 110 USP units PTE	2,713 $\pm$ 1,406	< 0.01
4	5	Control	1,285 $\pm$ 185	

The purpose of this study was to determine if treatment with both cold estradiol and parathyroid extract (PTE) for four successive days has an effect on the skeletal uptake of H^3-estradiol by mature rats. Preliminary investigations (2) had shown that radioactive estradiol uptake was near maximal at about 4 hr after s.c. injection using our injection medium. Nonradioactive estradiol (E_2) was administered for four consecutive days at three dose levels (0.1, 0.5 and 2.5 µg) in 0.2 ml of 50% ethanol. One hundred and ten USP units of PTE (Lily, courtesy of Dr. Joseph McGuire) in 0.5 ml of diluent were administered by the same route and at the same time but at a different site. One group of rats served as untreated controls. All rats (mean weight 170 g) received 6.06 µc of estradiol-2,4,6,7 T (New England Nuclear) in 0.2 ml 50% ethanol on the fifth day. The rats were killed 4 hr later, at which time both femurs were removed, rigorously cleaned of extraneous soft tissue, broken and placed in a 10% sodium EDTA (in 0.1 M PO_4 buffer at pH 7.0) solution for several days decalcification. Subsequently, the bone fragments were solublized in NCS™ (Nuclear-Chicago) for 16 hr at 37 C under moderate shaking and counted in the appropriate scintillation fluids. Mean skeletal uptake in disintegration/min per mg wet femur weight ($\pm$ 1 SD) per rat group is given in Table 1.

Priming with estrogen at the three dosages significantly increased the uptake of the subsequently injected radioactive estradiol by skeletal tissue, a so-called "non-target" tissue of this specific hormone, compared to unprimed control rats. Five- and 25-fold increments in the administered estrogen dose above a more nearly approximate physiologic dosage apparently had no greater effect than the physiologic dose on uptake of the label by the femur or in counteracting any resorptive effect on the mineralized tissue by PTE. The data obtained in this study are in agreement with an earlier experiment of the same type to the extent that the uptake differences between the primed and unprimed rats are comparable (2). However, in the present study the added treatment of PTE at the dosage used appeared to have no effect on the H^3-uptake by the femurs of the estrogen-primed rats. It is suggested that the estrogen priming may have influenced the metabolism of the bone cells so that they were not responsive to the action of a large dose of PTE.

In summary, the results indicate that the skeleton of the estrogen-primed rats is sensitized in such a way that it is more receptive to the subsequently injected H^3-estradiol than that of the nonprimed rats and that the uptake is not affected by a large dose of PTE which has a well-known resorptive function at the level of bone.

Supported in part by U.S.A.E.C. Grant AT(11–1)-1339.

REFERENCES

1. MAYER GP, RAMBERG CF JR and KRONFELD DS. Clin Orthop 62: 79, 1969.
2. ANDERSON JJB and FLOECKHER JM. Amer Zoologist 10: 494, 1970.

STIMULATION OF BONE RESORPTION BY PHOSPHORUS DEPRIVATION IN THE RAT

P. CUISINIER-GLEIZES, A. GEORGE, C. GIULIANO and H. MATHIEU

Unité de Recherches sur les Maladies du Métabolisme chez l'Enfant and Section de Pathologie Expérimentale, C.I.E., Paris, France

The effect of a low-P diet was studied in sham operated rats (SHAM), parathyroidectomized rats (PTX), thyro-parathyroidectomized rats injected with thyroxine (TPTX + T_4), and thyro-parathyroidectomized rats (TPTX). Two diets, were used: one with normal Ca and one with low Ca. For the normal-Ca and low-P diet bone resorption was measured by the changes in serum and urinary Ca, urinary hydroxyproline, and plasma Sr^{85} : tibial Sr^{85} and urinary Sr^{85} : tibial Sr^{85} ratios. In addition, the net intestinal Ca absorption was determined. For the low-Ca and low-P diet, bone resorption was measured only by the changes in serum and urinary Ca, and urinary hydroxyproline.

In the four groups, within five days of the normal-Ca and low-P diet, all parameters increased except the net intestinal Ca absorption which did not change significantly. Only urinary OH-P did not rise in the SHAM group. Moreover this group showed lesser changes than the others. Among the latter, the most marked effects were seen in the TPTX + T_4 group. The low-Ca and low-P diet, was studied only in TPTX + T_4 rats. Like the normal Ca diet, it induced an increase of serum and urinary Ca, and urinary OH-P.

These data suggest that 1) the low-P diet results in an immediate increase of bone resorption; 2) this effect is not mediated by the thyro-parathyroid glands; 3) the presence of the thyro-parathyroid glands seems partly to have a protective action not provided by thyroxine.

A second experiment was carried out to study the action of imidazole on the hypercalcemia induced by the low-Ca and low-P diet in TPTX + T_4 rats. Imidazole was injected s.c., 30 mg/100 g body wt. It resulted in a decrease of serum Ca 2 and 4 hr later. This action demonstrates the capacity of imidazole to inhibit the effect of P deprivation.

DENTAL CHANGES IN PARATHYROIDECTOMIZED AND THYRO-PARATHYROIDECTOMIZED RATS

MARCELA PITIŞ, Al. M. D. SERBAN and ADINA NEGREA

C. I. Parhon Institute of Endocrinology, Academy of Medical Sciences, Bucarest, Romania

Dentin calcification in parathyroidectomized (PTX) and thyro-parathyroidectomized (TPTX) young rats was studied. The experiments were performed on young rats from nine families that were operated on at the age of 24 days and killed 48 days later. The well-known slow growth of TPTX animals compared to the PTX intact controls of the same breed, and the high rate of postoperative mortality, especially among males, of PTX animals, as compared to TPTX animals were observed in this study.

The X-ray and histologic examination of the incisors of 28 animals (12 controls, 16 operated) showed significant differences in the calcification of the dentin. With PTX rats the alterations involved the whole predentin area, the predentin area being increased due to the corresponding noncalcification; there were also granular calcification areas with interglobular spaces and sometimes disorders in the odontoblastic layers. The enamel showed moderate hypoplasia and the ameloblastic layer had a normal aspect. In TPTX animals, except some cases that showed delays in calcification, especially at the crown levels, no important differences were encountered as compared with the controls.

The differences in the calcification of the dentin in PTX and TPTX animals suggest that the presence of the thyroid has an aggravating role; however, the mechanism to which this is due is difficult to specify. It is possible that the presence of abundant thyrocalcitonin blood calcium in rats interferes by decreasing the blood calcium values—a fact that may explain the high death rate of PTX animals compared to TPTX animals.

GLYCOSAMINOGLYCAN SECRETION
BY FETAL CARTILAGE CELLS *IN VITRO*

EFFECT OF PARATHYROID HORMONE

T. J. MARTIN, G. S. HARRIS and R. A. MELICK

University of Melbourne Department of Medicine,
Austin and Royal Melbourne Hospitals, Heidelberg, Victoria, Australia

Monolayer cultures have been established from the distal femoral epiphyses of fetal calves, and the secretions of the cells studied following incubation with C^{14}-glucose. Gel filtration on Sephadex G-200 of radioactive media resulted in two peaks of radioactivity, one emerging with the macroglobulins, the other with the albumin fraction of serum. Seventy percent of the radioactivity of the macromolecular peak was found to be contained in molecules which were degraded by bacterial hyaluronidase, whereas virtually all the radioactivity was recovered in low molecular weight components after digestion with testicular hyaluronidase. Macromolecular peak radioactivity was completely precipitated by cetyl trimethylammonium bromide, partly precipitated in the presence of 0.35 M potassium chloride, and eluted off DEAE Sephadex as a major peak with 2.0 M sodium chloride. It is concluded that the cells synthesize and secrete a mixture of sulfated (70%) and nonsulfated glycosaminoglycans (GAG). These studies were carried out on the media. The cell coat (trypsin supernatant) contained 15 to 25% of the GAG produced by the cells.

In previous experiments using such cultures, porcine calcitonin was found to stimulate C^{14}-glucose incorporation into medium GAG after 18 to 24 hr incubation (1). In the present work a pre-incubation period of 3 hr has been used before addition of isotope, and shorter incubation times have been used (usually 4 hr). The effect of parathyroid hormone (PTH) on C^{14}-glucose incorporation into GAG has been studied under these conditions, and compared with the effect of calcitonin. Highly purified bovine PTH (2 µg/ml) had a marked stimulatory effect on C^{14}-GAG

TABLE 1. *Effects of PTH and calcitonin on C^{14}-GAG synthesis (count/min)*

	Control	PTH (2 μg/ml)	α-TCT (3 μg/ml)
Medium	645 ± 88 (6)	1634 ± 108 (6)	820 ± 41 (6)
Cell coat	149 ± 25	793 ± 140	208 ± 13
P		⟨ 0.001	⟨ 0.1

Figures in parentheses indicate the number of experiments performed.

TABLE 2. *Effect of actinomycin D on response to PTH of medium $C\text{-}^{14}GAG$ (count/min)*

	Control	PTH (2 μg/ml)	P
− Actinomycin D	1150 ± 116 (5)	2639 ± 174 (5)	⟨ 0.001
+ Actinomycin D (2 μg/ml)	702 ± 121 (5)	992 ± 102 (5)	⟩ 0.2

Figures in parentheses indicate the number of experiments performed.

formation (Table 1), much greater than the effect of synthetic porcine calcitonin (α-TCT, 3 μg/ml). This was found consistently in repeat experiments. The stimulatory effect of PTH was abolished by actinomycin D (Table 2) at a concentration which inhibited H^3-uridine incorporation into total RNA synthesis by 90%. Neither calcitonin nor PTH was found to have any effect on C^{14}-leucine or H^3-uridine incorporation into total intracellular protein or RNA synthesized by the cells under the same conditions.

Most evidence indicates that the protein-polysaccharide complex is assembled intracellularly, and that protein and polysaccharide synthesis occur in parallel. Our lack of evidence for PTH-directed increase in protein or RNA synthesis does not exclude the possibility that a specific protein or RNA might be induced, concerned in protein-polysaccharide formation. The potent cation-binding properties of the GAG together with this demonstration of the effect of PTH on their synthesis and release from embryonic epiphyseal cells suggests the possibility that these molecules may mediate some of the effects of parathyroid hormone on movements of calcium into and out of cells.

REFERENCES

1. MARTIN TJ, HARRIS GS, MELICK RA and FRASER JRE *Experientia* **25**: 375, 1969.

HORMONAL EFFECTS ON CALCIUM METABOLISM: CALCITONIN

THYROCALCITONIN, A NEW CHAPTER IN HUMAN PATHOLOGY

GÉRARD MILHAUD, CLAUDE CALMETTES, GÉRARD COUTRIS
and M. S. MOUKHTAR

Laboratory of Isotopes, Saint-Antoine, Faculty of Medicine Paris, France

The discovery of thyrocalcitonin (TCT) (1) as a hormone existing in man (2), has led to a reappraisal of thyroid pathology taking into account the presence of two endocrine cell types in the thyroid, the "T-cells," producing T_4 and analogues, and the "C-cells" producing TCT. Hyper- and hypofunction of the thyroid gland should refer specifically to one system or the other, as well as to their possible inter-relationship. We have measured TCT content and studied the pathology of T- and C-cells in defined thyroid disorders.

Hypercalcitonism was found in: a) medullary cancer of the thyroid, with amyloid stroma, in metastatic tissue and in blood (3, 4) (23 cases); b) trabecular cancer of the thyroid, rich in acid mucopolysaccharide (5); c) thyroidal metastasis of bronchial carcinoid (6); d) C-cell rich adenomas (3 cases) with diarrhea (unpublished results); e) Graves' disease treated with synthetic antithyroidal drugs (2 cases); f) hyperparathyroidism.

Eucalcitonism was detected in a) thyroiditis; b) Hashimoto's disease; c) Graves' disease; d) follicular carcinoma of the thyroid; e) papillary carcinoma of the thyroid.

Hypocalcitonism was observed in follicular and toxic adenomas (two cases).

Ectopic production of TCT was found in one case of intestinal carcinoid and in one case of bronchial carcinoid (unpublished results).

Thus the production of a polypeptide with TCT activity confirms the close histological and enzymological relationship between the C-cells and the enterochromaffin cells. Both types of cells belong to the APUD series of polypeptidic hormone-producing cells (7), originating probably from the neural crest (8). A large group of endocrine polypeptide cells which share several common characteristics were described by Pearse as APUD cells (7). The three most reliable characteristics are A, fluorogenic amine content; PU, amine precursor uptake; D, amino acid decarboxylase. Ectopic TCT production by other members of the series is likely.

REFERENCES

1. HIRSCH PF, VOELKEL EF and MUNSON PL. *Science* **146**: 412, 1964.
2. MILHAUD G, MOUKHTAR MS, BOURICHON J and PERAULT AM. *CR Acad Sci [D] (Paris)* **261**: 4513, 1965.
3. MILHAUD G, TUBIANA M, PARMENTIER C and COUTRIS G. *CR Acad Sci, [D] (Paris)* **266**: 608, 1968.
4. MILHAUD G, COUTRIS G and TUBIANA M. *Presse Med* **77**: 2129, 1969.
5. MILHAUD G, CALMETTES C, DREYFUS G and MOUKHTAR M S. *Experientia* **26**: 1381, 1970.
6. MILHAUD G, CALMETTES C, RAYMOND JP, BIGNON J, MOUKHTAR M S. *CR Acad Sci [D] Paris* **270**: 2195, 1970.
7. PEARSE AGE. *Proc Roy Soc Biol* **170**: 71, 1968.
8. PEARSE AGE. in: Taylor S (Ed), "Calcitonin 1969." London, W Heinemann Medical Books, 1970, p 125.

THE EFFECT OF CALCITONIN ON BONE CELLS IN YOUNG RATS

AN ELECTRON MICROSCOPIC STUDY

LUDWIG ZICHNER

Department of Pathology, University of Zurich, Switzerland

Calcitonin is secreted by the C-cells of the thyroid (1) and was found to be an antagonist of parathormone (2). Calcitonin produces hypocalcemia and hypophosphatemia in man and laboratory animals due to incorporation of calcium into the calcified and noncalcified matrix. The purpose of our experiments was to study the morphological changes of bone cells and bone matrix in response to calcitonin.

Methods. Fifty MRC munits porcine calcitonin with 16% gelatin were administered s.c. twice a day to four-week-old female Wistar rats (breed CFN) until they were killed at 12, 24 and 48 hr and one, two, three and four weeks, respectively. The rats were not parathyroidectomized and were given food and water ad lib.

The epiphysis and metaphysis of the tibia were fixed in 2.5% glutaraldehyde and buffered in sodium phosphate for 6 hr. They were then treated in 1% OsO_4 in s-Collidine, dehydrated and embedded in Epon and cut in ultrathin sections. The sections were stained with uranylacetate and lead citrate and examined by a Zeiss 9a electron microscope.

Results. In most of the papers on the effect of calcitonin on bone cells an inactivation of the osteoclasts is suggested. This can be shown by electron microscopy. Osteoclasts of the control rats (Fig. 1) show, besides the characteristic richness of nuclei and mitochondria, an abundantly folded membrane of cytoplasm, the so-called brush border (Fig. 1b). This brush-border is lacking in the osteoclasts of calcitonin-treated rats. Their membrane-surface is smooth (Fig. 2). Often the osteoclasts lie separated from the bone wall, and the bone surface is without signs of bone resorption, namely without lacunae and dissolved Ca-apatite-crystals.

Osteoblasts, normally cuboidal to longitudinal cells limiting the bone (Fig. 3), lie in one layer on a well-defined zone of osteoid. After calcitonin administration they become multiform and some resemble osteoprogenitor cells with their light cytoplasm (Fig. 4a). In some places they lie in two or three layers (Fig. 4b). Like the osteocytes they show a modified form of calcifying of the collagen fibers.

The osteocytes show biphasic behavior. During the first phase of calcitonin treatment one can see an enlarged zone of demarcation (Fig. 5). The areas of nucleation are large and of star-shaped structure and almost reach the cytoplasm. Some Ca-apatite-crystals are seen in the cytoplasm (Fig. 5b); they represent a picture of intracellular crystallization of Ca-apatite.

On the other hand, the older osteocytes (Fig. 6) in the thick calcified bone show a very different picture about one to two weeks after calcitonin injection. The rough endoplasmic reticulum is rarified and the cell surface is richly folded. It reaches the calcified matrix which obtains a reversed image of the cytoplasmic folds. Between the folds lie loose Ca-apatite-crystals. After being incorporated they accumulate in cell vesicles and mitochondria. These osteocytes show "osteoclastic activity."

Discussion. The appearance of inactive osteoclasts is not surprising. The loss of the brush-border and the retraction from the bone surface are signs of inactivity.

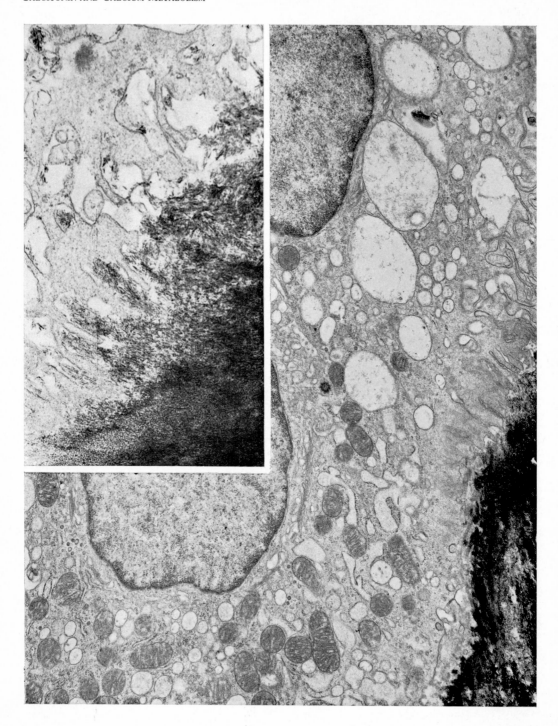

FIG. 1. Multinucleated osteoclast in the tibial metaphysis of a control rat with abundant mitochondria and rare endoplasmic reticulum. The cell surface is abundantly folded. × 9,300. In the inset a detail of the brush-border is seen. The cell folds have contact with the bone wall. Loose Ca-apatite-crystals lie between them and in cellular vesicles. × 18,000.

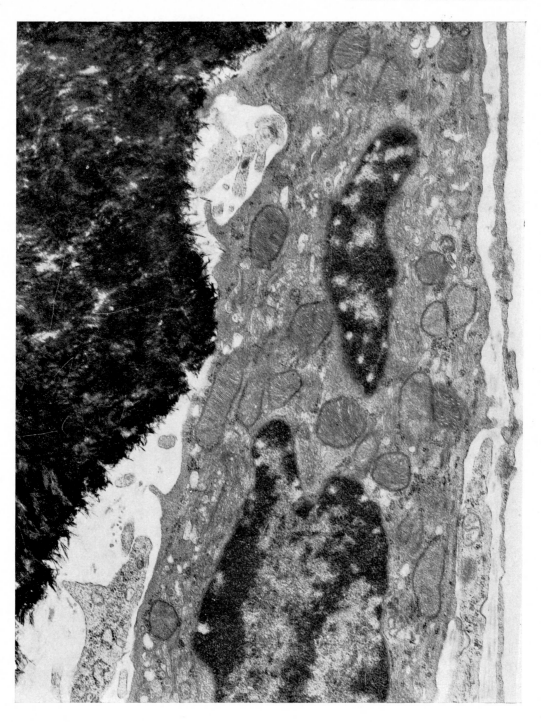

FIG. 2. Osteoclast of the tibial metaphysis after two weeks of calcitonin treatment: the cell surface is smooth, the bone wall shows no signs of resorption. A part of an osteoblast lies between osteoclast and bone wall. × 21,000.

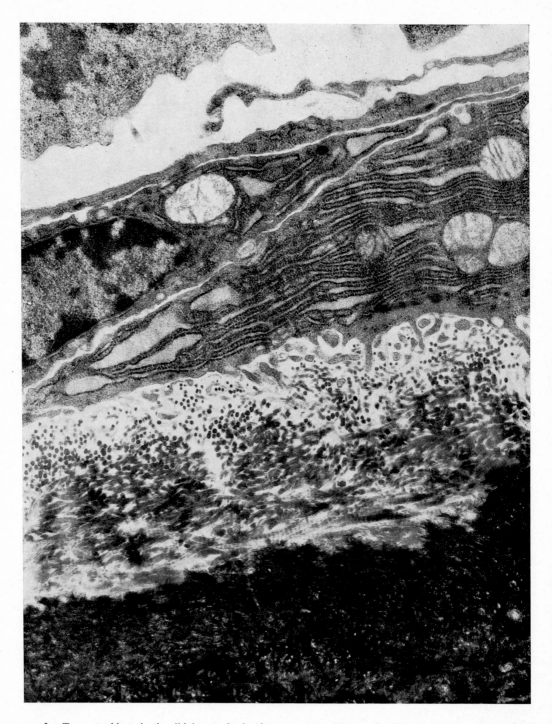

FIG. 3. Two osteoblasts in the tibial metaphysis of a control rat: Elongated cells with a circumscribed band of osteoid, zone of demarcation and calcified bone. × 14,000.

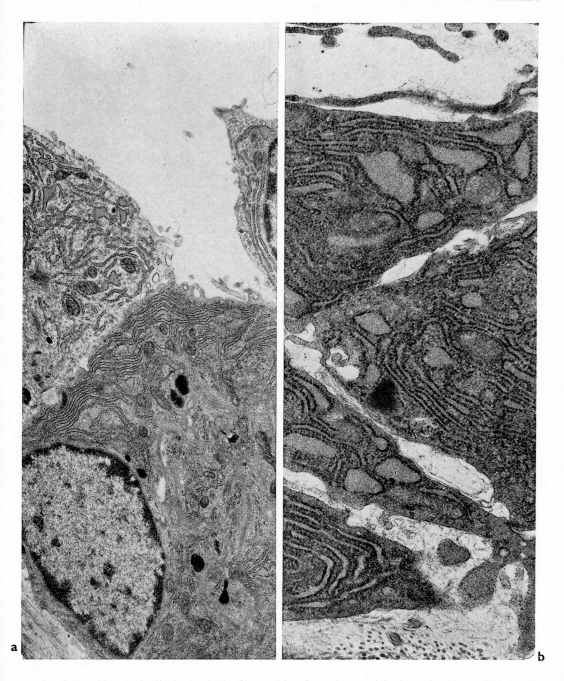

FIG. 4.   a) Osteoblasts in the tibial metaphysis of a rat 12 hr after calcitonin injection. The cell on the left side has a light cytoplasm, which is similar to that of the osteoprogenitor cell, as shown in the right upper corner × 8,700. b) Multilayered osteoblasts in the tibia metaphysis are shown after one week of calcitonin treatment. × 18,500.

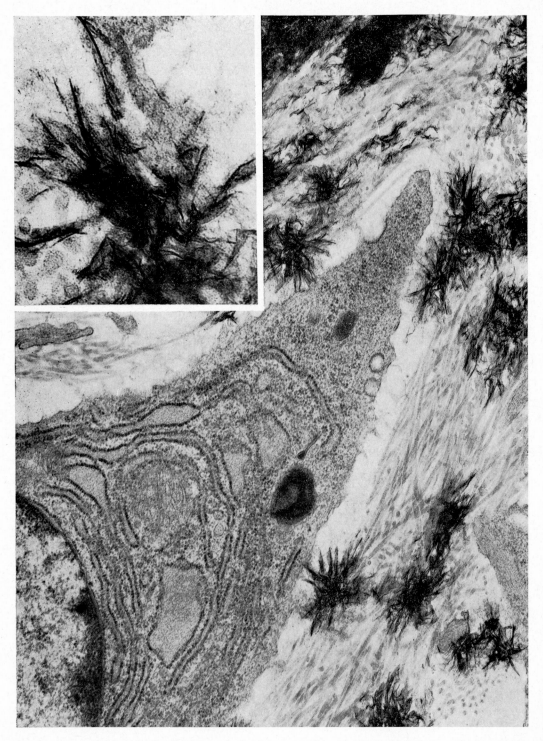

FIG. 5. Young osteocyte in the tibial metaphysis of a rat treated with calcitonin for one week: Ca-apatite-nucleation near the cell surface and in the cytoplasm. × 8,800. The inset shows Ca-apatite-crystals lying in cytoplasmic filopodia. × 70,450.

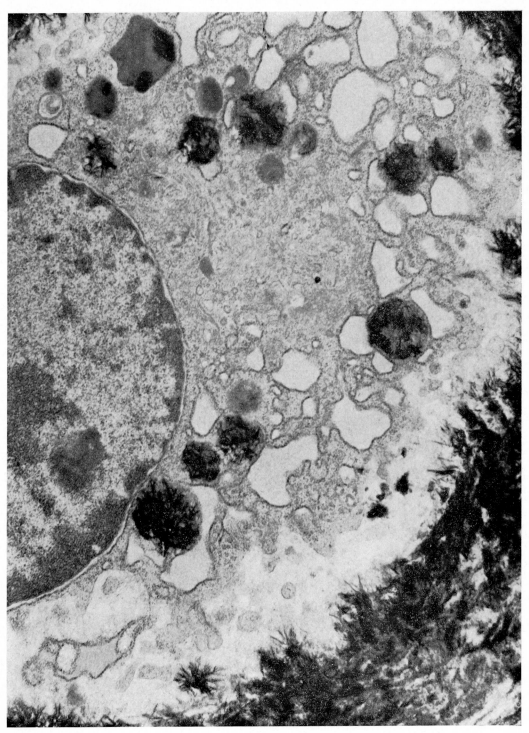

FIG. 6.   Old osteocyte with osteoclastic activity in the tibial metaphysis after calcitonin treatment for two weeks: the bone wall is rough, Ca-apatite-crystals lie between the abundant cell folds. After being incorporated in the cell, Ca-apatite-crystals accumulate in vesicles and mitochondria. $\times$ 11,500.

The behavior of the osteoblasts and osteocytes is striking. One can see two or three layers of osteoblasts and the interposition of osteoprogenitor-like cells. But the most important findings are the two kinds of activity of osteocytes in two following phases. The young osteocytes, just enclosed into the bone, are surrounded by an enlarged zone of demarcation, which closely reaches the cytoplasmic membrane. One can see, in addition, forms of intercellular Ca-apatite-crystallization. Here calcitonin diminishes and suppresses the protective zone of nucleation supported by the osteocytes. The normally present noncalcified band of osteoid is included in the zone of demarcation.

This dense and close calcification leads to micropetrosis, to an excessive mineralization of all remodeling surfaces. To prevent this Ca-impregnation a periosteocytic osteoclasia develops. This changed activity of the osteocytes is at that stage probably not the consequence of a secondary hyperparathyroidism.

REFERENCES

1. FORSTER GV, BAGHDIANTZ A, KUMAR MA, SLACK E, SOLIMAN HA and MACINTYRE I. *Nature (London)* **203**: 1303, 1964.
2. COPP DH, DAVIDSON AGF and CHENEY B. *Proc Can Fed Biol Soc* **4**: 17, 1961.

CALCITONIN IN HUMAN OSTEOPOROSIS

RESULTS OF PROLONGED ADMINISTRATION, ASSESSED BY METABOLIC BALANCE AND QUANTITATIVE HISTOLOGIC TECHNIQUES

M. A. DAMBACHER, A. J. OLAH, J. GUNCAGA, CH. LENTNER and H. G. HAAS

Division of Endocrinology and Metabolism, Departments of Medicine and Anatomy,
University of Basle, Switzerland

Fifty-day metabolic studies assessing the Ca, Mg, P and N balance as well as alkaline phosphatase activity and urinary hydroxyproline excretion were carried out on four women with idiopathic osteoporosis. After a ten-day base line period either synthetic porcine (three subjects) or synthetic human calcitonin (CT) (one patient), in doses of 0.5 mg/12 hr, was administered for 30 days and its effect was followed for ten additional days. Before and at the end of the CT-period iliac crest biopsies were taken and evaluated using morphometric (quantitative-histologic) methods.

A positive Ca and P balance was obtained in the youngest patient aged 28 years, but the remaining three subjects, aged over 50, did not show significant balance changes. However, urinary Ca increased in the older patients with a proportional fall of fecal Ca. An increase of hydroxyproline excretion was noted in the 28-year-old subject.

The paired bone biopsies revealed an increase of bone turnover in the 28-year-old patient, bone formation prevailing over bone resorption. The data of another patient were consistent with a slight increase of bone turnover, while in the remaining two subjects no definite CT-influence on bone remodeling could be detected.

These results emphasize the fact that a calcitonin influence on bone turn-over can be expected only in situations of relatively rapid bone remodelling. The observed increase of urinary Ca could be due either to a direct renal action of CT or to secondary parathyroid stimulation.

THE EFFECT OF CALCITONIN ON THE REGENERATION OF CIRCUMSCRIBED TIBIA DEFECTS AND ON MINERAL CONTENT OF BONE IN THE RAT

G. DELLING and W. GLUECKSELIG

Institute of Pathological Anatomy, University of Hamburg, Hambrug, German Federal Republic

The target organ of calcitonin is the skeletal system. The hormone causes hypocalcemia and hypophosphatemia by the inhibition of osteocytic osteolysis. In fracture healing the bone regeneration is accelerated by calcitonin. We attempted to study the influence of the hormone on circumscribed bone defects. There is no mechanical effect in this model. Certain physical properties of the femur were studied in addition.

Material and methods. We bored holes of 1.5 mm diameter in the tibial diaphysis of both hind legs of 120 Sprague-Dawley rats (body wt about 120 g). Four groups of 30 animals were used: intact controls, parathyroidectomized (PTX) controls, as well as intact rats treated with calcitonin, and PTX-rats treated with calcitonin. One hundred MRC munits calcitonin (extractive porcine calcitonin, CIBA Ltd., Basle) in 5% gelatin and acetate buffer pH 5.5 were injected s.c. daily. The control animals received the solvent vehicle alone. At weekly intervals five animals of each group were killed. All rats received, at the beginning of the experiment and 48 hr before the end, 1 mg tetracyclinehydrochloride/100 g body wt. The tibia and femur of each side were excised. Undecalcified cross sections of the bored diaphysis were stained with Goldner, periodic acid-Schiff-alcian blue, Kossa-methyl green-pyronine stains. The regeneration of the hole was measured by an integration eyepiece (Zeiss) and expressed as a percentage of the total area of the cortical defect of each histological cross section. In ultraviolet light (primary filter BG 12/4, barrier filter K 530) the tetracycline labeling showed exactly the margin of the defect and the newly-formed bone. In addition, we estimated the weight, volume, density, weight of bone matrix, ash weight and calcium content of the femur. The volume was calculated according to the Archimedes principle. Calcium content was determined by EDTA-titration.

The following observations were made: 1) Regeneration of bored holes: By calcitonin treatment the regeneration of the cortical defects was distinctly accelerated. Only in the calcitonin-treated groups did the formation of trabecular bone in the hole occur during the first week. In the second week the number of osteoclasts was reduced on the periosteal surface of the new-formed callus in the hormone-treated groups. After three weeks the percentage of the defect filled with bony callus in the intact controls was 45.9%, in PTX-controls 48.6%, in intact calcitonin-treated animals 76.2% and in the PTX calcitonin-treated animals 69.5%. After a period of six weeks the hole was substituted by newly formed bone in all four groups. The differences between the groups were smaller than in the third week (Table 1). 2) Physical pro-

TABLE 1. *Regeneration of the bored hole by bony callus as percentage of the total area of the defect (mean ±SD)*

Group	1st week	3rd week	4th week	6th week
Intact rats	—	45.9 ± 1.8	68.7 ± 1.4	89.7 ± 1.7
PTX rats	—	48.6 ± 1.9	62.4 ± 1.9	91.2 ± 2.1
Intact rats +calcitonin	9.2 ±1.4	76.2 ± 1.6	88.3 ± 1.8	98.5 ± 1.1
PTX rats +calcitonin	5.8 ±1.6	69.5 ± 1.5	79.5 ± 1.7	97.9 ± 1.4

perties of the femur: The hydrated density showed no obvious differences in the four groups. After a six-week period the values were: 1.46 ± 0.05 g/cm^3 in intact controls; 1.44 ± 0.06 in PTX controls; 1.48 ± 0.04 in calcitonin-treated rats; and 1.49 ± 0.05 in PTX calcitonin-treated rats. The dry density was slightly increased in the calcitonin-treated groups (intact controls 1.96 ± 0.03 g/cm^3, PTX controls 2.00 ± 0.04, intact calcitonin-treated rats 2.07 ± 0.06 and PTX calcitonin-treated rats 2.15 ± 0.06). The calcium content/100 mg bone matrix was 64.5 ± 0.2 mg in intact controls, 66.1 ± 0.3 mg in PTX controls, 71.3 ± 0.4 mg in intact calcitonin-treated rats, and 70.8 ± 0.4 mg in PTX calcitonin-treated rats.

Discussion. Under physiological conditions calcitonin inhibits osteocytic osteolysis (1). Baylink et al. (2) found a decreased rate of new formation of bone and of endosteal resorption under calcitonin treatment. The influence of the hormone on bone changes with high bone turnover is uncertain. In Paget's disease calcitonin causes a fall in urinary hydroxyproline excretion (3). Localized bone atrophy of an extremity remained unchanged in the dog (4) and in the rat (5) after prolonged calcitonin administration. In recent studies we observed an acceleration of fracture healing due to calcitonin in the rat (6). In experimental fracture healing many mechanical factors may influence the healing pattern. Pallasch (7) described the regeneration of circumscribed cortical defects by means of tetracycline labeling. In this model it seems to be possible to define the influence of drugs on bone healing processes. It can be assumed from the results obtained in our experiment that the osteoblastic activity is increased by calcitonin. This is expressed in the accelerated regeneration of the cortical defect under calcitonin treatment in intact and PTX rats. In addition, the acceleration may occur by the inhibition of osteoclastic resorption. In the final phase of the regeneration there is no great difference between treated and untreated animals. The slight changes in the physical properties of the femur show that the skeletal system is more or less unchanged after a period of six weeks of treatment with calcitonin. The increased dry density and the slightly increased calcium content per bone matrix might be an indication of increased bone mineralization.

REFERENCES

1. BELANGER LF and RASMUSSEN H. In: Talmage R V and Belanger LF (Eds) "Parathyroid hormone and thyrocalcitonin (calcitonin)." Amsterdam, Exerpta Medica, 1968, p 156.
2. BAYLINK D, MOREY E and RICH C. *Endocrinology* **84**: 261, 1969.
3. WOODHOUSE NYJ, REINER M, KALU DN, GALANTE L, LEESE B, FOSTER GV, JOPLIN GF and MACINTYRE I. in: "Calcitonin 1969." *Proc 2nd Int Symp London*, London, Heinemann, 1970, p 504.
4. CHIROFF RT and JOWSEY J. *J Bone Joint Surg* **52**A: 1138, 1970.
5. DELLING G, SCHAFER A and ZIEGLER R. in: "Calcitonin 1969." *Proc 2nd Int Symp London*. London, Heinemann, 1970, p 175.
6. DELLING G, SCHAFER A, SCHLEICHER HJ and ZIEGLER R. *Calcif Tissue Res* **6**: 143, 1970.
7. PALLASCH TJ. *Calcif Tissue Res* **2**: 334, 1968.

THE EFFECT OF THYROCALCITONIN ON CALCIUM UPTAKE BY ISOLATED BONE CELLS

I. BINDERMAN and A. HARELL

Department of Endocrinology, Hard Tissue Research Unit, Municipal-Government Medical Center, Ichilov Hospital, Tel Aviv, Israel

The great potency of thyrocalcitonin (TCT) as a hypocalcemic agent, and its release from the thyroid gland in response to hypercalcemia, suggest that it may be a hormone of importance in maintaining the blood calcium at a normal constant level (1). Hypocalcemia, in response to TCT, can be attributed to inhibition of bone resorption or enhancement of bone accretion. Most studies support the assumption of a direct effect of TCT on bone, but there is less definitive evidence regarding the mode of action.

Recent studies by Borle have shown that TCT had a direct effect on the uptake of calcium by cultured kidney cells (2). These findings correlate well with the conclusions of Rasmussen et al. that TCT directly influences the cellular exchange of calcium (3).

Using a method that was recently described by Hekkelman and Moskalewski for isolation of bone cells (4), we have shown that the "bone-cells" respond to TCT by accumulation of intracellular calcium. The effect of TCT on the calcium accumulation within the "bone-cells" is directly dependent upon the calcium concentration in the medium bathing the cells. of calcium is dependent on the calcium con-

Rodan (5), studying the physiological effects of TCT hormone on the plasma calcium level in hypercalcemic conditions of a perfused dog limb, came to the same conclusion and claimed that the fall in plasma calcium is probably due to an enhanced calcium accretion in the bone.

The lack of response by fibroblasts and fibrocytes under the same experimental conditions suggests that the action of TCT is probably a specific one, which affects only certain cells, the "bone-cells."

Increasing the calcium concentration in the medium without TCT did not influence the Ca-uptake by the "bone-cells" thus confirming the hypothesis that the enhancement of calcium uptake by "bone-cells" is an effect of TCT (Table 1).

The character of the correlation between the calcium concentration in the medium and the calcium uptake by the "bone-cells" under the influence of TCT seems to indicate an enzymatic-like mechanism (Fig. 1). The extrapolation of the curve (Fig. 1) towards zero shows that the influence of TCT on the uptake centration in the medium which has to be higher than 1.75 mM calcium (5).

TABLE 1. *The calcium uptake by isolated cells*

Calcium in the medium (mg/100 ml)	"Bone-cells"	"Bone-cells" + TCT	Fibrocytes	Fibrocytes + TCT
10	9.9 ± 0.01	9.1 ± 0.2 $P < 0.005$	9.9 ± 0.6	9.5 ± 0.2 n.s.
14	13.6 ± 0.2	11.7 ± 0.2 $P < 0.001$	12.8 ± 0.2	12.3 ± 0.2 n.s.
18	16.5 ± 0.8	11.1 ± 0.8 $P < 0.001$	13.6 ± 0.1	13.4 ± 0.1 n.s.

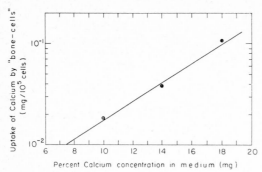

FIG. 1.　TCT effect on calcium up take by "bone-cells" at different calcium concentrations in medium

In recent studies on the protective mechanism of TCT, similar results were obtained by Rodan (5) and by Cooper et al. (6) in counteracting hypercalcemia. This observation may be the explanation for the difficulty

in measuring TCT-like activity in serum of patients with calcium levels under 1.75 mM calcium.

In summary, the "bone-cell" suspension system might be a versatile tool in studies of bone metabolism because it combines cellular integrity with an easier exposure at cell surfaces (7).

REFERENCES

1. HIRSCH PF and MUNSON PL. *Physiol Rev* **49**: 548, 1969.
2. BORLE AB. *Endocrinology* **85**: 194, 1970.
3. RASMUSSEN H, FEINBLATT J, NAGATA N and PECHETT M. *Fed Proc* **29**: 1190, 1970.
4. HEKKELMAN JW and MOSKALEWSKI S. *Exp Cell Res* **58**: 283, 1969.
5. RODAN GA. Ph.D. thesis, June 1970, Wezmann Institute, Rehovot.
6. COOPER CW, HIRSCH PF and MUNSON PL. *Endocrinology* **86**: 406, 1970.
7. MICHELAKIS AM, *Proc Soc Exp Biol Med* **135**: 13, 1970.

PLASMA CALCITONIN IN PRIMARY AND SECONDARY HYPERPARATHYROIDISM

G. F. MAZZUOLI, G. COEN, I. ANTONOZZI and L. BASCHIERI

1st Clinica Medica II, University of Rome and 1st Medicina del Lavoro, University of Pisa, Italy

Plasma calcitonin was determined in normal subjects, in six patients with primary hyperparathyroidism before and after i.v. calcium load and in five patients with chronic renal insufficiency. Determination of plasma calcitonin levels was repeated in four patients with primary hyperparathyroidism after correction of the hypercalcemia by surgery.

The extraction of plasma calcitonin was performed using the method of Gudmundsson et al. and the activity estimated by standardized biological assay method. In the normal subjects plasma calcitonin levels ranged from 154 to 300 MRC munits/liter, increasing to levels two to three times higher following i.v. calcium load.

In two of the six patients with primary hyperparathyroidism the calcitonin levels were above the normal values (381 and 560 MRC munits/liter). The other four cases had values within normal limits. After the i.v. calcium load a slight increase in plasma calcitonin was found. In all the hyperparathyroid patients the hormonal activity decreased to lower values following the removal of the parathyroid adenoma with correction of the hypercalcemia. The results suggest that in primary hyper-parathyroidism the functional reserve of the calcitonin secreting cells is decreased. The patients with normal plasma levels suggest the possibility of functional exhaustion of the C-cells.

In the pateints with chronic renal insufficiency, the calcitonin values were within normal limits, suggesting that the secretion rate of the hormone is independent of that of the parathormone, when blood calcium is within normal limits.

HORMONAL EFFECTS ON CALCIUM METABOLISM: CORTISONE, GROWTH HORMONE

CITRATE METABOLISM IN GROWTH CARTILAGE IN RICKETS AND FOLLOWING CORTISONE ADMINISTRATION

A. S. KUNIN and W. L. MEYER

Departments of Medicine and Biochemistry, University of Vermont College of Medicine, Burlington, Vermont, USA

Osseous tissue contains the ighest citrate content in the body (1). It has been speculated that citrate in bone regulates the size of apatite crystals (2). In the cell, citrate occupies a multifaceted position in its role in the Krebs cycle and ATP production, as a source of reducing power and acetyl groups for biochemical synthetic pathways, and as a controlling substance modulating the activity of certain key enzymes (3). It was thus of interest to investigate citrate oxidation and the enzymes concerned with citrate synthesis, *citrate synthase* (EC 4.1.3.7), and degradation, *isocitrate dehydrogenase* (EC 1.1.1.42), in growth cartilage in two model systems in the rat in which bone elongation is inhibited: in rickets, and that following cortisone administration.

Methods. Slices of tibial epiphyseal cartilage were obtained from rachitic or cortisone-treated rats and their respective normal controls as described previously (4, 5). Citrate oxidation by such slices was assayed as described elsewhere (6). Enzyme assays were performed on tissue slice homogenate supernatant and pellet fractions prepared as we have described (7) with the exception that NaCl was substituted for NaF in the extraction buffer. Citrate synthase was assayed by the method of Srere (8); values given are for the sum of pellet and supernatant fractions,

the latter accounting for about 75% of the total. Isocitrate dehydrogenase (IDH) activity, all of which appeared in the supernate, was measured spectrophotometrically at 340 nm using NADP and DL-isocitrate as substrates. No activity with NAD was detected. All activities were measured at 30 C and are expressed in terms of µmoles substrate converted/min (enzyme units, EU). DNA was determined in samples of the cartilage slice pools as has been described (5).

Results. Results of tissue slice incubations with 6-C^{14}-citrate and 1,5-C^{14}-citrate for

TABLE 1. *Production of $C^{14}O_2$ from 6-C^{14}-citrate and 1,5-C^{14}-citrate by slices of rat tibial epiphyseal cartilage*

Experimental group	$C^{14}O_2$ from	
	6-C^{14}-citrate (count/min per µg DNA)	1,5-C^{14}-citrate (count/min per µg DNA)
Normal	1,413 ± 123 (9)	307 ± 30 (9)
Cortisone-treated	674 ± 42 (8)	234 ± 37 (8)

Each flask contained cartilage slices (40 to 60 mg) from a pool derived from eight to 12 animals and approximately 830,000 count/min 6-C^{14}-citrate with a specific activity of 3.3×10^6 count/min per µmole, or 850,000 count/min 1,5-C^{14}-citrate with a specific activity of 4.6×10^6 count/min per µmole. Results are normalized to equal specific activities and are given as the mean ± 1 SE. Numbers in parentheses refer to the number of separate experiments performed.

TABLE 2. *Activity of citrate synthase and IDH in homogenates of rat tibial epiphyseal cartilage*

Experimental group	Citrate synthase	IDH (mEU/μg DNA)
NC	2.8 (4)	1.2 (4)
C	2.2 (4)	0.8 (4)
NR	3.3 (2)	1.4 (2)
R	2.7 (2)	1.4 (2)

Values are the averages obtained from analysis of pooled cartilage from the number of separate groups of experimental animals indicated in parentheses. C = cortisone-treated; NC = the corresponding normal controls; R = rachitic; NR = the corresponding normal controls.

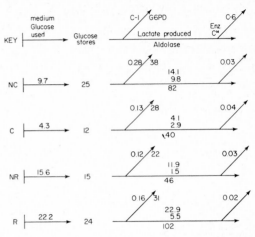

FIG. 1. Citrate metabolism by cartilage. Citrate synthase and IDH activities are given as nmoles substrate converted/hr per μg DNA. Citrate content is given as nmoles/μg DNA and is calculated from data of Ref. 6 and 9. Rates of CO_2 evolution from citrate labeled in the positions indicated in the key are given as nmoles/hr per μg DNA; the rachitic series values are calculated from Ref. 6. The value above the oblique arrow is the calculated difference between the citrate flux through the IDH step and the next step of the Krebs cycle. Abbreviations are defined in Table 2.

normal and cortisone-treated animals are given in Table 1. The administration of cortisone significantly rednced $C^{14}O_2$ formation from 6-C^{14}-citrate ($P < 0.01$). There was no significant effect of cortisone on $C^{14}O_2$ formation from 1,5-C^{14}-citrate. $C^{14}O_2$ formation from 6-C^{14}-citrate was greater both in the normal and cortisone-treated rats than that from 1,5-C^{14}-citrate. Enzyme activities found are given in Table 2. No significant differences were found in the rachitic series and the decreased activities in cortisone-treated samples were less marked than those found in the metabolic studies shown in Table 1.

Discussion. The above data combined with previous results are analytically portrayed in Fig. 1 and lead to the following conclusions: a) enzymatic capacity sufficient to turn over citrate stores in a matter of minutes is present in cartilage; b) nevertheless, the actual flux of citrate through the cartilage system observed *in vitro* is 0.5% or less of this capacity, and 10 hr or more would be required to turn over citrate stores; c) the high enzymatic capacity and general lack of correlation between citrate oxidation and IDH activity suggest that citrate utilization is controlled largely by metabolic factors as opposed to levels of enzyme present; d) the data for the cortisone series indicate that a significant portion of the citrate passing through the IDH step in an

hour does not proceed further around the Krebs cycle. This latter phenomenon may be only apparent due to 1) the existence of a pool of α-ketoglutarate sufficient to dilute significantly the labeled metabolite passing through or 2) a significant leakage of this metabolite from the cell, or it may result from a large alternative pathway for citrate in cartilage. An interesting possibility is that this other pathway is through α-ketoglutarate and L-glutamate to L-proline which would be incorporated into collagen, an important component of cartilage and bone. Cortisone treatment affects cartilage by either reducing the α-ketoglutarate pool or leak or both, or it leads to a much larger decrease in the alternate fate for citrate than in the Krebs cycle. The alternate, L-proline pathway for citrate is intriguing in the light of the relative insignificance of the Krebs cycle in cartilage (see

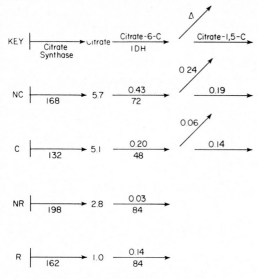

FIG. 2. Glucose metabolism by cartilage. *Aldolase* (EC 4.1.2.7) and G6PD (EC 1.1.1.49) activities are given as nmoles substrate converted/hr per μg DNA. Glucose stores are tissue free plus polymer bound glucose (mostly glycogen) given as nmoles glucose/μg DNA. Lactate produced is given as nmoles of glucose equivalents elaborated into medium/hr per μg DNA, the upper value based on enzymatically measured lactate and lower value calculated from labeled lactate produced from C^{14}-labeled glucose. Medium glucose used by cartilage slices is given as nmoles/hr per μg DNA. The extent of glucose contribution to the pentose phosphate pathway and Krebs cycle is indicated by the nmoles of labeled CO_2 which arose from C-1 labeled and C-6 labeled glucose, respectively. The values are calculated from the data of Ref. 4, 5, 7 and 11. Abbreviations are defined in Table 2.

below). The depression of the alternate pathway by cortisone treatment and the suggestion in the data (see also ref. 6) that it may be stimulated in rickets would be consistent with the loss and accumulation of matrix, respectively, in these circumstances (10; W. L. Meyer and A. S. Kunin, unpublished experiments).

The metabolism of citrate in cartilage may be better appreciated by contrast with that of glucose (Fig. 2). The contrast illustrates the well-documented heavy reliance of cartilage on anaerobic glycolysis for energy (see discussion and references in ref. 4 and 7). A number of features stand out: a) the larger glucose stores turn over in 1 to 3 hr; b) very little of the glucose used is oxidized through either the Krebs cycle or the pentose phosphate pathway; c) this is despite the fact that enzyme capacities such as IDH and glucose-6-phosphate dehydrogenase (G6PD) far exceed the flux through their pathways; d) these oxidative enzyme capacities rival those of the more rate-limiting enzymes of glycolysis such as aldolase (illustrated in Fig. 2) which latter only exceed the observed flux through the glycolytic pathway by four- to 10-fold. It is interesting that the low flux to capacity system, glycolysis, does appear to be governed in part by the varying level of enzymes present (4); compare the lactate produced to aldolase present shown in Fig. 2.

Besides the loose experimental ends remaining in the work discussed above, an important question is raised. Why are the oxidative enzyme capacities so high in the absence of any demonstrated use? Perhaps there are times in growth and calcification when these enzymes do process large amounts of their substrates which are, after all, present in cartilage. Does IDH contribute toward L-proline for collagen synthesis? Does G6PD contribute reducing power for collagen hydroxy-L-proline synthesis, for lipid synthesis important to calcification (12), or carbon chains for mucopolysaccharide and nucleic acid synthesis?

Supported by Grant AM-09632 from the N.I.H., USPHS.

REFERENCES

1. DICKENS F. *Biochem J* **35**: 1011, 1942.
2. KRANE SM, SHINE KI and PYLE MB. in: Greep RO and Talmage RV, "The parathyroids." Springfield Ill, Charles C Thomas 1961, p. 298.
3. SRERE PA. *Nature* (*London*) **205**: 766, 1965.
4. MEYER WL and KUNIN AS. *Arch Biochem* **129**: 438 1969.
5. KUNIN AS and MEYER WL. *Arch Biochem* **129**: 421, 1969.
6. KUNIN AS and KRANE SM. *Biochim Biophys Acta* **111**: 32, 1965.
7. MEYER WL and KUNIN AS. *Arch Biochem* **129**: 431, 1969.

8. PARVIN R. *Methods Enzymol* **13**: 16, 1969.
9. SIMMONS DJ and KUNIN AS. *Clin Orthop* **55**: 201, 1967.
10. RANG M. "The growth plate and its disorders." Baltimore, Williams and Wilkins, 1969.
11. KUNIN AS and KRANE SM. *Biochim Biophys Acta* **107**: 203, 1965.
12. IRVING JT and WUTHIER RE. *Clin Orthop* **56**: 237, 1968.

IN VITRO EFFECT OF OXYGEN, HYDROCORTISONE AND TRIIODOTHYRONINE ON CELLS OF MECKEL'S CARTILAGE

A. H. MELCHER

Faculty of Dentistry, University of Toronto, Toronto, Ontario, Canada

Meckel's cartilage, which is present in the mandibular process of the first branchial arch at the onset of ossification of the mandible, makes little contribution in the rat to the substance of the developing mandible posterior to the mental foramen, and disappears (1). Meckel's cartilage in 18-day *in utero* Connaught-strain mouse fetuses exhibits evidence of destruction in the vicinity of the mental foramen. The progressive destruction of the cartilage which accompanies further development results in two distinct fragments of the cartilage being present in the mandible: a proximal (or posterior fragment) and a distal (or anterior fragment). Chondrocytes of the proximal fragment lying posterior to the area of destruction are small and many of them exhibit pyknotic nuclei; more posterior still, the cells exhibit nuclei which are varyingly condensed and surrounded by scant cytoplasm (Fig. 1). Eleven days postpartum, no evidence of the proximal fragment can be found in the mandible. There appears to be little information on the factors which promote resorption of the proximal fragment of the cartilage. Many of the tissues in mandibles of 18-day *in utero* mouse fetuses can be maintained *in vitro* on a chemically defined medium for periods up to 14 days (2), and there is biochemical evidence that the cells of the explants are able to synthesize collagen (A. H. Melcher, R. Burgess and S. Kucey, unpublished observations). This *in vitro* system consequently offers a controlled environment in which the factors governing resorption of the posterior fragment of Meckel's cartilage could be investigated.

Explants were maintained in plastic Trowel-type culture dishes (Falcon plastics). The culture dishes were housed in gastight Plexiglass boxes and incubated at 38 C. The Plexiglass boxes were filled with appropriate mixtures of gases, the oxygen content of which was monitored with a Servomex oxygen analyzer. The

FIG. 1. Proximal fragment of Meckel's cartilage in the mandible of an 18-day *in utero* mouse. a) × 200. b) × 1,000.

FIG. 2. Proximal fragment of Meckel's cartilage in mandible cultured for 14 days on WFeA + 95% O. a) × 200. b) × 1,000.

FIG. 3. Proximal fragment of Meckel's cartilage in mandible cultured for 14 days on WFeAHc + 40% O. a) × 200. b) × 1,000.

FIG. 4. Proximal fragment of Meckel's cartilage in mandible cultured for 14 days on WFeAHcTt + 95% O. a) × 200. b) × 1,000.

FIG. 5. Radioautograph of proximal fragment of Meckel's cartilage in mandible cultured for 14 days in 95 O_2 and on WFeAHcTt to which 1.0 μc/ml H^3-thymidine had been added from ninth through 12th day.

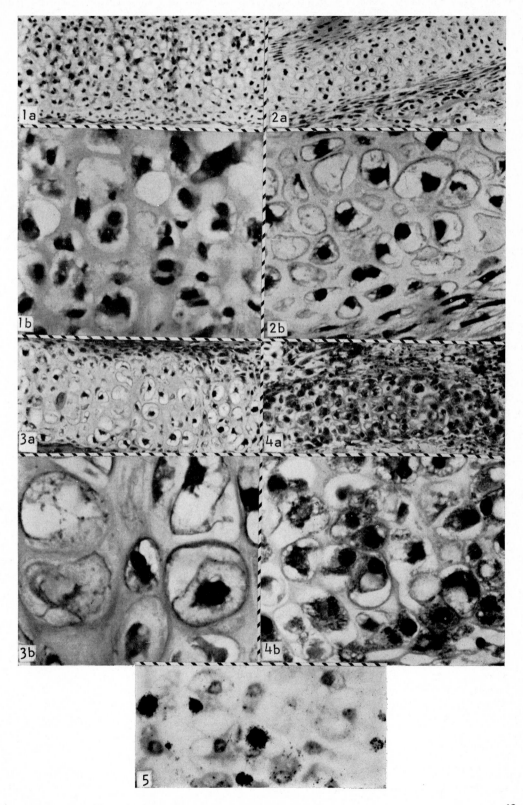

medium and gas mixture were changed every two or three days.

Explants were cultured on Waymouth's (3) 752/1 chemically defined medium supplemented with 0.45 µg/ml ferrous sulphate and 300 µg/ml ascorbic acid (WFeA), and in an atmosphere comprising 40% O_2, 5% CO_2 and 55% N_2, for a period of 14 days. This period of culture corresponds chronologically with the period of development of an 11-day post-partum mouse. Most of the proximal fragment of Meckel's cartilage was still present at the end of the period of culture. The nuclei of the chondrocytes were mostly pyknotic, and the extracellular substance largely intact. When cultured for the same period on the same medium, but in an atmosphere comprising 95% O_2 and 5% CO_2, the result was similar, although maintenance of the chondrocytes was improved (Fig. 2). Addition of 1.0 µg/ml hydrocortisone succinate to the medium (WFeAHc) led to a further improvement in the maintenance of the chondrocytes of the posterior fragment of Meckel's cartilage. After 14 days culture the nuclei tended to be more open-faced than those seen in similar situations at the time of explant, and the cytoplasm was more abundant and contained hematoxyphilic thread-like structures, and vesicles. Furthermore, there was evidence peripherally that the extracellular substance of the cartilage was being replaced by cells. These changes were evident when explants were maintained in 40% O_2 (Fig. 3), were more noticeable in 95% O_2, and were most marked when maintained in 95% O_2 and on medium to which 1.0 µg/ml triiodothyronine (WFeAHcTt) had also been added (Fig. 4). The areas of the cartilage in which hypertrophy of the chondrocytes had occurred were marked by a considerable reduction in extracellular substance, and this was well demonstrated in sections stained with alcian blue.

Radioautographs of explants which had been maintained for 14 days in an atmosphere of 95% O_2, and on WFeAHcTt to which 1.0 µc/ml medium H^3-thymidine had been added from the ninth through 12th day, showed that many of the cells in the hypertrophic area had been synthesizing DNA during that period (Fig. 5).

This investigation has shown that many chondrocytes, which at the time of explant may have been destined to die *in vivo*, can be maintained *in vitro*, be stimulated to hypertrophy, and be stimulated to synthesize DNA. The morphology of the cells and the surrounding extracellular substance suggests that the hypertrophic cells and the cells at the periphery of the cartilage may play some part in removing extracellular substance of the cartilage. Bhaskar et al. (1) have described replacement of the cartilage circumferentially by cells. However, as far as is known, no observation has been made indicating that the chondrocytes of the proximal fragment of Meckel's cartilage remove the surrounding extracellular substance *in vivo*. This possibility is currently being investigated. The changes that have been shown to occur *in vitro* appear to be controlled largely by hydrocortisone, and to have been intensified by increased oxygen tension and triiodothyronine. However, it is evident that a factor, which *in vivo* promotes complete removal of the cartilage, is absent from this system.

Supported by Grant MA-3803 of the Medical Research Council of Canada.

REFERENCES

1. BHASKAR SN, WEINMANN JP and SCHOUR I. *J Dent Res* **32**: 398, 1953.
2. MELCHER AH and HODGES GM. *Nature (Lond)* **219**: 307, 1958.
3. WAYMOUTH C. *J Nat Cancer Inst* **22**: 1003, 1959.

EFFECT OF GROWTH HORMONE ON
LONGITUDINAL BONE GROWTH IN HYPOPHYSECTOMIZED RATS

LARS INGVAR HANSSON and KARL-GÖRAN THORNGREN

Departments of Orthopaedic Surgery and of Histology, University of Lund, Sweden

It has been known for some time that the rate of longitudinal bone growth is reduced after hypophysectomy and that substitution with growth hormone increases this reduced growth rate.

The methods used earlier to determine the rate of longitudinal bone growth have, however, been unsatisfactory. In this investigation the growth rate was determined using tetracycline as a bone marker. This method has made it possible to determine with great accuracy the growth per day at different growth zones.

Young female rats (Sprague-Dawley) were hypophysectomized by the parapharyngeal route at different ages. The completeness of the operation was determined on microscopical sections. The growth rate from the proximal growth plate of the tibia was determined by means of nontoxic doses of oxytetracycline (TERRAMYCIN®). The longitudinal bone growth in animals at 40 days of age decreased rapidly during the first 10 days and then proceeded at a low rate. The accumulated growth after hypophysectomy was about 470 µ after four days and about 590 µ after 10 days compared to about 690 µ 40 days postoperatively. When the operation was performed at 60 days of age the total growth was lower, and growth almost ceased within 15 days after hypophysectomy.

The effect of bovine growth hormone (NIH-GH-B15) was investigated. The hormone was given to hypophysectomized female rats beginning 15 days postoperatively. The hypophysectomy was performed at 40 days of age. It was found that a highly significant increase in growth rate was achieved when the daily s.c. dose was as low as 5 µg for 10 days or longer. Administration of 100 and 400 µg daily for 20 days gave a total growth of about 1,370 and 1,670 µ, respectively, compared with a basal growth of about 200 µ in untreated animals. When 25 µg was given daily for periods of 10, 20 and 30 days there was a total growth of about 250, 750 and 1,500 µ, respectively. Thus the result was dependent on the dose and the length of the administration period.

This investigation is being continued and the purpose is to develop a bio-assay for growth hormone according to the principles given above.

BONE FORMATION BY INDUCTION UNDER THE INFLUENCE OF GROWTH HORMONE AND CORTISONE

ERKKI V. S. KOSKINEN, SOINI A. RYOPPY and T. SAM LINDHOLM

University of Helsinki, Finland

The main shortcoming of bank bone compared to autogenous bone—its inability to contribute directly to osteogenesis—would be compensated for if the ability of the implant to induce osteogenesis could be increased sufficiently (1). It has been demonstrated in previous studies, that an HCl-decalcified implant, placed in a heterotopic site, produces new bone by its contact with mesenchymal cells in the host bed (2, 3).

It has also been found in previous studies on fracture repair that somatotropic hormone (STH) combined with thyrotropin (TSH) exerts an accelerating and strengthening effect on the maturation of callus, and that cortisone delays the reparative process (4, 5).

The present study concerns hormonal effects on decalcified bone implants and observations of callus formation under the influence of the same hormones. Lyophilized, totally or superficially decalcified pieces of rat's cortical bone, 10 mm in length and implanted in muscle, were observed for one to 14 weeks under the influence of growth hormone, thyrotropin and cortisone. The following studies were made after various periods: radiological, histoquantitative line sampling, Ca^{45} autoradiography and measurements of radioactivity.

Results. Radiography: In totally decalcified implants, increased radiological density was observable three weeks after implantation. During the 14-week observation period, formation of new ossicle was seen. Stronger formation of calcified tissue was noted in the group with STH + TSH treatment than in the control and cortisone-treated groups. The difference between the groups is illustrated by the fact that the formation of calcified

tissue in the STH + TSH group at six weeks is equivalent to that at nine weeks in the controls. Ossicle formation was delayed in the cortisone-treated group.

The development was similar in the superficially decalcified implants, but only slight changes in density and structure of the grafts were noted at the early stage.

Histoquantitative examination: Analysis by line sampling (Fig. 1a,b) showed that STH and TSH, administered in combination, accelerated the maturation of fracture callus, especially at the early phase of repair, while cortisone retarded the reparative process. In totally decalcified implants, the hormones elicited effects resembling the above. However, as a result of the different character of new bone formation, the proportions of new bone and other tissue components were different, and the changes proceeded at a slow rate.

Formation of new bone was somewhat stronger under STH + TSH influence, and the proportion of other active components, such as hypertrophic mesenchyme, was higher. Under cortisone effect there was less new bone than in the controls, but intense cartilage formation occurred.

The old bone matrix, fairly equal in amount at the initial stage, decreased markedly in the STH + TSH group and less so in the controls, while the proportion of cavities increased. In the cortisone-treated group the diminution of old matrix was very slight, and cavities at the end of the observation period amounted to only half of those in the other two groups. This may be an indication of the immunosuppressive action of cortisone on the reaction between implant and host bed.

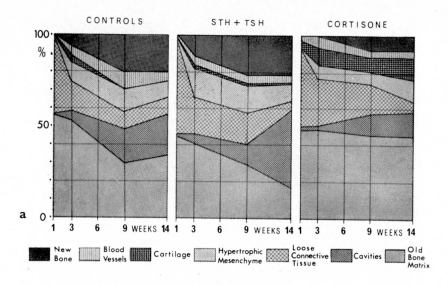

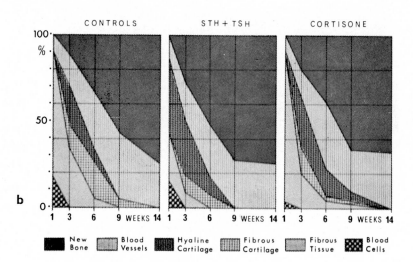

FIG. 1. Distribution of tissue components at different times in different treatment groups.

a) Upon implantation of totally decalcified bone grafts.

b) During maturation of fracture callus.

Low intensity and slow rate of reparative changes were even more pronounced with superficially decalcified implants. It is noted, however, that the formation of calcified tissue seen at radiography and that of new bone in the histological analysis are consistent in the different groups. As an example of simultaneous microradiography and labeling techniques, a superficially decalcified graft implanted in muscle for six weeks is seen in Fig. 2.

Ca^{45} radioactivity: The mineral content of the implants and of fracture callus was assessed by measurements of total radioactivity of sections and by densitometric scanning. The technique employed on implants is illustrated

47

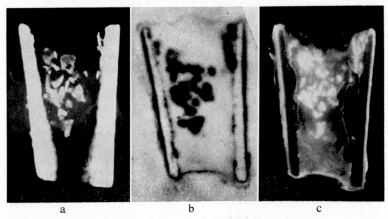

FIG. 2. Superficially decalcified graft implanted in muscle for six weeks and examined by a) microradiography b) Ca⁴⁵ autoradiography and c) oxytetracycline fluorescence technique. Incipient ossicle formation is seen in the medullary cavity.

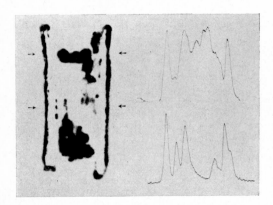

FIG. 3. The technique of scanning autoradiographs of implants.

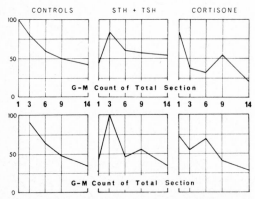

FIG. 4. Total Ca⁴⁵ activities of superficially decalcified implants (top) and of fracture callus (bottom). Abscissae: time in weeks.

in Fig. 3. The total Ca^{45} activity of implants, during the observation period, was higher in the STH + TSH group, and lower in the cortisone group, than in the controls (Fig. 4), and this was corroborated by the results of scanning. The course of the graphs generally corresponds with the corresponding findings relating to fracture callus.

Conclusions. It may be concluded that: a) The osteogenic capacity of decalcified allogenic bone implants, previously described, could be verified. b) By employing radiographic, histoquantitative and Ca^{45} techniques, new information could be obtained concerning formation of new bone and ossicle. c) The combination of STH, TSH and cortisone elicited effects in the implants resembling the influence of these hormones in fracture repair.

REFERENCES

1. BURWELL RG. in: Apley A G (Ed), "Recent advances in orthopaedics." London, J & A Churchill Ltd, 1969.
2. URIST MR, HAY PH, DUBUC FL and BÜRING K. *Clin Orthop* **64**: 194, 1969.
3. URIST MR, SILVERMAN BF, BÜRING K, DUBUC FL and ROSENBERG JM. *Clin Orthop* **53**: 243, 1967.
4. KOSKINEN EVS. *Ann Chir Gynaec Fenn* Suppl **90**: 1, 1959.
5. KOSKINEN EVS, RYÖPPY SA and LINDHOLM TS. *Proc McLean Conf Cell Mechanisms for Calcium Transfer and Homeostasis* (in press).

CALCIUM TRANSPORT IN BIOLOGICAL SYSTEMS

BIOCHEMICAL AND PHYSIOLOGICAL ASPECTS OF ADAPTATION

R. H. WASSERMAN, R. L. MORRISSEY, A. N. TAYLOR and R. A. CORRADINO

Department of Physical Biology, New York State Veterinary College,
Cornell University, Ithaca, New York, USA

The capacity of the gastrointestinal tract to alter its efficiency of absorption of calcium in response to the dietary intake of calcium or phosphorus or both has been known for many years. Also documented have been the observations that calcium-demanding processes, such as growth, lactation, pregnancy and egg-laying, are associated with (cause?) a greater rate of calcium absorption. Significant questions are: a) What is the detector of the calcium "status" of animal? b) What is the message connecting the detector with the response? c) What is the nature of the physiological change in calcium absorption? d) What is the nature of the biochemical and molecular alteration?

Past experimentation disclosed that adaptation is a vitamin D-dependent process (1, 2) which occurs more readily in younger than in older individuals (1), appears to be correlated with the degree of mineralization of the skeleton (1) and can take place in animals from which the parathyroid glands have been excised (2). One molecular change is an elevation in the vitamin D-induced calcium-binding protein in the adapted animal (3). More recently, detailed studies on the effect of various diets (varying in Ca and P content and Ca/P ratio) indicated that the estimated rate of Ca^{47} absorption from chick duodenum *in situ* was directly related, with a high correlation coefficient, to the CaBP content of the duodenal mucosa. The degree of miner-

alization (percent of ash on a fat-free, dry weight basis) of the tibiae was inversely related to the rate of Ca^{47} absorption, suggesting an interdependency of these two parameters. Other results from this experiment also tend to eliminate the parathyroid gland as the primary mediator of adaptation. Alterations in the intestinal alkaline phosphatase and Ca-sensitive adenosine triphosphatase activities, as a consequence of adaptation, will be reported.

Possibly related to adaptation is the recent finding that dietary stable strontium inhibits CaBP synthesis and depresses calcium absorption (4). Strontium may inhibit by a direct action at the gut level or via an inhibition of the calcification process or both.

Studies on the unidirectional fluxes of Ca^{47} across the duodenum *in situ* suggest that: a) Ca^{47} transfer across the microvillar border is slightly greater in the adapted animal; b) initial accumulation of Ca^{47} by mucosal tissue is not significantly different and c) the primary difference seems to lie in the greater rate of transfer of Ca^{47} from mucosal tissue to blood. A somewhat different pattern was observed when rachitic and vitamin D-replete animals were previously compared (3).

These observations, as well as those of others, will be discussed in relation to some of the physiological and biochemical factors involved in the phenomenon of adaptation.

REFERENCES

1. NICOLAYSEN R, EEG-LARSE N and MALM OJ. *Physiol Rev* **33**: 424, 1953.
2. KIMBERG DV, SCHACHTER D and SCHENKER H. *Amer J Physiol* **200**: 1250, 1961.
3. WASSERMAN RH and TAYLOR AN. in: Comar CL, Bronner F (Eds), "Mineral metabolism, an advanced treatise." New York, Academic Press, 1969, p 321.
4. CORRADINO RA and WASSERMAN RH. *Proc Soc Exp Biol Med* **133**: 960, 1970.

RELATIONSHIP OF CALCIUM-BINDING PROTEIN TO CALCIUM ABSORPTION IN THE FOWL

ARIE BAR and SHMUEL HURWITZ

Volcani Institute of Agricultural Research, Rehovot, Israel

A protein with a high affinity for calcium (CaBP) was isolated from intestinal mucosa cells by Wasserman and co-workers (1). It was characterized and implicated in the translocation of calcium across the mucosa. However, evidence for the participation of CaBP in calcium transport has remained circumstantial. We, therefore, tried to obtain additional evidence of such participation by following changes in CaBP in systems where the absorption capacity for calcium is known to vary. The systems, all involving the fowl, were as follows: System A, laying hens during periods of shell formation as compared to periods of inactivity of the uterus; System B, young pullets at the onset of egg production; System C, laying hens and chicks during short- or long-term periods of calcium depletion; System D, laying hens in which shell deposition was interrupted by intermittent feeding of nicarbazin. In all cases, CaBP was estimated by the Chelex method as described by Wasserman and Taylor (2).

System A. We have previously demonstrated a most remarkable regulation of calcium absorption in the laying hen, depending on its physiological state (3). The hens were found to absorb almost twice as much calcium during shell formation as compared to periods of uterine inactivity. Intestinal samples were thus taken from birds during those periods and analyzed for CaBP. The mean activity during shell formation $\pm$ SE was $110 \pm 4.5\%$ higher during shell secretion compared to periods of inactivity. This difference was not significant ($P > 0.05$).

System B. The onset of egg production precipitates a remarkable increase in calcium absorption (4). During the deposition of the first shell, calcium absorption does not reach its maximum value and the hen is in a negative calcium balance. After about four weeks, calcium absorption reaches its maximum which is maintained during the months of intensive egg laying. Since dietary regime remains the same through these phases, the actual absorption reflects the absorption capacity of the intestine. It was of interest to check whether these changes are associated with corresponding ones in CaBP. Indeed, CaBP already increases to normal "laying" level after the deposition of the first shell (Table 1).

TABLE 1. *Changes in calcium-binding activity in intestinal mucosa associated with initiation of egg laying*

Stage	Calcium-binding activity[a]
Nonlaying pullet	7.8 $\pm$ 0.7
1st egg	18.8 $\pm$ 1.4
35th egg	40.1 $\pm$ 4.0
Adult hen	22.0 $\pm$ 0.7

[a] Mean $\pm$ SE.

TABLE 2. *The effect of intermittent arrest of egg production on calcium-binding activity in intestinal mucosa*

Dietary treatment	Stage	Calcium-binding activity % of laying control[a]
Control	Nonlaying	46 ± 7
Control	Laying	100 ± 4
Nicarbazin, 4 days	Last egg	85 ± 10
Nicarbazin, 9 days	Nonlaying	42 ± 2
Control, 10 days[b]	1st egg in uterus	75 ± 5
Control, 14 to 16 days	5th egg	108 ± 8

[a] Mean ± SE.
[b] Following nine days of nicarbazin feeding.

A further increase is noted during the first month of egg production during which calcium absorption further increases. However, later on CaBP decreases although calcium absorption does not.

System C. Wasserman and Taylor (5) and we (3) have shown that CaBP increases in chicks after a few days of calcium deprivation. Despite the increase in the absorption capacity of the laying hen intestine under a similar challenge (3), no increase in CaBP was observed (6). However, during a longer term depletion where a mild treatment is used (1.7% dietary calcium), CaBP gradually increases: 100 ± 4% at day 0, 119 ± 5% after 16 days and 142 ± 10% after 32 days of treatment (means ± SE).

System D. Egg formation can be arrested at the terminal stages of the formation of the ova by including 0.04% nicarbazin in the diet (7). Under those conditions, the estrogen-dependent calcium metabolism (e.g. high plasma calcium and the presence of medullary bone) remains unchanged. Upon withdrawal of the drug, egg production resumes in eight to 10 days. Due to the absence of shell formation, calcium absorption markedly decreases during nicarbazin feeding and increases again when egg production resumes after the withdrawal of the drug. In this system, CaBP decreased, in two days after the last egg had been laid, to "nonlaying" level (Table 2). During the calcification of the first shell after the pause caused by nicarbazin, CaBP increases to 75% of its original value and reaches its original value four to six days later.

Conclusions. In the fowl, some but not all of the changes in the calcium absorption capacity are associated with corresponding changes in calcium-binding protein. Initiation of shell formation either through the natural processes or following an interruption by drug administration, is always associated with an increase in calcium-binding activity. On the other hand, the fine regulation of absorption capacity triggered by shell formation or short-term calcium deprivation is not associated with any changes in calcium-binding activity.

In the laying hen, either two stages of induction or two calcium-binding fractions are suggested: a short-term one with an induction time of a few days and another with an induction time of two to four weeks.

REFERENCES

1. WASSERMAN RH, CORRADINO RA and TAYLOR AN. *J Biol Chem* **243**: 3978, 1968.
2. WASSERMAN RH and TAYLOR AN. *Science* **152**: 791, 1966.
3. HURWITZ S and BAR A. *Amer J Clin Nutr* **22**: 391, 1969.
4. HURWITZ S and GRIMINGER P. *J Agric Sci* **54**: 373, 1960.
5. WASSERMAN RH and TAYLOR AN. *J Biol Chem* **243**: 3987, 1968.
6. HURWITZ S and BAR A. *J Nutr* **99**: 217, 1969.
7. WEISS HS, FISHER H and GRIMINGER P. *Poult Sci* **39**: 1221, 1960.

THE INFLUENCE OF A DIPHOSPHONATE
ON THE INTESTINAL ABSORPTION OF CALCIUM

D. B. MORGAN, J.-PH. BONJOUR, A. B. GASSER, K. O'BRIEN and H. A. FLEISCH

Department of Pathophysiology, University of Berne, and
Laboratory for Experimental Surgery, Davos Switzerland

Diphosphonates, such as ethane-l-hydroxy-l, 1-diphosphonate (EHDP) and dichloromethylenediphosphonate (Cl_2MDP), are potent inhibitors of calcium phosphate precipitation (1, 2) and dissolution (3, 4) *in vitro*. *In vivo* they prevent ectopic calcification induced by various means (3, 5), and EHDP slows the progress of ectopic bone formation in myositis ossificans (6). They also inhibit bone resorption in tissue culture (4), reduce hypercalcemia induced by PTH in rats (4) and reduce osteoporosis induced by immobilization in rats (7, 8 and R. C. Mühlbauer et al., in preparation). Cl_2MDP diminishes bone resorption in growing rats as measured by

Ca^{45} kinetics (9) according to the technique of Aubert and Milhaud (10).

In the present work we have investigated, using the same technique, the effect on Ca^{45} kinetics of EHDP given s.c. daily, for seven days at different intakes of calcium. This diphosphonate diminishes bone resorption, but to a lesser degree than with equivalent doses of Cl_2MDP. Both compounds increased the calcium balance when given at a dose of 1 mg P/kg. At a dose of 10 mg P/kg, Cl_2MDP still increases the calcium balance, but EHDP causes a large reduction in calcium balance and calcium accretion rate (Fig. 1a) with morphologic changes of rickets (11). The net

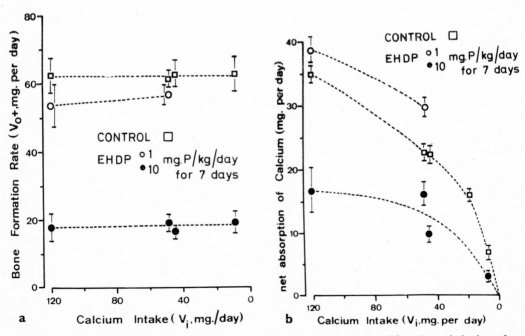

FIG. 1. The effects of EHDP (1 and 10 mg P/kg s.c. for seven days in 61-day-old rats) on a) the bone formation rate (V_{o+}, mg/day) and b) net absorption of calcium (mg/day), according to the intake of calcium.

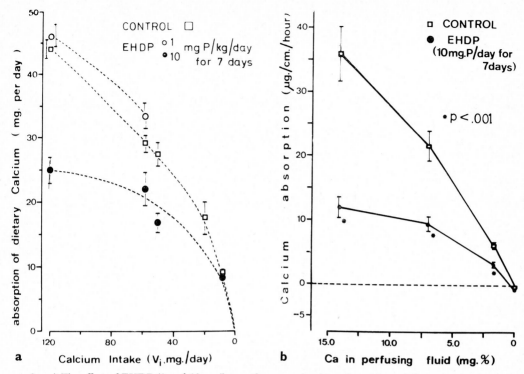

FIG. 2. a) The effect of EHDP (1 and 10 mg/kg s.c. for seven days) on absorption of dietary calcium; b) The effect of EHDP (10 mg P/kg s.c. for seven days) on the net absorption of calcium from duodenum perfused *in vivo*, according to the calcium concentration in the perfusing fluid.

absorption of calcium (dietary calcium minus fecal calcium) (Fig. 1b) and the absorption of dietary calcium (dietary calcium minus fecal calcium plus endogenously secreted calcium) (Fig. 2a) are increased with the small dose of EHDP (1.0 mg P/kg) but much decreased after the large dose of EHDP (10 mg P/kg). The large dose of Cl_2MDP caused neither rickets nor a reduction in calcium absorption from the intestine.

We have investigated the decrease of calcium absorption after large doses of EHDP in greater detail. The lumen of the rat duodenum has been perfused *in situ*. The bile was diverted from the intestine through a cannula in the bile duct, collected and analyzed. In each rat, net calcium absorption was measured from solutions containing 2, 7 and 15 mg calcium/100 ml. After the adminis-

tration of EHDP (10 mg P/kg) for seven days, the net calcium absorption from the duodenum was reduced at all calcium concentrations in the perfusate (Fig. 2b). The reduction in net absorption was not due to an increased secretion of calcium since there was no detectable secretion of calcium with this technique.

We are now investigating whether the diminution of absorption from the duodenum is associated with a change in the active transport of calcium as measured with the everted gut sac. In addition, the effect of EHDP on the calcium-dependent ATPase in the gut wall has been determined, since it has been suggested (12) that the calcium-dependent ATPase in the brush border of the mucosal cells of the intestine is part of the mechanism for the active transport of calcium across the intestine. Our preliminary results show that in rats, after seven days of treatment with large doses of EHDP, there is a decrease of calcium-dependent ATPase activity in the brush border of the duodenum. On the other hand, the same dose of Cl_2MDP causes an increase of the calcium-dependent ATPase activity.

Thus EHDP increases calcium absorption at smaller doses but reduces it strongly at doses producing rickets. Whether the effect on calcium absorption is a direct effect of EHDP on the gut or secondary to the change in bone mineralization is not known. The latter mechanism would need some sort of an information link between bone and the gut. This would ensure that the rate of absorption of calcium from the gut and the rate of entry of calcium into bone are of similar magnitude, thus avoiding a large urinary excretion of calcium which might damage the kidney. In this case diphosphonates would provide an excellent tool for studying the information mechanism.

Supported by the Procter & Gamble Company, Cincinnati, Ohio, USA, by the Swiss National Fund (No. 3567), and by the U.S. Public Health Service (AM-7266).

REFERENCES

1. FRANCIS MD. *Calcif Tissue Res* 3: 151, 1969.
2. FRANCIS MD, RUSSELL RGG and FLEISCH HA. *Science* 165: 1264, 1969.
3. FLEISCH HA, RUSSELL RGG and FRANCIS MD. *Science* 165: 1262, 1969.
4. RUSSELL RGG, MUHLBAUER RC, BISAZ S, WILLIAMS DA and FLEISCH HH. *Calcif Tissue Res* 6: 183, 1970.
5. FLEISCH HA, RUSSELL RGG, BISAZ S, MUHLBAUER RC and WILLIAMS DA. *Europ J Clin Invest* 1: 12, 1970.
6. BASSETT CAL, DONATH A, MACAGNO F, PREISIG R, FLEISCH HA and FRANCIS MD. *Lancet* ii: 845, 1969.
7. FLEISCH HA, RUSSELL RGG, SIMPSON B and MUHLBAUER RC. *Nature (London)* 223: 211, 1969.
8. MICHAEL WR, KING WR and FRANCIS MD. *Clin Orthop* (in press).
9. GASSER AB, FLEISCH HA and RICHELLE LJ. *Calcif Tissue Res* 4 (suppl): 96, 1970.
10. AUBERT JP and MILHAUD G. *Biochim Biophys Acta* 39: 122, 1960.
11. KING WR, FRANCIS MD and MICHAEL WR. *Clin Orthop* (in press).
12. MARTIN DL, MELANCON MJ JR and DELUCA HF *Biochem Biophys Res Commun* 35: 819, 1969

INFLUENCE OF SODIUM, GLUCOSE AND XYLOSE ON CALCIUM ABSORPTION

STUDIES WITH JEJUNAL PERFUSIONS IN FIVE HUMAN SUBJECTS

M. C. CHAPUY and D. PANSU

Laboratoire de Pathologie et Thérapeutique des Echanges Minéraux, Ecole Pratique des Hautes Etudes and Service du Professeur Vignon, Pavillon E, Hôpital Edouard Herriot, Lyon, France

Certain sugars and polyalcohols (lactose, xylose, sorbitol) stimulated calcium absorption when added in large quantities to the diet of rats (1) and humans (2). This effect required the simultaneous presence of both the active compound and calcium and was most effective when the sugars were poorly absorbed, causing hyperosmolar diarrhea (3). It has been suggested that the action is mainly an intestinal one and related to water exchange. This hypothesis was tested by the use of jejunal perfusion whereby the relationships between calcium, water and sodium transport were studied.

Methods. All experiments were conducted with four women volunteers and one man, all healthy and aged 25 to 50 years. A total of 18 studies were made. Perfusions were made using the general method for humans (4) with modification by triple lumen tube and the use of a balloon: intestinal secretions were stopped by the balloon and aspirated, perfusion

TABLE 1. *Calcium absorption with various concentrations of calcium, NaCl and sugars in infusion solutions*

	Solution I			Solution II				Solution III			
Cases	Ca (µEq)	Water (ml)	Na (µEq)	Ca (µEq)	Water (ml)	Na (µEq)	Xylose (mg)	Ca (µEq)	Water (ml)	Na (µEq)	Glucose (mg)
1	−5.1	−0.52	−210	−2.5	+1.51	+220	−35				
2	−4.5	−0.40	−220	−3.1	+1.67	+300	−62				
3	−6.2	−2.30	−150					−1.3	−2.32	+120	−174
4	−8.3	−0.86	−66	+1.6	+3.44	+470	−59				
5	−4.2	+2.39	+110	−3.0	+4.25	+243	−44				
5′				−4.3	+3.73	+320	−34	−2[a]	+0.8	+250	−100

Results expressed in quantities absorbed (–) or secreted (+) in 1 min and 25 cm.
Solution I   contains 150 mEq Cl, 150 mEq Na, 4.5 mEq Ca.
Solution II contains 50 mEq Cl, 50 mEq Na, 4.5 mEq Ca, 30 g xylose.
Solution III contains 50 mEq Cl, 50 mEq Na, 4.5 mEq Ca, 36 g glucose.
[a] Ca in perfusion 9 mEq/liter.

TABLE 2. *Calcium absorption by the same subject with various concentrations of calcium, NaCl and sugars in infusion solutions*

Infusion solution concentration per liter					Quantity absorbed in 1 min and 25 cm				
Na (mEq)	Calcium (mEq)	Xylose (g)	Glucose (g)	Theoretical osmolarity (m ω)	Calcium (µEq)	Water (ml)	Na (µEq)	Xylose (mg)	Glucose (mg)
150	4.5			310	−4.2	+2.39	+110		
50	4.5	30		310	−3.0	+4.25	+240	−44	
50	9	30		310	−4.3	+3.73	+320	−34	
50	9		36	310	−2.0	+0.81	+250		−100
100	9	30		360	−0.8	+2.86	+166	−18	
100	9		36	360	−2.5	+1.39	+96		−131
150	4.5		40	410	−1.6	+3.90	−110		−156

−   indicates net absorption.
+   indicates net secretion.

was infused below the balloon, 99 ml/min, and perfusates siphoned 25 cm beyond the site of infusion. The position of tubes in the last part of the duodenum or first part of the jejunum was checked fluoroscopically. Each test solution was perfused in fasting subjects for 1 hr, with a 30-min equilibration period and three collection periods of 10 min each. Solutions contained 1.50 g/liter of polyethylene glycol as a nonabsorbable volume marker, 3 or 9 g/liter of NaCl, calcium, gluconate at a calculated final calcium concentration of 90 or 180 mg/liter (2.25 or 4.50 mmole/liter), 15 or 30 g/liter of xylose, 18 or 36 g/liter of glucose (100 or 200 mmole/liter).

Results. The results are presented in Table 1 and are expressed in net quantities absorbed (—) or secreted (+).

In isotonic NaCl solution, calcium absorption varied from subject to subject as indicated by other authors (5). The variation was from 4.2 µEq/min per 25 cm to 6.2 µEq/min per 25 cm. Generally, simultaneous water and NaCl absorption was observed. When NaCl concentration decreased and sugar concentration increased in perfused isotonic solutions, calcium absorption decreased significantly in each subject. Although water secretion and calcium dilution were greater when xylose was used in place of glucose with the same molar concentration (200 mM), the fall of calcium absorption was not as significant.

Serial perfusions in the same subject (Table 2) confirmed that the best condition for calcium absorption was realized with isotonic NaCl solution but not with hypertonic NaCl solution or low NaCl concentration in isotonic solution with sugar. In the latter case xylose was capable of maintaining a better absorption than glucose. In all cases calcium can be absorbed when water and NaCl are secreted.

Discussion. Studies of calcium absorption in the first part of jejunum with jejunal perfusion indicate that:

1)   Calcium absorption is not saturated with time in this segment.

2)   There are large individual variations in water transport and calcium transport.

3)   The presence of NaCl appears to facilitate calcium absorption. With low NaCl concentration in the perfusion solution, calcium absorption decreases. The presence of 200 mM glucose does not change this effect. The presence of 200 mM xylose permits a better calcium absorption.

4)   No relation was found between calcium absorption and water or sodium transfer. The real mechanism of action of xylose on calcium absorption may be related to an increase in negative electrical potential in serosal fluid as indicated by Martin and de Luca (6).

REFERENCES

1. FOURNIER P. *Path Biol (Paris)* **13**: 143, 1965.
2. PANSU D and CHAPUY MC. *CR Acad Sci [D] (Paris)* **270**: 3103, 1970.
3. PANSU D and CHAPUY MC. *Calcif Tissue Res* **4**: 155, 1970.
4. COOPER H, LEVITAN R, FORDTRAN JS and INGELFINGER FJ. *Gastroenterology* **1**: 50, 1966.
5. WENSEL RH, RICH C, BROWN AC and VOLWILER W. *J Clin Invest* **48**: 1768, 1969.
6. MARTIN DL and DE LUCA HF. *Amer J Physiol* **216**: 1351, 1969.

RELATION BETWEEN CALCIUM ABSORPTION AND THE LEVELS OF CALCIUM IN SERUM AND URINE

V. NUNZIATA, M. REINER, A. NADARAJAH, N.J.Y. WOODHOUSE, M. FISHER and G. F. JOPLIN

Royal Postgraduate Medical School and Department of Medicine, Hammersmith Hospital, London, England

Using the double isotope test of calcium absorption previously described (1), studies were made on groups of patients with acromegaly, hyperparathyroidism, Cushing's disease, thyrotoxicosis and other disorders of calcium metabolism. Simultaneously, the prevailing levels of serum and urine calcium were established, and in some patients external balances were carried out.

The results suggest that calcium absorption plays an important role in regulating the serum and urine calcium in acromegaly and hyperparathyroidism. In Cushing's disease and thyrotoxicosis, isotope absorption was poor in comparison with the urine calcium, from which a negative balance could be inferred.

REFERENCE

1. REINER M, NADARAJAH A, LEESE B and JOPLIN GF. *Calcif Tissue Res* **4** (Suppl): 95, 1970.

EFFECT OF LACTOSE ON THE ABSORPTION OF
ALKALINE EARTH METALS AND INTESTINAL LACTASE ACTIVITY

P. FOURNIER, Y. DUPUIS and A. FOURNIER

Study Group on Nutritional Factors in Ossification, E.P.H.E., Paris, France

This study is a continuation of work presented in two other reports. In the first (1) the effect of lactose on calcium utilization in the rat was studied and it was found that the continued presence of sugars in the intestine altered absorption conditions. In our second report (2), it was shown that in man ingested lactose further increases calcemia, that it has less effect on glycemia and that fewer symptoms of intolerance, such as osmotic diarrhea, occur. The present study concerns the extent to which lactase activity influences species differences in the effect of lactose on calcium utilization.

Methods. Twenty-four Swiss mice and eight Wistar rats, aged six weeks or six months, were separated into two equal groups. Those in the control groups received a diet previously described (3), based on starch, with a regular calcium content but without the utilization factor for this element. The diet of the lactose-group animals differed from the above diet in that sugar was substituted for 30% of the starch. After the animals had received the diets for a week, they were tested as follows: 1) The daily calcium balance was determined. 2) A comparison was made between the effects of glucose and lactose. For each group, half the animals received by esophageal tube a solution containing extra alkaline earths, Ca or Sr[85], and in one group 10% glucose and in the other 20% glucose. Blood glucose, calcium and radioactivity (due to Sr[85]) were measured on blood samples, collected by cutting the ends of the rat's tails and by killing the mice, 30 min, 90 min and 4 hr later. 3) Lactase activity was determined according to Dahlquist (4) on a jejunum suspension.

Results. Lactose produced a greater increase in absorption in the young rat than in the adult and, despite a high level of urinary secretion, a greater calcium retention. Compared with the feces of the controls, the rats on the lactose diet were more hydrated. While the ingestion of glucose immediately caused symptoms of hyperglycemia, followed by a rapid return to normal levels, administration of lactose only influenced glycemia slightly and slowly (see Fig. 1). On the other hand, under the influence of lactose a steady and significant increase of blood alkaline earths, Ca or Sr[85], was seen—the action of the glucose thus being quite distinct in this context. In the rat, lactase activity varied little with age.

Calcium balance in the mouse, unlike that in the young or adult rat, was slightly affected by dietary lactose. In this case there was no noticeable diarrhea. In the adult mouse, the balance data show that lactose had little effect on calcium absorption though with several significant individual differences. The findings on the effects of ingestion of glucose or lactose on glycemia, calcemia and strontemia in mice are so far inconsistent, and will not be reported. As far as lactase activity is concerned, this is found to be greatest in the young mice and varies from one animal to another, generally decreasing in adults. Young or adult rats had an enzyme activity 50 to 70% lower than mice of the same age (see Table 1).

Discussion. There is a great difference in

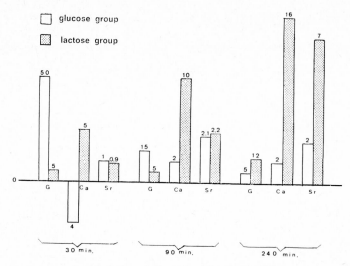

FIG. 1. Variation of glycemia and calcemia (% starting value) and strontemia (‰ of dose administered).

TABLE 1. *Calcium balance and lactase activity in control and lactose-fed animals Ca (mg/day)*

	Ingested	Absorbed	Excreted	Retained	Lactase activity (units[a]/g)
		Control diet			
Rats					
6 weeks	71	23	1.3	21.7	1.3
	(60 to 99)	(17 to 28)	(0.9 to 1.5)	(16 to 32)	(0.8 to 1.1)
6 months	104	1.3	1.1	0.2	0.8
	(92 to 126)	(–2 to 4)	(0.8 to 1.9)	(–3 to 2.6)	(0.4 to 1.7)
Mice					
6 weeks	26	5.2	0.2	5	2.3
	(21 to 30)	(3.1 to 7.5)	(0.16 to 0.27)	(3 to 7.3)	(1.6 to 2.6)
6 months	24	1	0.6	0.4	1.2
	(16 to 37)	(–3 to 7)	(0.4 to 1.2)	(–3 to 6)	(0.5 to 2.6)
		Lactose diet			
Rats					
6 weeks	69	39	4.5	34.5	1.7
	(61 to 87)	(31 to 46)	(3 to 7)	(27 to 44)	(1.3 to 2.3)
6 months	91	31	13	18	0.8
	(80 to 109)	(21 to 52)	(9 to 21)	(12 to 34)	(0.3 to 1.4)
Mice					
6 weeks	27.5	6	0.3	6.7	2.9
	(22 to 33)	(4.6 to 7.2)	(0.15 to 0.5)	(4.2 to 8.6)	(2.0 to 3.3)
6 months	30	1.5	0.9	0.6	1.3
	(17 to 41)	(–0.5 to 8)	(0.6 to 2)	(–1 to 6)	(0.6 to 2.6)

Results expressed as the arithmetic mean of groups of five animals with ranges given in parentheses.
[a] One enzyme unit hydrolyzes 1 μmole lactose/min.

the effects of lactose on calcium utilization in the two species. In rats, the effect of lactose can, in agreement with the theory that the animals' reactions develop freely, be considered as poor intestinal utilization. The lack of hyperglycemia is attributable to the defective hydrolysis equivalent to the state appearing in diarrhea due to the prolonged presence of sugars in the intestine.

The minor effect of lactose on alkaline-earth utilization in mice is difficult to understand in view of a lack of adequate analytical data. It seems to be an isolated finding since we have seen that other sugars, D-xylose and sorbitol, administered by esophageal tube, are just as effective in mice (even in the very young) as in rats. Using old mice of another stock, it has been shown that adding lactose to the diet increases calcium absorption. It seems, however, that mice are less sensitive to lactose although they can react to the administration of the sugar differently, according to age, breed and diet. Regarding the rat, which is much more sensitive, the lactose effect differs from that in the mouse in intensity rather than in nature.

The question arises whether this difference is due to a difference in lactase activity. It has been reported that lactase activity in the jejunum is greater in mice, and it is understood that lactose, hydrolyzed to a greater degree, interferes less with intestinal absorption. This argument is strengthened by the fact that the rat, which eats more, has more lactose to hydrolyze but this is not in fact so because the rat's intestine has greater overall lactase activity. But other factors should also be considered such as alimentary rhythm, transit rate, rate of secretion of the intestinal juices, and in influence of intestinal flora on lactose.

In man, the relationship between the effects of lactose and lactase activity is much closer. Lactose intolerance, very widespread in some races, is incontestably attributable to lactase deficiency (5). In many individuals in whom lactose only slightly influences glycemia, their lactase activity is found to be minimal (6). Those subjects in whom digestive intolerance for lactose is accompanied by strongly increased calcemia have much lower lactase activity than those who can hydrolyze this sugar well (D. Pansu, personal communication). At the present time, the whole range of lactase activities in rats and mice seems too insignificant to be solely responsible for the large differences in their handling of lactose between the two species.

REFERENCES

1. FOURNIER P and DUPUIS Y. in: "Les tissues calcifiés." Paris, 1968, p 283.
2. PANSU D and CHAPUY MC. *Calcif Tissue Res* **4** (Suppl): 155, 1970.
3. DUPUIS Y. *CR Acad Sci* [D] (*Paris*) **251**: 2587, 1960.
4. DAHLQUIST A. *Anal Biochem* **7**: 18, 1964.
5. BAYLESS T and ROSENWEIG N. *JAMA* **197**: 968, 1966.
6. WELSH J and ROHRER V. *Arch Intern Med* (*Chicago*) **120**: 251, 1967.

INTESTINAL TRANSPORT OF CALCIUM IN EXPERIMENTAL UREMIA

E. RITZ and K. ANDRASSY

Medizinische Universitätsklinik, Heidelberg, German Federal Republic

Chronic renal insufficiency is associated with an impairment of the intestinal transport of calcium which can be overcome by large doses of vitamin D (vitamin D resistance). It was the purpose of the present investigation to see whether there are analogies between the changes of intestinal Ca transport in vitamin D deficiency and in uremia.

In five-sixths nephrectomized (N) male 100 g Wistar rats [controls (Co) sham operated; pair feeding] *in vivo* efflux of Ca across the duodenal mucosa was decreased (N $33.7 \pm 2.3\%$ dose/180 sec; Co $44.7 \pm 2.09\%$; $P < 0.01$); the effect was specific for Ca and PO_4; the efflux of Na (N 24.5 ± 2.81; Co 28.9 ± 2.52; $P > 0.10$) was unchanged. There was also indirect evidence for a decrease of plasma to lumen flux of Ca in uremia.

The decrease of Ca efflux was not caused by loss of renal parenchyma (also occurring after ligature of ureters), by elevation of serum urea (urea in drinking water), by increased fecal phosphate or by acidosis (NH_4Cl). After bilateral nephrectomy there was a rapid decrease of duodenal Ca efflux [Co 25.0 ± 2.6; 3 hr 16.0 ± 0.25 ($P < 0.05$); 24 hr 10.1 ± 1.79 ($P < 0.01$)].

The decrease of Ca efflux *in vivo* was accompanied by a decreased mucosal uptake of radiocalcium. *In vitro* Ca transport against chemical gradients (C/M ratios in everted sacs: N 1.78; Co 6.69) and radiocalcium concentrations in mucosal and serosal layers were decreased in O_2 but not in N_2 atmosphere. Ca diffusion across duodenal mucosa at 0 C *in vitro* was also marginally diminished.

After bilateral nephrectomy Ca binding activity (CaBA) of duodenal mucosa fell rapidly [Co $5.85 \pm 0.26\%$ Ca^{45} in supernatant fluid 10^{-6} g protein; 12 hr after nephrectomy 4.51 ± 0.14 ($P < 0.10$); 24 hr 4.05 ± 0.19 ($P < 0.05$)]; the decrease of CaBA in the Chelex 100-test was accompanied by a diminished concentration of the Ca binding protein on polyacrylamide gel electrophoresis. CaBA was diminished after bilateral ligature of the ureters (2.85 ± 0.28; Co 3.42 ± 0.24; $P < 0.10$) but not after elevation of serum urea (urea in drinking water) or after induction of acidosis (0.75 M NH_4Cl).

Peritoneal dialysis of parathyroidectomized (PTX) rats with Ca free dialysate did not increase CaBA [PTX 4.68 ± 0.37; PTX-N 2.85 ± 0.42 ($P < 0.05$); PTX-N Ca free dialysate 3.18 ± 0.37; not significant]. Dialysis with 10 mval Ca increased CaBA over that of PTX controls however (PTX-N 10 mval Ca in dialysate 6.09 ± 0.14). This finding points to a possible role of the intracellular Ca pool in the control of Ca-binding-protein synthesis.

In the laying chicken, where the metabolic pattern of uremia is quite different from that in mammals, there was no decrease of Ca efflux over the duodenal mucosa (Co $39.0 \pm 6.2\%/180$ sec; N 39.2 ± 2.8; not significant) and no decrease of CaBA in the mucosa of the uterus (Co $6.05 \pm 0.53\%$ Ca^{45} in supernatant fluid; N 5.0 ± 0.61; not significant) five days after subtotal bilateral ligature of the ureters.

The impairment of the intestinal transport of Ca could be overcome both by vitamin D and by 25-hydroxycholecalciferol. In the log-dose response curve vitamin D was less effective in uremic rachitic animals at all dose levels studied, however. Vitamin D resistance was found in the log-dose response curves of both target organs of vitamin D, intestine (decrease of O_2 dependent accumulation of Ca) and bone [diminished width of the zone of primary calcification (line test); persistence of osteoid in the metaphysis]. Vitamin D and 25-hydroxycholecalciferol were equally effective.

In conclusion, experimental uremia in mammals (not in birds) causes a rapid impairment of various parameters of intestinal transport of Ca which closely resembles that seen in vitamin D deficiency. Elevation of serum urea, acidosis, retention of dialyzable substances and loss of nephron mass do not explain the effects observed. In view of the rapidity with which the changes appear, a derangement of vitamin D metabolism seems less likely than a direct alteration of target organ responsiveness.

THE EFFECT OF HYDROCHLOROTHIAZIDE AND OF SODIUM IN THE DIET ON CALCIUM AND STRONTIUM TRANSPORT IN INTESTINE AND KIDNEY

A. DONATH, S. NORDIO, F. MACAGNO and R. GATTI

Children's Hospitals of the University of Berne, Switzerland and of Genoa, Italy

In a case of idiopathic hypercalciuria the authors observed that hydrochlorothiazide, in spite of a prolonged normalization of calciuria, does not induce any improvement in either osteoporosis or growth retardation. A hypothesis was put forward that the drug inhibits calcium absorption from the intestine. This was confirmed by the study of fecal elimination of calcium and intestinal absorption of Sr[85]. Hydrochlorothiazide does not increase the secretion of Ca[47] into the intestine and it reduces urinary elimination of Ca or radiocalcium injected i.v. A sodium-poor diet reduces calciuria in normal children. It increases the fecal elimination of calcium and reduces, more or less, the intestinal absorption of Sr[85] either under basic conditions or under vitamin D supplementation. A sodium-rich diet increases both calciuria and the fecal elimination of calcium in normal children. The relationships between the transport of Ca and Na and the pathogenesis of the effect of the drug on Ca transport is discussed. This effect may represent an interesting *in vivo* test for evaluating the mechanism regulating calcium transport.

DIFFERENT BEHAVIOR OF Ca[45] AND Sr[89] AS TRACERS IN A KINETIC MODEL OF CALCIUM METABOLISM

G. MEYER, W. REMAGEN and P. GROSSE

Institute of Pathology and Computer Center, University of Kiel, Kiel, German Federal Republic

The relation between strontium and calcium metabolism has been repeatedly investigated using the radioactive isotopes of these elements. On the one hand Sr has been used as a tracer for Ca, and on the other it has been studied on its own because of its importance in radioactive fallout (1).

There are considerable differences in our knowledge of the metabolism of the two elements. Therefore, it is difficult to define synonymous parameters for them, and the results differ considerably: Absorption from the intestine is lower for Sr (2, 3); curves of specific radioactivity are qualitatively equal, but the Sr curve is somewhat steeper (4, 5). In all investigations the considerably higher urinary excretion of Sr seems to be the most marked difference (1, 2, 5–8). The results concerning fecal excretion differ; in men and rats some workers found a higher output of Sr (4), whereas others did not (8). The bone turnover rates are equal (4, 7) in rats; a certain preference for Sr has been found in men (7) and, by some investigators, in rats (2). Even considering only the work dealing with rats, a direct comparison of the results is most dif-

TABLE 1. *Parameters of the model; mean values* $\pm$ SD *calculated with* Sr^{89} *and with* Ca^{45}

Parameter		Sr^{89}		Ca^{45}
Body	(G)	136.429	g	136.429
weight		±2.042		±2.042
Serum Ca	(S)	12.056	mg/100 ml	12.056
level		±0.160		±0.160
Ca intake	(v_i)	130.845	mg/d	130.845
with food		±7.404		±7.404
Total fecal	(v_F)	85.726	mg/d	85.726
loss		±5.325		±5.325
Urinary excretion	($v_{u\ exp}$)	1.843	mg/d	1.843
chem. est.		±0.119		±0.119
Compartment	(P)	28.593	mg	29.194
fast exchange		±1.097		±1.097
Compartment	(E)	75.427	mg	94.618
low exchange		±5.814		±6.428
Exchange	(v_e)	109.062	mg/d	122.480
P–E		±6.050		±5.488
Total loss	(v_T)	110.106	mg/d	101.595
from P		±3.124		±2.577
Urinary	(v_u)	20.517	mg/d	1.800^a
excretion		±1.131		±0.194
Endogenous	(v_f)	16.655	mg/d	11.770^a
fecal Ca		±0.978		±0.671
Bone	(v_{o+})	72.934	mg/d	88.025^a
accretion		±2.977		±2.519
Overall	(Δ)	$+24.602$	mg/d	$+43.319^a$
balance		±3.283		±3.256
Bone	(v_{o-})	48.332	mg/d	44.704
resorption		±3.009		±2.979

^{a} Difference between mean values of Sr^{89} and Ca^{45} significant at $P < 0.001$.

ficult, since the methods used have been based on different concepts (2, 6, 8), the material has not been homogenous (6) or the isotopes have not been injected simultaneously (8). Furthermore, the small number of animals used did not allow a statistical evaluation (2, 6, 8).

We therefore considered it useful to compare the behavior of Ca^{45} and Sr^{89} in the model of Ca metabolism conceived by Aubert and Milhaud (9), and slightly modified by us (3, 9, 10). We reduced the variables by simultaneously injecting the two isotopes into the same group of animals large enough for statistical evaluation. The use of Sr as a tracer in a model of Ca metabolism does not allow conclusions concerning the Sr metabolism proper, but the results have to be considered in their relation to those obtained with Ca.

The implications and criticisms of the model of Aubert and Milhaud, as well as the techniques, have been discussed in detail elsewhere (4, 9, 10). We used 21 female Wistar rats (CFN) with a mean weight of 136 g. They were fed a commercial diet (Altromin) with a controlled Ca content of 1.38%, a P content of 0.94%, and 100 IU% vitamin D_3, and distilled water ad lib. The animals were killed after the experiments and parts of the skeleton were dissected free and ashed. The ratio of the radioactivities was then estimated in the ash. The values for the two elements in the different samples were obtained by measuring each sample twice, the Ca radiation being absorbed at the second time by an aluminum filter, and comparing the results with those obtained from single and mixed standard samples. The calculation of the individual and the group values was done with the help of a computer.

In Table 1 the mean values $\pm$ SD for the parameters of the model are listed. The values for the first five parameters are identical for Sr and Ca, because they were measured directly. All the mean values are highly significant. There are highly significant differences between the Sr and the Ca values of v_u, v_f, v_{o+}, and Δ. A significant correlation between v_u and $v_{u\ exp}$ for Ca was not obtained; it had, however, been found in former investigations (3, 10). The mean value of the

ratio $\dfrac{Sr^{89}/Ca^{45}\ \text{injected}}{Sr^{89}/Ca^{45}\ \text{in bone}}$ for all animals is

1.226, and the individual figures vary very little from the mean.

In spite of the somewhat steeper slope of the Sr serum activity curve, there are no significant differences between the Sr and the Ca values for P and E. It is meaningless to compare P and E in our experiments with the compartments of other workers (8, 11) because they are defined in different ways. The sum of both, which expresses the total pool of exchangeable Ca, should, however, be roughly the same. This is not the case, as P + E in our experiments are about 1.6 times larger than $C_1 + C_2$ in the model of Cohn et al. (8). The reason may be the i.v. injection and resultant steeper serum activity curve in our animals, instead of i.p. injection with a consecutive delayed resorption. This is most probably as true for Ca as for Sr, Cohn et al. (8) also having found slightly larger Ca compartments,

$v_u Sr$ is 11.4 times higher than $v_u Ca$. This is in agreement with findings of others (6, 8). It is a consequence of the fact that only the ionized Ca is filtered in the kidney and may thus be excreted (12); Sr is completely filtered as it is not at all bound to proteins of the blood plasma (13). Furthermore, concerning tubular reabsorption, there is a competitive

mechanism with a preference for Ca (14).

The difference between $v_f Sr$ and $v_f Ca$ may be explained by the somewhat higher Sr content of the digestive juices (15) and by the difference between the (re-)absorption rates, with a factor of between 2 and 2.5 in favor of Ca (16).

There is a highly significant higher Ca bone accretion rate; this is in contradiction to the results of other authors (2, 6, 8), who have found equal rates. v_{o+} depends on v_T and thus on the serum activity curve ($v_T = v_u + v_f + v_{o+}$), since v_u and v_f are estimated directly from the excreted radioactivity. Under these circumstances, it is of relevance to control the figures for v_{o+} derived from the model by direct estimation. The mean value

of the ratio $\dfrac{Sr^{89}/Ca^{45}\ \text{injected}}{Sr^{89}/Ca^{45}\ \text{in bone}}$ (1.226) indi-

cates that more Ca than Sr is deposited in bone. If we set the deposition of Ca at 100%, then that of Sr is 81.6%. If we likewise set $v_{o+}Ca$ at 100%, then $v_{o+}Sr$ is 82.9%. The close correlation between these two figures strongly supports the validity of the model and of the calculated bone accretion rates. It cannot be determined from our results if the lower Sr accretion rate is the consequence of the higher total excretion ($v_u + v_f$), or if it is an independent process.

The difference between the values for the balance only reflects the one between $v_u Ca$ and $v_u Sr$, as Δ is calculated from $v_i - (v_F + v_u)$, where v_F and v_u are identical. v_{o-} is calculated from $v_{o+} -\Delta$, and thus depends on v_u and v_{o+}, which are inverse in quantity.

In conclusion, our results confirm the findings in the literature about the different urinary excretion of Ca and Sr. Yet in contrast to the results of others, we present good evidence that there is a positive discrimination for Ca concerning deposition in bone. We consider it no more meaningful to use Sr isotopes as tracers in experiments on Ca metabolism, as all important vectors differ for the two elements.

Part of this paper has been submitted as a doctoral thesis to the Medical Faculty, University of Kiel, Germany.

Supported by a grant from the Deutsche Forschungs-gemeinschaft.

REFERENCES

1. BRONNER F, AUBERT JP, RICHELLE LJ, SAVILLE PD, NICHOLAS JA and COBB JR. *J Clin Invest* **42**: 1095, 1963.
2. COMAR CL, WASSERMAN RH and NOLD MM. *Proc Soc Exp Biol Med* **92**: 859, 1956.
3. REMAGEN W and OEFF K. *Z Ges Exp Med* **139**: 574, 1965.
4. AUBERT JP, BRONNER F and RICHELLE LJ. *J Clin Invest* **42**: 6, 1963.
5. HARRISON GE, CARR TEF and SUTTON A. *Int J Radiat Biol* **13**: 235, 1967.
6. BAUER GCH, CARLSSON A and LINDQUIST B. *Acta Physiol Scand* **35**: 56, 1955.
7. COHN SH, BOZZO SR, JESSEPH JE, CONSTANTI-NIDES C, GUSMANO EA and ROBERTSON JS. *J Appl Physiol* **21**: 67, 1966.
8. COHN SH and GUSMANO EA. *Proc Soc Exp Biol Med* **126**: 79, 1967.
9. AUBERT JP and MILHAUD G. *Biochim Biophys Acta* **39**: 122, 1960.
10. REMAGEN W. "Calciumkinetik und Knochen-morphologie." Stuttgart, G Thieme, 1970.
11. GUSMANO EA, CONCANNON JN, BOZZO SR and COHN SH. *Radiat Res* **33**: 540, 1968.
12. NEUMAN WF and NEUMAN MW. "The chemical dynamics of bone mineral." Chicago, Chicago University Press, 1968.
13. CREGER CR, ANSARI MNA, COLVIN LB and CROUCH JR. *Proc Soc Exp Biol Med* **124**: 799, 1967.
14. SPENCER H, LEWIN I and SAMACHSON J. *Radiat Res* **31**: 876, 1967.
15. GREENBERG DM and TROESBER FM. *Proc Soc Exp Biol Med* **49**: 488, 1942.
16. PANY JE. *Wein Klin Wschr* **79**: 489, 1967.

CALCIUM BINDING PROTEIN IN HUMAN INTESTINAL MUCOSA

J. MENCZEL, G. EILON, A. STEINER, C. KARAMAN, E. MOR and A. RON

Research Laboratory, Department of Medicine and Department of Surgery,
Shaare Zedek Hospital, Jerusalem, Israel

Administration of vitamin D to rachitic animals induced the appearance of a calcium binding protein (CaBP) which is required for calcium absorption (1, 2). CaBP was also isolated from duodenal mucosa of nonrachitic animals and was found in several species of animals such as chicks, dogs, rats and monkeys (3). The molecular weight of the protein was assessed as 28,000 by gel filtration and from 24,000 to 26,000 by sedimentation studies (3, 4). Wasserman and Taylor have shown that a gross correlation exists between the time of appearance of the CaBP in the mucosal tissue and an increase in cal-

TABLE 1. *The specific activity of CaBP in duodenal and jejunal mucosa in four patients.*

| | Duodenum | Jejunum | |
| | Specific activity of CaBP (Ca^{45}) count/min per µg protein | Specific activity of CaBP (Ca^{45}) count/min per µg protein | Percentage of specific activity of jejunum as compared to duodenum |
Case no.			
1	22.5	2.7	12.0
2	20.4	4.2	20.6
3	13.8	4.2	30.4
4	19.5	3.9	20.0
Mean ± SD	19.05 ± 1.74	3.75 ± 0.358	19.96

TABLE 2. *CaBP in five additional intestinal biopsies*

Case no.	Duodenum Specific activity of CaBP (Ca^{45}) count/min per µg protein	Jejunum Specific activity of CaBP (Ca^{45}) count/min per µg protein	Percentage of specific activity of jejunum as compared to duodenum
5	34.0		
6	46.8		
7	15.2		
8		3.96	
9	16.2		
Mean ± SD for cases in Tables 1, 2	23.56 ± 8.9	3.79 ± 0.28	20.6

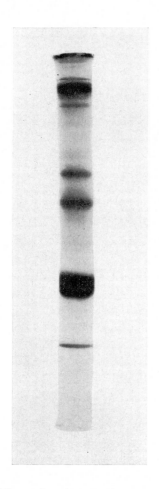

FIG. 1. Electrophoresis of acrylamide gel of partly purified CaBP from duodenal homogenates. Received from Case 1.

cium absorption (3, 5). A dose-time relationship was also observed: a higher dose of vitamin D caused the shortening of the lag period of CaBP appearance (5).

CaBP is found in all parts of the intestine, with the highest concentration in the duodenum and the lowest in the ileum. The concentration is higher in the jejunum than in the ileum. The rate of calcium absorption follows the same order. Luca and co-workers have reported that vitamin D_3 is transformed to 25-hydroxycholecalciferol by the liver and therefore the effect on the appearance of CaBP could be through the vitamin D metabolite (6).

The purpose of the present study was to investigate the presence of CaBP in human intestinal mucosa.

Methods. Biopsies from different parts of the intestine were obtained during gastrectomy or other intestinal operations. The duodenal mucosa was separated by scraping and the CaBP assayed by the method described by Wasserman (7). The assay system for CaBP is based upon the competition between CaBP and an ion exchange resin for added Ca^{45}.

Disk electrophoresis was performed on partly purified CaBP (8). Sliced disks of the gel were eluted and the CaBP determined.

TABLE 3. *CaBP in eluted electrophoretic acrylamide gels: upper and lower disks*

Case no.	Duodenum		Jejunum	
	Lower disk (Ca^{45}) count/min per µg protein	Upper disk (Ca^{45}) count/min per µg protein	Lower disk (Ca^{45}) count/min per µg protein	Upper disk (Ca^{45}) count/min per µg protein
1	358.0	344.0	189.0	77.0
2	64.7	54.9	32.0	33.1
5	795.0	270.0		
10	169.2	90.0		

Protein estimation was determined by the method of Lowry (9).

Results. Intestinal biopsies were obtained from nine patients: in four of them the samples were obtained from the duodenum as well as from the jejunum.

The specific activity of CaBP in the duodenal and jejunal samples of the same four patients is summarized in Table 1. The mean specific activity found in the duodenum was 19.05 ± 1.74 count/min per µg protein. The activity in the jejunum was about 20% of that in the duodenum. The CaBP in the five additional intestinal biopsies is given in Table 2. The mean of the specific activity of CaBP in the duodenum in the eight samples examined was 23.56 ± 8.9 count/min per µg protein compared to 3.79 ± 0.28 count/min per µg protein for the jejunal specimens.

Electrophoresis of acrylamide gel of partly purified CaBP from human duodenum was performed (Fig. 1). After elution of the different bands it was found that the two lowest bands contain the CaBP.

These two disks were eluted and the binding capacity was determined (Table 3). In about half of the eluted bands the major part of the CaBP was concentrated in the lower disk. But in the other half there was no significant difference in the amount of CaBP between the higher and the lower disks.

The demonstration of CaBP in human mucosa similar to that found in animals, suggests the important role of the CaBP in the active transport of calcium in the duodenum. As found in other species, the concentration of CaBP in human duodenal mucosa was five times higher than that in the jejunum. Wasserman and his co-workers have shown that the concentration of CaBP correlates directly with the ability to absorb calcium. The proteins were found in a soluble phase in the tissue homogenate suggesting that CaBP is readily released (3).

The role of vitamin D in rickets and osteomalacia is well known, the finding of a CaBP in the human duodenal mucosa suggest that vitamin D or its metabolites act through this protein.

Supported by Grant 4 X 5113, National Institute of Dental Research, National Institute of Health, Bethesda, Maryland.

REFERENCES

1. WASSERMAN RH and TAYLOR AN. *Science* **152**: 791, 1966.
2. DeLUCA HF, LUND J, ROSENBLOOM A and LOBECK CC. *J Pediat* **70**: 828, 1967.
3. WASSERMAN RH, CORRADINO RA and TAYLOR AN. *J Biol Chem* **243**: 3978, 1968.
4. TAYLOR AN and WASSERMAN RH. *Arch Biochem* **119**: 536, 1967.
5. EBEL JG, TAYLOR AM and WASSERMAN RH. *Amer J Clin Nutr* **22**: 431, 1969.
6. PONCHON G and DeLUCA HF. *Fed Proc* **28**: 759, 1969.
7. WASSERMAN RH, TAYLOR AN and KALLFELZ FA. *Amer J Physiol* **211**: 419, 1966.
8. SULITZEANU D, SLAVIN M and YECHESKELI E. *Annal Biochem* **21**: 59, 1962.
9. LOWRY OH, ROSENBROUGH NJ, FARR AL and RANDALL RJ. *J Biol Chem* **193**: 265, 1951.

ENHANCEMENT OF CALCIUM ABSORPTION IN HYPOTHYROIDISM

Observations with a New Method Measuring Calcium Absorption

J. F. F. LEKKERKERKER, F. VAN WOUDENBERG, H. BEEKHUIS and H. DOORENBOS

Division of Endocrinology, Department of Internal Medicine and Isotope Service, University Hospital, Groningen, The Netherlands

Patients totally thyroidectomized for functioning thyroid carcinoma and on intermittent therapy with triiodothyronin (T3) show a spontaneous rise in serum calcium and increased sensitivity to dihydrotachysterol during the myxedematous phase. This phenomenon can be explained by: increased absorption; decreased urinary calcium excretion; decrease of calcium pool; decreased secretion of calcium by the gut; relative increased skeletal breakdown.

Calcium absorption was studied by the following method: After i.v. injection of 2 µc Ca^{45} the serum radioactivity was measured in blood samples drawn after 10, 20, 30, 45, 75 and 120 min. Disappearance curves were constructed according to the formula $Rs(t) = A \cdot t^{-b}$ (t < 1,000 min) in which $Rs(t)$ is the radioactivity at time t, and A and b are constants (1) (Fig. 1). Two hours after the i.v. injection an oral dose was given containing 5 to 10 µc Ca^{45} in 150 ml of distilled water with 55 mg calcium as chloride. Serum radioactivity was measured in blood samples taken 15, 30, 60, 90, 120 and 180 min after the oral dose.

Assuming pulse-like absorption of calcium at the beginning of every minute and assuming disappearance of the radioacitvity, absorbed in every minute, according to the formula t^{-b}, cumulative absorption was calculated from both curves by a computer. The absorption was expressed as percent of the dose per liter calcium pool at 1 min. By multiplying these data by the size of this pool (= 1/A, A of the i.v. curve) we obtained the fraction of the oral dose absorbed. With this method we were able to measure in 5 hr the fractional absorption of an oral dose with the use of only one calcium isotope.

Nine totally thyroidectomized patients, three of whom were being treated with dihydrotachysterol for hypoparathyroidism, and three patients with primary myxedema were studied in the untreated phase and after six to eight weeks of substitution therapy with T3. All patients received diets with constant levels of calcium and phosphorus equal to their home diets. The results are given in Table 1 and Fig. 2 and 3. In the hypothyroid phase the calcium absorption was increased after 2 hr as well as after 3 hr; the urinary calcium excretion was increased and the calcium pool was unaltered. These results confirm the inhibitory effect of thyroxin on calcium absorption in rats (2). It is concluded that calcium absorption increases in hypothyroidism. This effect is probably not mediated by parathormone since increased absorption is accompanied by higher serum calcium le-

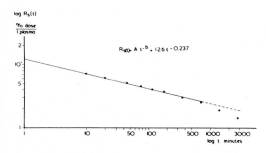

FIG. 1. Disappearance of radioactivity after i.v. injection of Ca^{45}.

TABLE 1. *Results in hypothyroid phase (–T3) and with substitution therapy (+T3)*

	Serum phosphorus (mg/100 ml)	Creatinine clearance (ml/min)	Phosphate clearance (ml/min)	Calcium pool t = 60 min l/kg body wt
– T3	4.0	73	10	0.246
+T3	3.2	116	17	0.266
P	< 0.02	< 0.01	< 0.01	ns

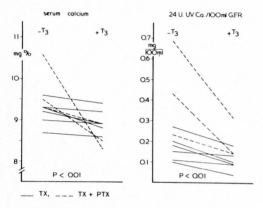

FIG. 2. Influence of T3 on serum calcium and urinary calcium excretion.

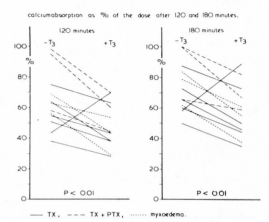

FIG. 3. Influence of T3 on calcium absorption.

vels and was also observed in three patients with hypoparathyroidism. It could be caused by an *in vivo* alteration of metabolism of vitamin D in the absence of thyroid hormone.

REFERENCES

1. ANDERSON J, TOMLIMSON RWS, OSBORN SB and WISE ME. *Lancet* i: 930, 1967.
2. NOBLE HM and MATTY AJ. *J Endocr* 37: 111, 1967.

BIOCHEMICAL AND BIOPHYSICAL ASPECTS OF CALCIFIED TISSUE

ACID PYROPHOSPHATASE, PHOSPHOPROTEINPHOSPHATASE AND PHOSPHOMONOESTERASE ACTIVITIES IN BONE TISSUE

G. VAES and J. VREVEN

Laboratory of Physiological Chemistry, University of Louvain, Belgium

As reviewed elsewhere (1), acid phosphatase is abundant in the osteoclasts and its activity has been found to be increased in the bones of rats or mice treated with parathyroid extract or by other agents which stimulate bone resorption. In the same way as alkaline phosphatase has been viewed as an index of osteoblastic activity, acid phosphatase in bone has been considered to reflect an osteolytic process (2).

However, acid phosphatase activity in bone should not be considered as the manifestation of a single enzyme. Vaes and Jacques (3) have shown that the activities assayed with phenylphosphate and β-glycerophosphate as substrates appear to be due largely to two different enzymes: acid phenylphosphatase is particularly labile and readily inactivated by various physical or chemical agents, while acid β-glycerophosphatase is more stable; acid phenylphosphatase activity is markedly dependent on the ionic strength and is more readily inhibited by formaldehyde, but less readily by tartrate, than β-glycerophosphatase. Both activities were found to be largely associated with cytoplasmic particles showing the main characteristics of lysosomes. On fractionation of the homogenates (4, 5) by differential centrifugation, both phosphatases sedimented in a similar way, becoming most concentrated in the L or "light mitochondrial" fraction; subfractionations by isopycnic centrifugation in density gradients did not succeed in separating the two phosphatase activities. Moreover, both enzymes displayed a typical structure-linked latency: they did not display most of their activity, unless some treatment injurious to the membranes of the particles had been applied (6). However, about 50% of the acid phenylphosphatase, although bound in a latent form to cytoplasmic particles having the main properties of lysosomes, was more resistant to activating treatments, suggesting its association either with particles distinct from the lysosomes, or with a special fraction of the total population of lysosomes present in the homogenates: on the basis of arguments developed elsewhere (1) it was speculated that this fraction could represent the lysosomes of the osteoclasts.

Further consideration has been given to the existence of several acid phosphatases in bone cells and to their intracellular distribution (Vreven and Vaes, in preparation). Cytoplasmic extracts from bone cells were found capable of splitting several phosphomonoesters at acid pH, not only β-glycerophosphate and phenylphosphate, but also α-glycerophosphate, paranitrophenylphosphate, phosphoethanolamine and phosphoserine. Acid pyrophosphatase activity was also demonstrated, using inorganic pyrophosphate as substrate, and phosphoproteinphosphatase, using casein as substrate. All these activities are optimal around pH 5. All of them, except the two glycerophosphatases, are rather labile in the conditions of the assays: they are then stabilized by the presence of ascorbic acid or other reducing agents such as cysteine or dithiothreitol, which thus sometimes appear to "stimulate" these activities; the addition of ascorbate to the incubation mixtures also permitted recovery of some of the activity which had been progressively lost in the extracts when kept for some time at 0 C. Acid pyrophosphatase activity was inhibited by the addition of magnesium ions to the incubation mixture.

Quantitative assays have been devised for all these activities: in acetate buffer, at or about their optimal pH and in the presence of ascorbic acid (5 mM), the rate of reaction was constant with time up to at least 2 hr for all, except acid pyrophosphatase, which leveled off earlier; for all activities, the rate of reaction was proportional to enzyme concentration up to 16 mg of tissue (cytoplasmic extract) per ml of assay mixture. Michaelis constants and maximal velocities were measured in these conditions.

Upon fractionation of the bone homogenates by differential centrifugation, all the activities occurred partly in soluble and partly in particulate fractions, with their highest specific activity in the light-mitochondrial fraction. In cytoplasmic extracts, all of these activities occured in latent form to the extent of 50 to 70 % of their total activity, depending on the enzyme; the latency of acid α-glycerophosphatase was, however, smaller (30%) than that of the other enzymes. The latency was decreased or suppressed by various physical or chemical agents: some of the activities, however, were less readily released than others remembering the difference previously observed between acid phenylphosphatase and acid β-glycerophosphatase. All these properties suggest strongly the association of acid pyrophosphatase, phosphoproteinphosphatase and phosphomonoesterase activities with lysosome-like particles.

While it is already known that acid phosphatase activities assayed on β-glycerophosphate and on phenylphosphate are due to two different enzymes, further studies, now in progress (Vreven, Lieberherr and Vaes), are still required to establish the molecular basis of the various activities demonstrated in the present work and their possible interrelationships. Their behavior during bone resorption is also being studied. We have already observed that a much higher amount of all these enzymes, but particularly of acid paranitrophenyl (+ 190%), phenylphosphatase (+ 230%) and pyrophosphatase (+ 370%) are found in embryonic calvaria which have been cultivated during a few days with parathyroid hormone.

Supported by Grant 1209 from the Belgian Fonds de la Recherche Scientifique Médicale.

REFERENCES

1. VAES G. in: Dingle JT and Fell HB (Eds), "Lysosomes in biology and pathology." Amsterdam, North Holland Pub Co, 1969, v 1, p 217.
2. McLEAN FC and URIST MR. "Bone", 2nd edn. Chicago, University of Chicago Press, 1961.
3. VAES G and JACQUES P. Biochem J 97:380, 1965.
4. VAES G. in: Richelle LJ and Dallemagne MJ (Eds), "Calcified tissues." Liège, University of Liège, 1965, p 51.
5. VAES G and JACQUES P. Biochem J 97: 389, 1965.
6. VAES G. Biochem J 97: 389, 1965.

AMINOPEPTIDASE PROFILE AND PROTEASE ACTIVITY IN RAT CARTILAGE AT PHYSIOLOGICAL pH

ALBERT HIRSCHMAN and MILDRED HIRSCHMAN

Department of Anatomy, Downstate Medical Center, State University of New York, Brooklyn, New York, USA

The presence of lysosomal acid hydrolases in the cartilage of developing bone, possibly involved in the degradation of cartilage matrix, was reported by Fell and Dingle (1). The concept that protein-polysaccharide degradation was an important step in preparing cartilage matrix for calcification was developed by Weinstein et al. (2) and Dziewiatkowski (3).

Inasmuch as the pH of tissue fluid in general is near neutrality, it was considered possible that physiological alterations in cartilage matrix may be brought about by hydrolytic enzymes with pH optima near or slightly above pH 7. Bélanger and Migicovsky (4), using a gelatin film method, reported the presence of proteolytic activity in bone at pH 7.6, with particular reference to resorption, but they did not find much activity in cartilage. Wergedal (5) showed the presence of proteolytic activity at pH 8 in metaphyseal and diaphyseal bone. Burstone (6) reported the presence of leucine amino-peptidase in bone cells by histochemical methods, but no specific reference to epiphyseal cartilage was made. Yeager et al. (7) and Johnson (8) reported the presence of leucine aminopeptidase in periosteal cells and in chondrocytes underlying surgically stimulated periosteum. Tanaka (9) and Mori and co-workers (10) found aminopeptidase only in small amounts in cartilage cells. Thus, although proteolytic activity has been found in bone, only small amounts, if any, have been reported by various investigators in epiphyseal cartilage.

The aminopeptidases are enzymes which split off N-terminal amino acids from polypeptide chains. There may be several aminopeptidases, each active against a more or less specific group of N-terminal amino acids. The present investigation is a study of the aminopeptidases of epiphyseal and costal cartilage of the rat, and of the general proteolytic activity in extracts of these tissues.

Methods. Extracts of epiphyseal and costal cartilage of young rats were made by grinding with sand and water (1 g tissue/15 ml H_2O), followed by centrifuging at about $800 \times g$ for 20 min.

The substrates used were 21 amino acid β-naphthylamides. Five mg of each were dissolved in 25 ml of 0.1 M PO_4 buffer at pH 7.0. The assay is a modification of that of Goldbarg and Rutenberg (11). The aminopeptidase profiles were made by calculating the ratios of the rate of hydrolysis of the various amino acid β-naphthylamides to that of leucine β-naphthylamide. The effect of pH was determined by using different phosphate buffers.

Some extracts were passed through a Sephadex G-200 column (2.5 × 90 cm) in 0.5% NaCl in 0.01 M PO_4 buffer at pH 7.4, and the fractions were assayed for aminopeptidase activities. Proteolytic activity of the extracts was measured by the Kunitz method (12). Aminopeptidase activity was demonstrated histochemically by incubating unfixed, cryostat-cut sections of tibial epiphyseal cartilage in some of the β-naphthylamide substrates, in the presence of fast garnet GBC or fast red B.

Results. The aminopeptidase profiles of epiphyseal and costal cartilage are shown in Table 1. The values given represent the activities relevant to leucine aminopeptidase activity in the same sample. Several points of

TABLE 1. *Aminopeptidase profiles of rat epiphyseal and costal cartilage[a]*

β-naphthylamide of	Epiphyseal	Costal
Leucine	1.00	1.00
Methionine	1.45	0.81
Alanine	1.40	0.81
Arginine	0.44	0.94
Glutamic acid (α)	0.42	0.43
Phenylalanine	0.40	0.32
Lysine	0.37	0.70
Histidine	0.17	0.17
Tyrosine	0.14	0.17
Asparagine	0.09	—
Valine	0.09	0.12
Glycine	0.07	0.08
Glutamic acid (γ)	0.07	0.08
Isoleucine	0.06	0.06
Aspartic acid (α)	0.05	0.12
Threonine	0.04	0.07
Proline	0.04	0.07
Serine	0.04	0.04
Aspartic acid (β)	0.02	0.005
Hydroxyproline	0.02	0.03

[a] Figures represent the ratios of the rate of hydrolysis of the individual amino acid β-naphthylamide to that of leucine β-naphthylamide.

difference between epiphyseal and costal cartilage may be seen: 1) Methionine and alanine aminopeptidase activities are much higher than leucine aminopeptidase activity in epiphyseal cartilage, but lower than leucine aminopeptidase activity in costal cartilage; 2) the ratios of arginine, phenylalanine, aspartic acid, threonine and proline aminopeptidase activities relevant to leucine aminopeptidase activity are higher in costal cartilage than in epiphyseal cartilage. In contrast to these results, a commercial hog kidney leucine aminopeptidase (Worthington) showed activity primarily against leucine β-naphthylamide.

The activity in the cartilage extracts was measured at pH 6.5, 7.0 and 7.5. In this range, the pH-activity curves were flat, or with the highest activity at pH 7.0 or 7.5, except for phenylalanyl and isoleucyl β-naphthylamides, for which highest activity was at pH 6.5.

On passing cartilage extracts through Sephadex G-200, the aminopeptidase activities against the β-naphthylamides of alanine, methionine, tyrosine, arginine, glutamic acid (α) and phenylalanine were all found only in the fraction immediately following the void volume, indicating mol wt greater than 200,000. This is in agreement with the value of about 300,000 reported for hog kidney aminopeptidase by Himmelhoch and Peterson (13).

General proteolytic activity, as measured by the Kunitz method using a casein substrate, was present in greater amount in extracts of epiphyseal cartilage than in extracts of costal cartilage. The activity was measured at pH 5.6, 6.6, 7.6 and 8.4; the greatest activity was at pH 7.6. These results differ from those of Ali (14) who used rabbit ear cartilage and a hemoglobin substrate.

Histochemical studies showed moderate amounts of leucine and methionine aminopeptidase activities in most cells of epiphyseal cartilage, but relatively little activity in the matrix. The cells of articular cartilage, particularly in the middle and inner zones, also showed activity. Under the same conditions, the activity in the metaphysis and marrow was so strong as to obscure precise cellular localization.

Conclusion. The presence of proteolytic and aminopeptidase activities in epiphyseal cartilage at near-neutral pH supports the view that these presumably nonlysosomal enzymes may be active in altering the cartilage matrix, possibly as part of the calcifying mechanism. The actual role of the aminopeptidases in protein metabolism is not known. Inasmuch as there is a wide spectrum of aminopeptidase activity in cartilage, it is conceivable that the cartilage aminopeptidases may break down, in a stepwise fashion, proteins and also protein fragments resulting from endopeptidase action.

The aminopeptidase activity was found principally in the chondrocytes, with relatively little activity in the matrix. Some loss from the matrix could have occurred by diffusion during incubation of the fresh, cryostat-cut sections. The failure of some other investigators to find appreciable amounts of aminopeptidases in cartilage may be due to the fact that they used specimens which had been subjected to histological fixatives.

Differences in the aminopeptidase profile of epiphyseal and costal cartilage may be related to the fact that, in contrast to epiphyseal cartilage, only a small proportion of costal cartilage is actively engaged in endochondral ossification. However, the role of the aminopeptidase is, as yet, unknown.

Supported in part by Grant AM 05922 from the National Institutes of Health.

REFERENCES

1. FELL HB and DINGLE JT. *Biochem J* **87**: 403, 1963.
2. WEINSTEIN H, SACHS CR and SCHUBERT M. *Science* **142**: 1073, 1963.
3. DZIEWIATKOWSKI DD. *Clin Orthop.* **35**: 189, 1964.
4. BÉLANGER LF and MIGICOVSKY BB. *J Histochem Cytochem* **11**: 734, 1963.
5. WERGEDAL J. *Calcif Tissue Res* **3**: 55, 1969.
6. BURSTONE MS. *Ann NY Acad Sci* **85**: 431, 1960.
7. YEAGER VL, JOHNSON MF, SETHER LA, SEVERSON AR, HENDRICKSON RR, FRYATT EA and HUGHES RA. *J Path Bact* **93**: 699, 1967.
8. JOHNSON MF and YEAGER VL. *J Path Bact* **93**: 703, 1967.
9. TANAKA K. *Acta Histochem (Jena)* **23**: 53, 1966.
10. MORI M, ITO M and FUKUI S. *Histochemie* **5**: 185, 1965.
11. GOLDBARG JA and RUTENBERG AM. *Cancer* **11**: 283, 1958.
12. KUNITZ M. *J Gen Physiol* **30**: 291, 1947.
13. HIMMELHOCH SR and PETERSON EA. *Biochemistry (Wash)* **7**: 2085, 1968.
14. ALI SY. *Biochem J* **93**: 611, 1964.

CHARACTERIZATION OF AMINOPEPTIDASES AND PHOSPHATASES OF HUMAN FETAL PERIOSTEUM

KAUKO K. MÄKINEN and PIRKKO-LIISA MÄKINEN

Institute of Dentistry and Department of Forensic Medicine, University of Turku, Turku, Finland

The aminopeptidase and phosphatase activity of human fetal periosteal membrane, parietal bones and cartilaginous epiphysis were investigated. The material was obtained from four to 16-week-old fetuses. After homogenization, the tissue samples were analyzed by isoelectric focusing and DEAE cellulose chromatography. The aminopeptidase activity was determined by an azo-coupling method using various N-L-aminoacyl-2-naphthylamines as the main substrates. The phosphatase activity of the samples was measured with p-nitrophenyl phosphate. The effect of various peptide hormones on the rate of hydrolysis of the above substrates was studied.

Attention was paid to the possible presence of aminopeptidase B in the tissues mentioned. Isoelectric focusing in the pH range 3 to 10 revealed only one peak with activity toward N-L-arginyl-2-naphthylamine. The isoelectric point of the enzyme was 4.3 and the enzyme hydrolyzed the corresponding derivative of L-lysine at a high rate. It is likely that the enzyme does not represent aminopeptidase B, a widely distributed mammalian arginine aminopeptidase. The occasionally observed activity of aminopeptidase B was considered to represent traces of blood. Aminopeptidase activity in periosteum, parietal bones and cartilaginous epiphysis was much lower than in blood or liver, and fewer substrates were hydrolyzed by preparations from the former tissues than by those obtained from the latter. Isoelectric focusing yielded several peaks hydrolyzing p-nitrophenyl phosphate. All these enzymes needed Mg^{2+} ions for maximum activity and most enzymes were maximally active at alkaline pH values.

Vasopressin inhibited the hydrolysis of p-nitrophenyl phosphate. Luteinizing hormone and luteotropic hormone activated this reaction. In general, the effect of peptide hormones seemed to be selective.

INFLUENCE OF SODIUM ETHANE-1-HYDROXY-1, 1-DIPHOSPHONATE AND Mg^{2+} ON THE INORGANIC PYROPHOSPHATASE IN CALCIFYING HAMSTER-MOLARS

J. H. M. WÖLTGENS, S. L. BONTING and O. L. M. BIJVOET

Department of Biochemistry, University of Nijmegen, Nijmegen, The Netherlands

Sodium ethane-1-hydroxy-1, 1-diphosphonate, $CH_3 C(OH) (PO_3HNa)_2$ (EHDP) inhibits the formation (1) and dissolution of calcium phosphate crystals *in vivo* at lower levels than inorganic pyrophosphate (2). It contains a P-C-P bond instead of the P-O-P bond in the latter substance. Fleisch et al. (2) suggest that this compound is more effective than inorganic pyrophosphate by virtue of its being more resistant to chemical and enzymatic hydrolysis.

The purpose of our study was to determine whether EHDP inhibits the inorganic pyrophosphatase (PP_i-ase) known to be present in calcifying hamster molars and whether such inhibition could be modified by Mg^{2+}.

Homogenates of molars from three-day-old hamster molars were used in these experiments. An inhibition curve of the PP_i-ase, with 50 % inhibition occurring at 1 mM EHDP, could be obtained by varying the EHDP concentration from 0 to 2.10^{-2} M.

In order to determine whether this inhibitory effect could be due to chelating properties of EHDP, the effect of Mg^{2+} with varying inhibitor-concentrations on PP_i-ase was studied. Without an inhibitor, a maximal stimulation of the PP_i-ase activity was obtained at a substrate/Mg^{2+} ratio of 1. The inhibition of the PP_i-ase by EHDP was Mg^{2+}-dependent. Maximal inhibition was obtained at a (substrate + inhibitor)/Mg^{2+} ratio of 1, suggesting that the inhibitory substance is a Mg-EHDP complex of molar ratio 1:1. Therefore a Lineweaver-Burke plot, with and without 1.65 mM Mg-EHDP complex, was determined and a competitive inhibition of the PP_i-ase by the Mg-EHDP complex with a $K_M = 1$ mM and a $K_I = 0.72$ mM was observed. These findings suggest that EHDP inhibits the PP_i-ase by a competition of its 1:1 Mg complex with the 1:1 Mg-pyrophosphate complex for the active site. The affinity to the enzyme of the Mg-EHDP complex appears to be the same as for the Mg-pyrophosphate complex.

REFERENCES
1. FRANCIS MD, RUSSELL RGG and FLEISCH H. *Science* **165**: 1264, 1969.
2. FLEISCH H, RUSSELL RGG and FRANCIS MD. *Science* **165**: 1262, 1969.

CARTILAGE LYSOZYME, AN EXTRACELLULAR BASIC (CATIONIC) PROTEIN

KLAUS E. KUETTNER, NINO SORGENTE, CHARALAMPOS ARSENIS and
REUBEN EISENSTEIN

Department of Orthopedic Surgery, Department of Biochemistry and Division of Pathology, Rush Presbyterian-St. Luke's Medical Center and Department of Biological Chemistry, University of Illinois College of Medicine, Chicago, Illinois, USA

Sir Alexander Fleming (1), while searching for antibacterial substances, discovered an enzyme in tissue extracts and body secretions as well as in egg whites of birds, which had "the power of rapidly dissolving certain bacteria." He called this enzyme lysozyme and found it present in cartilage. Cartilage contained more of this protein than any other tissue he studied.

Lysozyme is present in mammalian and avian preosseous cartilage, with the highest concentration in the area of cartilage undergoing transformation into bone (2). Its concentration seems to be dependent on the age, or better, the rate of cartilage transformation into bone and is modified by factors known to influence the state of cartilage, such as vitamin D (3). Exogenous egg white lysozyme when added to cultures of embryonic chick bones or mammalian epiphyseal growth plates, but not to cartilage which lacks a growth plate, induces specific but reversible morphologic changes, which are quite precise in their distribution and which appear to be due to binding to specific matrix components such as chondromucoproteins (4, 5). Such changes are noted in the resting zone, are most impressive in the lacunae of columnar zones, and spare the hypertrophic zone, where lysozyme is present in its highest concentration *in vivo*. Electron microscopic observations of these binding sites have permitted a number of conclusions as to the organization of cartilage matrix, including the first demonstration of a 640 Å periodicity related to cartilage collagen (6). To determine further what the physiological role of lyso-

zyme might be, we asked whether this basic protein was absorbed from the serum by strong anionic cartilage constituents, such as mucoproteins, or whether it was synthesized by chondrocytes.

Chicken embryonic cartilage was therefore incubated in glucose containing Krebs-Ringer buffer, to which C^{14} lysine was added (lysozyme contains six lysine residues per 129 amino acids, approximately 47 residues per 1,000). After 3-hr incubation the cartilage was homogenized, extracted and the tissue bound lysozyme was quantitatively obtained by treatment of the residue with the cation exchanger Sephadex CM-50. All the lysozyme activity (derived from the original incubation media as well as extracted from the tissue) was then absorbed on a cation exchanger, eluted with potassium chloride and the effluent passed through Sephadex G-25. The isolated protein peak coincided with that of both the lysozyme lytic activity and radioactivity indicating that lysozyme was biosynthesized by the embryonic chicken cartilage *in vitro*. The rate of biosynthesis of cartilage lysozyme as a function of time was then studied. One gram of cartilage was incubated in Krebs-Ringer bicarbonate buffer (pH 7.4) containing glucose (3 mg/ml) C^{14} lysine (0.5 μc/ml of buffer) at 37 C for 20, 40, 60, 90, 120 and 180 min, respectively, in a shaker water bath in air. After incubation, the tissue was immediately removed, homogenized and frozen in order to halt the cellular activity. It was then digested with trypsin (lysozyme is resistant to breakdown by trypsin). The trypsin digest as well as the incubation media were passed through a cationic exchanger Sephadex CM-50 which was extensively washed with deionized water in order to remove all noncationic protein components. Using a potassium chloride gradient of 0.01 to 4.0 M the lysozyme was quantitatively eluted. The peak of lytic activity corresponded to the peak of radioactivity. Quantitative evaluation of the biosynthesis of lysozyme indicated that after 60 min of incubation, the maximum amount of lysozyme was biosynthesized by the tissue. After 90 min of incubation, a sharp decline of lysozyme activity was evident. After 180 min, the amount of lysozyme had fallen to the level detectable after 20 min of incubation. These data indicated that the lysozyme was rapidly catabolized. In order to test the possibility of degradation by lysosomal enzymes, lysosomes were obtained from isolated chondrocytes. When such lysosomes were lysed and incubated with lysozyme no degradation of lysozyme could be observed. Lysozyme thus appears to be resistant to breakdown by lysosomal enzymes, suggesting that an as yet unidentified non-lysosomal protease is involved in lysozyme catabolism. Another aspect of our studies was to determine the locus of lysozyme in cartilage using immunofluorescent technique. Since the only lysozyme available for use as an antigen was egg white lysozyme, it became important to determine whether or not chicken cartilage lysozyme and chicken egg white lysozyme, which have identical electrophoretic mobility, were immunologically similar. Rabbits were therefore immunized with highly purified recrystallized egg white lysozyme. The antigen-antibody complex was then precipitated from the serum by the addition of antigen and the isolated complex was separated into lysozyme and purified specific antibody by column chromatography at pH 1.8 on Sephadex G-75. An embryonic chicken bone was then submerged in agar. The specific purified anti-egg lysozyme antibody (in a concentration of 2.5 mg/ml) and the specific antigen egg white lysozyme (in a concentration of 50 μg per ml) were placed into the wells one centimeter from the bone. After incubation at 37 C for 36 hr, precipitin lines formed between the antigen and the antibody, identical to those observed in an Ouchterlony plate. In addition, however, precipitin lines were also formed at the interface between the antibody and the bone. This indicated that lysozyme diffused out of the tissue and reacted with the anti-egg white lysozyme. The contiguous ends of both precipitin lines merged, thus establishing immuno-identity between egg white lysozyme and cartilage lysozyme of the chicken. The specificity of the antibodies obtained against egg white lysozyme was confirmed by incubating freshly biosynthesized radioactive cartilage lysozyme with the purified anti-egg white γ-globulin fraction. Over 90% of the radioactivity was removed from the solution and was recovered in the antigen-antibody precipitate. Using anti-egg white lysozyme in the indirect fluorescent antibody technique and appropriate controls, we were able to demonstrate that, in cartilage, lysozyme is located primarily in an area in the immediate vicinity of the chondrocyte, the lacunae.

Our working hypothesis, based on these observations, remains that the biological role of lysozyme is related to its properties as a basic protein, and involves an interaction with anionic polymers to alter their biological function. Current theory strongly indicates that such reactivity is primarily related to change and molecular dimensions, so as to affect water and ion binding in the connective tissues. Such a hypothesis then regards the relationship between lysozyme and the acidic mucoproteins as analogous to the one postulated between DNA and histone to regulate genetic activity. In this regard, it is of interest that during our experiments in which we have measured tissue lysozyme levels, it became clear that significant amounts of lysozyme are bound, rather than free.

REFERENCES

1. FLEMING A. *Proc Roy Soc* (*Biol*) **93**: 306, 1922.
2. KUETTNER K, GUENTHER H, RAY R and SCHU-MACHER G. *Calcif Tissue Res* **1**: 298, 1968.
3. EISENSTEIN R, ARSENIS C, LISK P and KUETTNER KE. *Fed Proc* **29**: 553, 1970.
4. KUETTNER K, SOBLE L, EISENSTEIN R and YAEGER J. *Calcif Tissue Res* **2**: 93, 1968.
5. KUETTNER KE, SOBLE LW, GUENTHER HL, CROXEN RL and EISENSTEIN R. *Calcif Tissue Res* **5**: 56, 1970.
6. EISENSTEIN R, ARSENIS C and KUETTNER KE *J Cell Biol* **46**: 626, 1970.

STUDIES ON THE NON-COLLAGENOUS PROTEINS OF BONE

B. A. ASHTON, G. M. HERRING, M. E. OWEN and I. T. TRIFFITT

Medical Research Council External Scientific Staff, Bone Research Laboratory,
Churchill Hospital, Headington, Oxford, England

Adult bovine cortical bone was powdered and extracted with sodium EDTA solution at pH 7.5 (1). The EDTA was found to solubilize between 4 and 6% of the organic matrix and this extract was fractionated according to the scheme shown in Fig. 1.

The separation of the G2 fraction on DEAE-cellulose (DE 32), using a gradient of 0 to 0.3 M sodium chloride in 0.05 M Tris (pH 7.2), is shown in Fig. 2. The analyses of the column fractions showed that these gly-

coproteins are not as acidic as the sialoprotein and chondroitin sulphate fractions, but that they contain appreciable amounts of carbohydrates.

The G1 and G2 fractions and the G2 subfractions were tested by immunodiffusion and microimmunoelectrophoresis for the presence of serum proteins. Both the G1 and G2 fractions gave two precipitin lines against anti-bovine serum antiserum on Ouchterlony plates, and these corresponded on immuno-

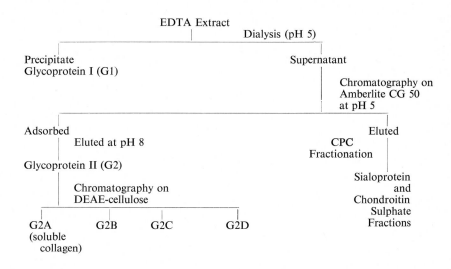

FIG. 1. Flow sheet illustrating the isolation of the glycoprotein fractions from bone.

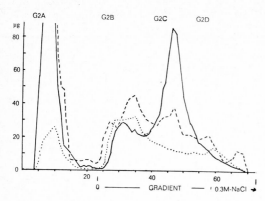

FIG. 2. The fractionation of the bone glycoprotein fraction G2 on DEAE-cellulose. —— U.V. E_{280}; ____ hexose; ...... sialic acid.

electrophoresis to bands against bovine serum albumin (BSA) and immunoglobulin G (IgG). Only G2B of the G2 subfractions showed the presence of serum proteins, and this fraction was investigated further by chromatography on DEAE-cellulose and Sephadex G-200. The column fractions were analyzed for protein (E_{280}), for BSA by the modified Laurell technique of Rose and Harboe (2) and by double immunodiffusion, and for IgG by double immunodiffusion. The elution patterns obtained for G2B are shown in Figures 3 and 4.

The quantitative determination of BSA and IgG by the Laurell method and single radial immunodiffusion showed that BSA forms 50 to 60% and IgG approximately 10% of the G2B fraction. To quantitate the amount of BSA present in bone, immunological techniques were applied to samples of a collagenase digest of bone matrix prepared by the method of Oldroyd and Herring (3). Immunoprecipitation, single radial immunodiffusion and the Laurell technique, gave values for BSA of between 3 and 4% of the collagenase digest, that is approximately 0.4% of the total organic matrix.

It has generally been assumed that BSA and IgG, appearing in extracts of bone and teeth, are derived from the serum contained in blood vessels. However, in other connective tissues these proteins have been demonstrated in extravascular sites (4), or isolated from the tissue in slightly modified forms, usually containing additional carbohydrate (5). In this laboratory, the localization of albumin in frozen undecalcified sections of rabbit bone is being studied by fluorescence microscopy and autoradiography after injection of tritiated-, FITC- and rhodamine-labeled protein.

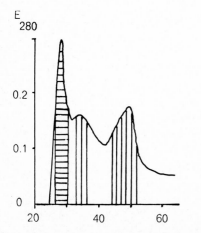

FIG. 3. Fractionation of G2B on Sephadex G-200. — Protein (E_{280}); ≡ IgG present; ||||| BSA present.

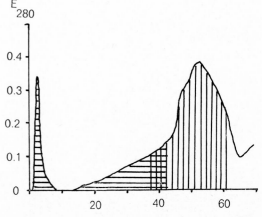

FIG. 4. Fractionation of G2B on DEAE-cellulose. — Protein (E_{280}); ≡ IgG present; ||||| BSA present.

REFERENCES

1. HERRING GM in: Blackwood HJJ (Ed) *First European Symposium on Bones and Teeth.* Oxford, Pergamon Press, 1964, p 263.
2. ROSE C and HARBOE NMG. in: Peeters H (Ed), "Protides of the biological fluids," *Proc 17th Coll Bruges,* 1969, p 397.
3. OLDROYD D and HERRING GM. *Biochem J* **104**: 20P, 1967.
4. MANCINI RE, VILAR O, DELLADIA JM, DAVIDSON OW, GOMEZ CJ and ALVAREZ B. *J Histochem Cytochem* **10**: 194, 1962.
5. BERMAN ER. *Biochim Biophys Acta* **83**: 27, 1964.

THE DISTRIBUTION OF MINERAL IONS IN CELLULAR ORGANELLES OF CALCIFYING CHICK BONE

IRVING M. SHAPIRO

Center of Oral Health Research, School of Dental Medicine, University of Pennsylvania, Philadelphia, Pennsylvania, USA

The literature abounds with morphological and biochemical studies describing the many different aspects of the calcification process. In spite of these numerous studies, the details of this mechanism are still obscure. For example, it is not known how calcium and phosphorus ions reach the mineralizing zone. Furthermore, the specific biochemical role of cells in this process has yet to be elucidated. Recently, however, it has been speculated that mitochondria of hard tissue cells play a specific role in mineralization. Indeed, indirect evidence has implicated the mitochondria of these cells in the transport of ions to the calcification site. To obtain further information on this possible role for these organelles, the ionic composition of mitochondria and the other cellular organelles of a mineralizing tissue was examined.

Six-week-old chicks were sacrificed and the liver and the long bones were immediately removed and stored in 0.25 M sucrose at 5 C. Each bone was carefully dissected and the zones of newly formed bone, hypertrophic and calcifying cartilages were isolated. The cells were liberated from the tissues by gentle trituration in a porcelain mortar. The liver cells and the cells from the three calcified tissue regions were homogenized in a glass-Teflon homogenizer and then subjected to differential centrifugation in 0.25 M sucrose. This procedure permitted isolation of nuclei, mitochondria and microbodies. The organelles were purified further by centrifugation, washed with water and freeze dried. Each cellular fraction was analyzed for DNA, RNA, cytochrome oxidase, protein and nitrogen. Perchloric acid extracts of the tissue were analyzed by atomic absorption spectroscopy for Ca^{++} and Mg^{++}. Inorganic phosphate (Pi) analysis was also determined on the acidic extracts.

TABLE 1. *The distribution of mineral ions in cell organelles of the epiphyseal apparatus and liver (mg/g of nitrogen)*

	Ca^{++}/N	Pi/N	Mg^{++}/N
Liver			
Nuclei	1.62	0.91	2.3
Mitochondria	3.08	1.58	2.6
Microbodies	1.69	0.62	2.2
Bone			
Nuclei	5.0	2.3	1.3
Mitochondria	6.6	3.2	2.8
Microbodies	3.1	1.5	3.5
Calcified cartilage			
Nuclei	7.8	2.18	2.2
Mitochondria	11.8	6.80	5.4
Microbodies	7.3	2.1	4.6
Hypertropic cartilage			
Nuclei	8.1	1.25	6.3
Mitochondria	28.9	15.6	2.4
Microbodies	14.7	1.9	3.4

The results of these analyses indicated that in both liver and epiphyseal cartilage, the Ca^{++} and Pi levels were higher in the mitochondria than in either the microbody or nuclear fractions (Table 1). In the mitochondria of the calcified tissues, the highest levels of Ca^{++} and Pi were found in hypertrophic cartilage and the lowest were in bone. The level of Ca^{++} and Pi in the mitochondria of bone cells was considerably higher than in the soft tissue.

The distribution of Mg^{++} differed from that of Ca^{++} and of Pi. High levels of Mg^{++} were found in all microbody and nuclear fractions, and there did not appear to be any correlation between the degree of calcification and the levels of this ion.

The results of this experiment supported the view that mitochondria could act as a store for Ca^{++} and Pi for the mineralization process. The findings could be interpreted to indicate that the organelles of the premineralized zone (hypertrophic cartilage) stored Ca^{++} and Pi and that the mitochondria gradually gives up these ions to the extracellular matrix as mineralization proceeds. This study also indicated that there did not appear to be a specific organelle concerned with Mg^{++} storage. It is therefore not possible to speculate on the pathway by which this ion reaches the extracellular matrix of cartilage and bone.

RNA AND MUCOPOLYSACCHARIDE METABOLISM
IN RACHITIC CARTILAGE AND BONE

D. J. SIMMONS and A. S. KUNIN

Radiological Physics Division, Argonne National Laboratory, Argonne, Illinois and
University of Vermont, Burlington, Vermont, USA

Qualitative and quantitative aspects of mucopolysaccharide (MPS) and RNA metabolism in rat cartilage and bone during the development and healing of rickets were studied by autoradiography following injection of labeled precursor substances. The animals were made rachitic by feeding them a semisynthetic, high calcium (1.2%), low phosphate (0.1%), vitamin D-free diet for two weeks. Healing was achieved during the third week when the rats were fed a basal rachitogenic ration supplemented by phosphate (Ca:P = 1.4:1) and vitamin D (10 IU/g diet).

H^3-uridine was employed to follow the synthesis and turnover of RNA; S^{35}-sulfate was used to study MPS synthesis. These radioactive precursors were administered in single injections, i.p. The rats labeled with uridine were killed 1, 4, and 72 hr after injection; the S^{35}-labeled rats were killed after 3 hr. The autoradiographs were prepared by the dipping method in Kodak NTB-2 liquid emulsion, and they were quantitated by grain counting.

Cartilage. From the S^{35}-sulfate series, we were able to demonstrate and confirm Hjertquist's observations (1) that while most of the cells throughout the normal cartilage plate (ad lib. and pair-fed rats) are competent to synthesize MPS, the most mature hypertrophic cells in rachitic cartilage have lost this ability. But the grain counts suggested that the rate of MPS synthesis by cells in the proliferative zones of rachitic cartilage was entirely normal.

Nearly every cell in normal cartilage was

engaged in RNA synthesis, as discerned by the pattern of H³-uridine incorporation. But the grain counts suggested that the cells in the hypertrophic zone were three to four times more active than the cells in the proliferative zone. This activity gradient was not evident in rachitic cartilage. Cellular tracer incorporation was normal in the upper third of the plate, subnormal (40%) in the youngest hypertrophic cells and markedly reduced in the oldest juxtametaphyseal cells. RNA turnover, defined as a decrease in nuclear and cytoplasmic grain counts 72 hr after injection, may be impaired in nutritional rickets, for while normal chondrocytes lost 75% of their activity, rachitic cells lost only 50%. These differences may not solely reflect an extended zonal cell longevity in rachitic cartilage owing to impaired endochondral ossification and stunted linear bone growth. While the data do not bear directly upon rates of enzyme synthesis, the *in vitro* data (2–4) on increased glycolytic enzyme concentrations in rachitic cartilage may now be interpreted as reduced enzyme turnover rather than as increased RNA-dependent synthesis. The enzymes may simply accumulate because they are not destroyed. In rickets healed by phosphate, the tracer distribution and pattern of synthesis and turnover was normal.

Bone. The uptake and turnover of H³-uridine by tibial osteoblasts along the endosteum and proximal metaphyseal trabeculae were quantitatively similar in normal and rachitic rats healed by phosphate. These data, as well as prior information about endosteal cells (5), permit us to conclude that the pace of metaphyseal bone formation by individual osteoblasts in rickets is not abnormal. Moreover, it is likely that changes in the rate of urinary hydroxyproline excretion in phosphate-healed rickets (6) reflect the populations of competent osteogenic cells, not their individual levels of activity.

Performed under the auspices of the U.S. Atomic Energy Commission.

REFERENCES

1. HJERTQUIST SO. *Acta Path Microbiol Scand* Suppl **154**: 99, 1962.
2. MEYER WL and KUNIN AS. *Arch Biochem* **129**: 438, 1969.
3. KUNIN AS and KRANE SM. *Biochim Biophys Acta* **107**: 203, 1965.
4. DIXIT PK. *J Histochem Cytochem* **17**: 411, 1969.
5. SIMMONS DJ and KUNIN AS. *Clin Orthop* **68**: 261, 1970.
6. PARSONS V, STIRLING G and DAVIES C. *Calcif Tissue Res* Suppl **4**: 157, 1970.

SELECTIVE INTERACTION BETWEEN CA⁺⁺ AND CYTOCHROME COMPONENTS OF INNER MITOCHONDRIAL MEMBRANES

HERBERT ZIPPER and PHILIP PERSON

V. A. Hospital, Brooklyn, and Columbia University School of Dental and Oral Surgery, New York, New York, USA

The movement of Ca^{++} across cell membranes against electrochemical gradients is, in nature, always an obligatorily aerobic process. It is also known that both Ca^{++} and parathormone exert strong influences upon the redox state of mitochondria and mitochondrial derivatives; and it has been suggested by several groups of workers that mitochondria may play an important role in the mineralization process. In addition, there has been a recent renewal of interest in the detection and characterization of selective Ca^{++}

binding substances, which may be of importance in the transport and metabolism of Ca^{++}.

Recent studies in this laboratory have demonstrated that yeast and heart mitochondria may be solubilized without use of detergents or sonic oscillations by a variety of methods involving controlled use of high pH. In these methods, one finds direct and indirect evidence that such mitochondrial solubilizations are accompanied by removal of divalent cations from the insoluble membrane components. In the above perspective we now report on a newly discovered selective complexing between Ca^{++} and the high pH-solubilized a, b and c cytochrome components of the inner membranes of mitochondria isolated from yeast and heart muscle, which results in the quantitative precipitation of the entire cytochrome complex.

Yeast mitochondria were isolated from water suspensions (no salts or buffers used) by standard differential centrifugation procedures. The isolated mitochondrial pellets (200 mg protein) were solubilized by incubation with 0.05 M EDTA at pH 10.0 for 60 min, and the system spun at $144,000 \times g$ for 60 min. Conditions for solubilization of heart mitochondria differ somewhat in that high pH values and lower centrifugal forces are used. The clear supernatant liquid contained all of the a, b and c cytochromes in solution, and was dialyzed for 20 hr against four changes of distilled H_2O (four liters each). It was then divided into two equal aliquots. To one aliquot, 0.2 M Ca^{++}, and to the other aliquot, 0.2 M Mg^{++} were added dropwise with stirring. With Ca^{++} a heavy pale tan precipitate quickly appeared (0.001 M Ca^{++} final concentration); while with Mg^{++} (final concentration 0.022 M) the solution remained clear initially, but on standing for 15 to 30 min, fine, white, thread-like aggregates appeared. Both precipitates were spun down at $2,000 \times g$. They were washed. solubilized, and subjected to spectral and biochemical analyses. Ca^{++} had quantitatively precipitated all of the a, b and c cytochrome components originally solubilized from the mitochondria, and the system retained all of the cytochrome oxidase activity present in the originally solubilized material. In the Mg precipitated material, there was no spectral evidence of cytochrome components, and no cytochrome oxidase activity was detectable by assay. Electronmicroscope study of the Ca^{++} and Mg^{++} precipitated material is in progress. Preliminary observation of phosphotungstic acid-negatively stained material show that the Ca^{++} precipitated material consists of a background of randomly dispersed small granular components, among which are seen amorphous material and also larger, vesicular and myelin-like membranous components. In the case of the Mg^{++} precipitated material, there are also amorphous, vesicular and myelin-like membranous components, but the small granule components are lacking. The electron microscopic appearances of both Ca^{++} and Mg^{++} complexes are therefore similar in terms of content of lipid figures and amorphous material, but they differ in that the Ca^{++} complex only contains granular material. The latter may represent the cytochrome components according to our own and other studies in the literature. These observations provide a possible locus for Ca^{++} interactions with mitochondria, and as such, are relevant to problems of mineralization and to the many biochemical studies of the involvement of Ca^{++} in mitochondrial electron transport processes.

MUCOPOLYSACCHARIDES OF THE MATRIX OF EPIPHYSEAL GROWTH PLATE

REUBEN EISENSTEIN, CHARALAMPOS ARSENIS and KLAUS E. KUETTNER

Rush Presbyterian–St. Luke's Medical Center, Chicago, Illinois, USA

One of the problems in electron microscopy of cartilage is that conventionally prepared tissues appear to be relatively empty, an appearance which is inconsistent with what is known about the physical and chemical properties of this tissue. In recent years cationic substances have been used as electron stains for the anionic components of cartilage, which are largely mucopolysaccharide in nature. We have compared the morphology of cartilage epiphyseal growth plates from puppy scapulas and mouse embryo femurs, as visualized after staining with three cations: ruthenium red, protamine and egg white lysozyme. Ruthenium red is a small metal salt; protamine is a nucleoprotein of high charge density; lysozyme is a cationic protein with a mol wt of 14,500, lower charge density and a normal constituent of cartilage.

Protamine and lysozyme stain only extracellular matrix where three lines of evidence suggest that they form complexes with mucopolysaccharides: they form precipitates with them in test tube experiments, metachromasia is lost in tissue sites where they can be visualized, and digestion with hyaluronidase or papain results in loss of ability of these cations to complex with the tissue. Ruthenium red, in some areas, also stains intracellular materials.

With all three cations, complexes between the stain and some component of the tissue, apparently mucopolysaccharide in nature, are easily visualized as electron dense deposits. The volume of distribution of such deposits is much greater with the protein cations than with ruthenium red, most likely due to maintenance of polysaccharides in a more extended state during combination with the larger proteins than with the smaller metallic salt, ruthenium red.

A comparison of the staining reactions of cartilage matrix with these three materials permits the separation of two classes of mucopolysaccharides. One of these is associated with collagen, occupies a large volume when stained with lysozyme or protamine and a small volume when stained with ruthenium red, and forms an intensely dark precipitate with ruthenium red. The other is stained with protamine and ruthenium red, but not with lysozyme, stains less intensely with ruthenium red, and is not associated with collagen in its distribution through the tissue.

These reactions are interpreted as follows: The material which stains with all three cations and occupies a smaller volume when stained with ruthenium red is considered to be a larger, more glycosylated molecule with a greater anionic charge and volume of distribution. Of the chemically characterized major components of cartilage matrix, protein polysaccharide light-5 (PPL-5) seems to best fit such a description. This material is therefore termed "presumptive PPL-5." The other material, which does not stain with lysozyme and stains less intensely with ruthenium red is considered to be smaller, less glycosylated, with a smaller charge and volume of distribution. Such a description might well fit the other major chemical component of cartilage matrix, PPL-3. This material is therefore referred to as "presumptive PPL-3."

These two classes of mucopolysaccharides are not uniformly distributed in the different zones of cartilage. In the resting zone, particularly near the articular surface, both types of material are present and are relatively uniformly distributed in the tissue. In the columnar zone, both types of material are present within the lacuna, but only "presumptive PPL-5" is seen in the extralacunar space. In this space, however, it occupies a smaller volume of distribution than it does within the lacuna, suggesting that a different or more tightly cross-linked arrangement is present within the lacuna than in the extralacunar space. In the extralacunar space, the mucopolysaccharide is arranged in a regular array on the surface of collagen fibers, which do not have an intrinsic 640 Å periodicity in this area. This array is best demonstrated with lysozyme which, in the puppy scapula, demonstrates a regular 640 Å periodicity of lysozyme reactive mucopolysaccharide on the surface of collagen fibrils. In mouse embryo femur, where the collagen fibrils are narrower than in the puppy scapula, this arrangement is much less regular. In the hypertrophic zone, the "presumptive PPL-5" is not demonstrable.

Within chondrocytes, material stainable with ruthenium red is demonstrable in two types of vesicles, both derived from the Golgi apparatus. One type is large, and the other small. Small vesicles evert into larger ones or into the extracellular space, as do larger ones. The intensity of stain increases as the vesicles move toward the cell membrane, suggesting continuing growth of polysaccharide chains within these vesicles.

Aside from interpretation of the micrographs in chemical terms, which is admittedly speculative, this study of comparative staining reactions demonstrates at least three things. First, the matrix as well as the cells of the epiphyseal growth plate differentiate in the different anatomical areas of this tissue. Second, the nature of the mucopolysaccharides within the lacuna is different from those in the extralacunar area. Third, at least in some areas of cartilage there is a topographic interrelationship between collagen and mucopolysaccharide in molecular dimensions. All these conclusions fit certain data available in the biochemical literature.

THE MUCOPOLYSACCHARIDES (GLYCOSAMINOGLYCANS) IN FRACTURE CALLUS

KAARE SOLHEIM

Ullevål Hospital, University of Oslo, Oslo, Norway

The mineralization process in bone formation is far from understood. Glycosaminoglycans have been suggested as playing an important role in this process, however, they have not previously been chemically isolated and identified.

Since fracture callus grows and mineralizes rapidly, the glycosaminoglycans were examined in experimental fractures in rabbits. Three-day and four-week-old callus were studied, and the chemical analyses included determinations of calcium, phosphorus and hydroxyproline as an index of the mineral and collagen content, respectively. The cetyl pyridinium chloride method was used for the liberation, fractionation and identification of the glycosaminoglycans.

Glycoproteins and glycosaminoglycans were separated on Ecteola-cellulose columns and the hexosamines in the eluates were determined. While one-third of the total hexosamines in the dried callus powder from three-day-old fractures were derived from glyco-proteins and two-thirds from glycosamino-glycans; the glycoproteins had decreased to about 6% of the total hexosamines in four-week-old callus. The total content of glyco-saminoglycans, expressed as a percentage of organic dry weight, increased during the first two weeks after the fracture and then de-clined.

A minor component of the glycosamino-glycans in callus was identified as hyaluronic acid, the amount of which was highest in one- and two-week-old callus. Only small amounts were found at later stages of fracture repair. However, the hyaluronic acid isolated showed unchanged chemical and physical properties during all stages of fracture repair.

Chondroitin sulfate was the main compo-nent of the glycosaminoglycans in callus from all stages of fracture repair examined. The infrared spectra of the galactosaminoglycans in callus from all stages of fracture repair showed characteristics of both chondroitin 4-sulfate and chondroitin 6-sulfate with the former predominating. These sulfated galac-tosaminoglycans were probably of low molec-ular weight and/or sulfated to a low degree in the earlier stages of fracture repair and their degree of polymerization and/or sulfa-tion probably increased up to four weeks post-fracture. Any desulfation or depolymeriza-tion of the galactosaminoglycans in callus did not take place during the time period examined.

Thus, quantitative as well as qualitative variations in the glycosaminoglycans in callus occur during its development to highly min-eralized bone. These studies were extended to examine the protein component in the proteo-glycan-complex and also the occurrence of the glycosaminoglycans during pathologic calcification, as in myositis ossificans and os-teogenesis imperfecta. In myositis ossificans the glycosaminoglycans were found to be the same as in normal bone, whereas in osteo-genesis imperfecta the glycosaminoglycan pat-tern was totally disturbed. In nonunion, i.e. where the repair of a fracture fails, the min-eralization per se seems to proceed normally but the organic matrix is at fault, as studies in pseudarthrosis have shown.

BOVINE SERUM ALBUMIN-CALCIUM BINDING STUDIES

II. EFFECTS OF pH AND pCa VARIATIONS

CH. E. SACHS and A. M. BOURDEAU

Centre d'Etudes des Maladies du Metabolisme de l'Enfant, Hôpital des Enfants Malades, Paris, France

Our original purpose was to investigate the effect of pH on calcium-protein binding in patients in order to determine whether or not strict anaerobic conditions have to be ob-served in blood sampling for ionized calcium measurements. We have, however, become involved in a long-term *in vitro* study of bovine serum albumin (BSA) solutions. In a preliminary report (1) we discussed an ap-parent abnormality of the calcium-binding behavior under certain circumstances. Fur-ther critical studies are presented which ques-tion the reality of this abnormal behavior.

Methods. To obtain solutions of the same ionized calcium concentrations, referred to as isopotential for calcium or solutions of pCa, a dialysis equilibrium in a thermostated con-tainer between a dialyzing fluid and a series of cellophane bags (Cuprophane, Bemberg, Wüperthal, Germany), containing increasing concentrations of BSA was established. The dialyzing fluid was a 150 mM of sodium chloride solution with concentrations of calcium chloride from 0.5 to 2.4 mM. A few drops of triethanolamine were added to stabilize the solution to the desired pH (pH range 6.8 to 8). The solutions inside the bags were made from a commercially available bovine albumin solution of 200 g/liter (Biotrol Laboratories, Paris). The dilutions were made to the approximate desired albumin concentrations with the dialyzing fluid.

Preliminary tests showed that equilibrium for calcium exchanges was obtained in 12 to 16 hr at 27 C and that, because of some dilution in the bags, the usual final concentrations of albumin were 20, 40, 57, 70, 100 and 120 g/liter, respectively. Different equilibria were studied by varying pH and calcium concentrations in the dialysis fluid. After dialysis, bag solutions and dialysis fluid were analyzed for pH, sodium, chloride, total and ionized calcium and protein. Total calcium was measured by a complexometric method, and ionized calcium was measured with the flow-through liquid membrane electrode (Orion Research Inc., Mass., USA).

Results and discussion. In our previous report, data of a given isopotential experiment were analyzed as a whole according to a described theoretical basis of data processing. This can be summarized by equation 1:

$$(\text{total Ca}) = m \times (\text{total albumin}) + (\text{Ca}^{++}) \quad (1)$$

stating that in each experiment a total calcium vs. total albumin plot should be a straight line since m, mean number of calcium moles bound per albumin mole, and (Ca^{++}), ionized calcium in the bags, were constant.

The results of this global analysis showed, in fact, a decrease of m with increasing albumin concentrations. A critical review of the data was performed focusing on the slight differences in pCa and pH values of the solutions in the same experiment.

The relative inequality of ionized calcium in different bags of a same experiment, due to Donnan effect, could not be the cause of the observed variation of m, since ionized calcium increases slightly with albumin concentration and since m increases with ionized calcium according to equation 2:

$$\frac{1}{m} = \frac{1}{f}(1 + \frac{K}{\text{Ca}^{++}}) \quad (2)$$

The variations of pH can be summarized as follows: In experiments with dialysis fluid pH above 6.95, a decrease of bag-pH was observed with increasing albumin concentrations; below pH 6.90 the variation was reversed. The cause of this variation was the acid or alkaline-like behavior of the commercially available BSA solution we used, associated with the absence of any effective buffer capacity of our dialysis fluid. Since pH changes might affect the value of K, the observed variations of m have to be related to modifications of pH. Since evaluation of m from global analysis was subjected to criticism, the data were analyzed on an individual basis and m calculated according to equation 3:

$$m = \frac{\text{Ca bound}}{\text{total albumin}} = \frac{\text{total Ca} - \text{Ca}^{++}}{\text{total albumin}} \quad (3)$$

This indirect determination of the bound fraction of calcium was accurate since the use of the calcium selective membrane electrode permitted direct measurement of ionized calcium and since there was no diffusible calcium chelating agent in our system. (The calcium-chelating effect of most effective buffers in the pH range 6.5 to 8.0 was the reason for the use of a nonbuffered dialysis fluid.)

Variations of m with pH, calcium and BSA concentrations were studied on plots of m as a function of one of these variables: $m = f$ (pH), $\frac{1}{m} = f\left(\frac{1}{\text{Ca}^{++}}\right)$ according to equation 2, m = f (colog Ca^{++}). Overall plotting of the data did not allow us to ascribe simple relations to these variations. Data were arranged to obtain plots where two of the variables were constant: the preliminary results did not provide sufficient information in each category to permit any significant clarification.

Nevertheless the importance and non-linearity of pH effect on m is qualitatively evident. At ionized calcium concentrations of 1 mM, below pH 6.9, m increases from 0.08 to 0.40 mM/mM; it reaches a plateau between 6.9 and 7.2 and increases then for pH 7.2 to 7.9 from 0.40 to 1.4 mM/mM. The $\dfrac{1}{m} = f$ $\left(\dfrac{1}{Ca^{++}}\right)$ plot is not linear throughout and becomes curvilinear for values of ionized calcium above 1.5 mM. The slope of the linear part increases with increasing BSA concentrations.

No general conclusions can be drawn from these results. Some of the differences, such as a lower overall calcium binding capacity, between these results and data published by other authors (2) might be due to the quality of BSA studied (E. W. Moore, personal communication).

Supported in part by Grant 69–01–732 from the Delegation Generale à la Recherche Scientifique et Technique and Grant 11731–II/B6 from the Commissariat à l'Energie Atomique—EURATOM Joint Association.

REFERENCES

1. SACHS CH and BOURDEAU AM. *Clin Orthop* (in press).
2. CARR CW. *Arch Biochem* **43**: 147, 1953.

DISTRIBUTION OF WATER AND GLYCOSAMINOGLYCANS IN DIFFERENT LAYERS OF CATTLE ARTICULAR CARTILAGE

R. K. LEMPERG, S. E. LARSSON and S. O. HJERTQUIST

Department of Orthopedic Surgery, Umeå University and Department of Pathology. Sundsvall Hospital, Sundsvall, Sweden

The composition and concentration of the glycosaminoglycans of apparently normal human articular cartilage has been found to vary between birth and 20 years of age (1, 2 and S. O. Hjertquist, in preparation). With further increase of age, up to 80 to 90 years, no consistent changes were found in total hexosamines (1–3 and Hjertquist, in preparation) and in chondroitinsulphate (2, 4, 5). Cattle articular cartilage showed a decrease of total hexosamines and chondroitinsulphate between the ages of four months and 12 years (6). These results referred to "whole thickness articular cartilage." Since histochemical (7) and microchemical (8–10) studies have suggested that the glycosaminoglycans of adult individuals are unevenly distributed in different layers of articular cartilage, investigations involving "whole thickness articular cartilage" should be interpreted with some caution. It seemed therefore worthwhile to study the distribution of water and different glycosaminoglycans in different articular cartilage layers in growing and adult individuals.

From cattle varying between one month and 10 years of age, cartilage-bone cylinders (6 mm in diameter) were obtained from the femoral condyles within a few min after death and frozen in liquid nitrogen. Frozen sections were prepared. The outermost 20 μ section

TABLE 1. *The water content (% of wet weight) in different layers of articular cartilage from the femoral condyle of cattle. (Values given are mean* ± SE)

	Calf	Heifer	Cow
	n = 7	n = 6	n = 7
SL	81.10 ± 0.77[a]	72.90 ± 1.80[d]	71.10 ± 1.57
ML	74.70 ± 1.10	69.90 ± 1.37[b]	72.60 ± 0.41[c]
DL	71.80 ± 2.26	60.70 ± 0.93[e]	65.93 ± 0.77[f]

[a] Difference from ML: $P < 0.001$ [b] Difference from DL: $0.01 > P > 0.001$
[c] Difference from DL: $P < 0.001$ [d] Difference from calf: $0.01 > P > 0.001$
[e] Difference from calf DL: $P < 0.001$ [f] Difference from heifer: $0.01 > P > 0.001$

TABLE 2. *Total hexosamines (A) and hexosamines in the MgCl2 fraction—chondroitin-sulphate (B) in % of wet weight in different layers of articular cartilage from the femoral condyle of cattle. (Values given are mean* ±SE)

		Calf	Heifer	Cow
A		n = 5	n = 4	n = 4
	SL	1.180 ± 0.055[a]	1.605 ± 0.100[c]	1.393 ± 0.058[b]
	ML	1.336 ± 0.067	1.603 ± 0.065[d]	1.685 ± 0.100
	DL	1.754 ± 0.155	1.333 ± 0.122	1.703 ± 0.076
B	SL	0.838 ± 0.045[e]	0.995 ± 0.100	0.553 ± 0.041[h]
	ML	1.038 ± 0.067[f]	1.015 ± 0.087	0.630 ± 0.087[i]
	DL	1.434 ± 0.138	0.880 ± 0.087[g]	0.683 ± 0.065[j]

[a] Difference from DL: $0.01 > P > 0.001$ [b] Difference from ML: $0.05 > P > 0.01$
[c] Difference from calf: $0.01 > P > 0.001$ [d] Difference from calf: $0.05 > P > 0.01$
[e] Difference from ML: $0.05 > P > 0.01$ and from DL: $0.01 > P > 0.001$
[f] Difference from DL: $0.05 > P > 0.01$
[g] Difference from calf: $0.05 > P > 0.01$ [h] Difference from heifer: $0.01 > P > 0.001$
[i] Difference from heifer: $0.05 > P > 0.01$ [j] Difference from calf: $0.01 > P > 0.001$

constituting the surface layer was discarded due to uncontrollable contamination with synovial fluid. Thereafter, serial 200 μ thick sections were cut and three of these sections were analyzed: the superficial layer (SL), one section from the middle layer (ML) and the deepest layer (DL) close to the cartilage-bone junction. The water content was determined in each individual section and pooled sections (5 mg dry weight) from each layer were used for analysis of calcium, hydroxyproline and glycosaminoglycans. The analysis of the glycosaminoglycans was made by a micro-procedure with cetylpyridinium chloride (11). The results of the analyses of the water content (Table 1) and hexosamines (Table 2) are given for calves (one and five months), heifers (8 months) and cows (five and 10 years). The difference between total hexosamines and hexosamines in the $MgCl_2$ fraction (chondroitinsulphate) is mainly attributable to hexosamines in the CPC fraction (glycoproteins and possibly keratinsulphate) since the two other fractions, the 0.3 M NaCl fraction (mainly hyaluronic acid) and the 6.0 M HCl fraction, were quantitatively small.

1) The water content decreased significantly with the distance from the articular surface in all age groups. In the DL, a decrease was found between calves and heifers followed by a remarkable tendency to an increase in cows. The ML showed constant figures in all age groups while a decrease was found in the SL between calves and heifers. 2) The total hexosamines calculated in % of the wet weight showed an increase in the deeper layer in

calves and cows, while in heifers a tendency towards low values was found in the DL. Heifers showed higher values in the SL and ML compared to calves. There was no consistent difference between cows and heifers. 3) The MgCl$_2$ fraction (% of the wet weight) showed a clear increase with depth in calves but not in heifers and cows. Decrease of this fraction was found in DL of heifers compared to calves and in all layers of the cows. 4) The CPC fraction increased in cows approximately to the same extent as the MgCl$_2$ fraction decreased, resulting in constant total hexosamines values in comparison to heifers. 5) Solubility profiles of the chondroitinsulphate fractions in the SL suggested lower molecular weights or change densities in this layer compared to the DL.

Thus this investigation showed consistent differences in the water content and glycosaminoglycans concentration between different layers of articular cartilage and alterations with maturation and aging. These observations are roughly in accordance with previous investigations concerning adult individuals (9, 10). Isolation and characterization of the gly-

cosaminoglycans in different layers are in progress. Similar investigations in osteoarthritis may be of particular interest because, in this disease, the cartilage surface becomes eroded and studies of "remaining cartilage" would consequently involve layers of different depth.

REFERENCES

1. HJERTQUIST SO and ENGFELDT B. *Acta Path Microbiol Scand* Suppl, **187**: 40, 1967.
2. KUHN R and LEPPELMANN H-J. *Liebig Ann Chem* **607**: 202, 1957.
3. ANDERSSON CE, LUDOWIEG J, HARPER HA and ENGLMAN EP. *J Bone Joint Surg* **46A**: 1176, 1964.
4. BOLLET AJ and NANCE JL. *J Clin Invest* **45**: 1170, 1966.
5. KUHN R and LEPPELMANN H-J. *Liebig Ann Chem* **611**: 254, 1958.
6. BALAZS EA. in: "Aging of connective and skeletal tissue," *Thule International Symposia.* Stockholm, Nordiska Bokhandelns Förlag, 1969.
7. STOCKWELL RA and SCOTT JE. *Ann Rheum Dis* **24**: 341, 1965.
8. BALAZS EA, BLOOM GD and SWANN DA. *Fed Proc* **25**: 1813, 1966.
9. MAROUDAS A, MUIR H and WINGHAM J. *Biochim Biophys Acta* **177**: 492, 1969.
10. STOCKWELL RA and SCOTT JE. *Nature* (London) **215**: 1376, 1967.
11. ANTONOPOULOS CA, GARDELL S, SZIRMAI JA and DETYSSONSK ER. *Biochim Biophys Acta* **83**: 1, 1964.

EFFECT OF IONIC STRENGTH ON THE DISSOLUTION OF CALCIUM PHOSPHATES

YORAM AVNIMELECH

Soils and Fertilizers Laboratory, Technion—Israel Institute of Technology, Haifa, Israel

The purpose of this work is to present a generalized approach describing the effect of ionic strength of the solution on the composition of solutions of calcium phosphates and on the dissolution of calcium phosphates. The data obtained for dilute calcium phosphate systems may be applied to many systems of interest such as soils, fertilizer granules, sea water or biological fluids.

A very important parameter describing the

properties of a calcium phosphate solution is its Ca:P ratio. Changes in this ratio will impose changes on the composition of the solid if total calcium and phosphorus in the system are kept constant. If no electrolyte having a common ion with the ternary system (Ca(OH)$_2$–H$_3$PO$_4$–H$_2$O) is present, the Ca:P ratio of the solution is a function of the average valence, or the distribution of the the orthophosphoric acid species. This ratio

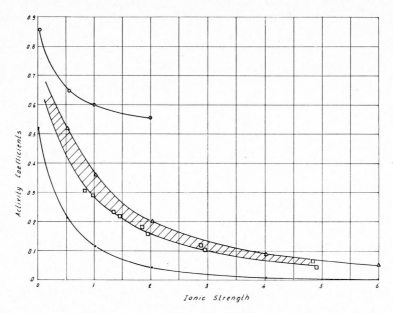

FIG. 1. Computed activity coefficients for $H_2PO_4^-$ and $HPO_4^=$ in NaCl solutions.

Open circles: values calculated for $H_2PO_4^-$ from Debye-Hueckel equation

$$(-\log f = \frac{AZ: \sqrt[2]{I}}{1 + Ba\sqrt{I}}).$$

Dots: values for $HPO_4^=$ in 3.10^{-2} M $Ca(H_2PO_4)_2$ solutions.
Triangles: values for $H_2PO_4^-$ in 3.10^{-2} M $Ca(H_2PO_4)_2$ solutions.
Squares: values for H_2PO_4 in solutions containing 2 to 2.10^{-1} M calcium and 6 to 7.10^{-1} M phosphorus.

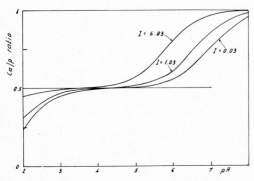

FIG. 2. Calcium: Phosphorus ratios of calcium phosphate solutions as a function of the pH and the ionic strength.

can be calculated with known dissociation constants of the orthophosphoric acid and the appropriate activity coefficients. The equation defining this ratio at the pH range 3 to 9, (H_3PO_4, $PO_4^\equiv$ and $Ca(H_2PO_4)^+$ being neglected) is

$$\frac{Ca}{P} = \frac{1}{1 + \dfrac{f_1}{f_2 K_2}(H^+) + \dfrac{f_2}{K_1 K_2}(H^+)^2} +$$

$$\frac{0.5}{1 + \dfrac{f_1 K_2}{f_2} \cdot \dfrac{1}{(H^+)} + \dfrac{f_2}{K_1}(H^+)} \qquad (1)$$

where K_1 and K_2 are, respectively, the first and the second dissociation constants of the phosphoric acid while f_1 and f_2 are the activity coefficients of $H_2PO_4^-$ and $HPO_4^=$ ions, respectively.

Equation 1 can be readily solved as long as the activity coefficients of the $H_2PO_4^-$ and $HPO_4^=$ an be estimated. The use of the Debey-Hueckle limiting law is restricted to concentrations lower than those existing in many systems of interest. In such systems other estimates for the above-mentioned activity coefficients at high ionic strength are needed. Relative activity coefficients can be estimated through the use of equation 2:

$$(H^+) = K_1\frac{[H_3PO_4]}{[H_2PO_4^-]\cdot f_1} = K_2\frac{H_2PO_4]^-f_1}{[HPO_4^=]f_2} \quad (2)$$

If the pH and the concentrations of the orthophosphoric acid species are known, the activity coefficients of the ions, relative to some standard activity, can be calculated.

The computed activity coefficients in solutions of NaCl are shown in Fig. 1. The activity coefficients were not unique functions of the ionic strength, as would be expected. These were lowered as the phosphorus and calcium concentration increased. However, the functions obtained could serve as an approximation to be used for the solution of equation 1, as given in Fig. 2. The above-mentioned considerations were verified experimentally. Dicalcium phosphate dihydrate was dissolved in water and in NaCl solutions. The Ca/P ratio calculated according to equation 1 was in good agreement with the experimental results.

SOME PHYSICOCHEMICAL ASPECTS OF THE ROLE OF CITRATE IN TISSUE MINERALIZATION

LJ. BREČEVIĆ and H. FÜREDI-MILHOFER

Department of Physical Chemistry, Rudjer Bošković Institute, Zagreb, Croatia, Yugoslavia

The suggestion of Neuman and Neuman (1) that citrate plays a major role in the resorption of bone and in the mobilization of skeletal calcium is still being discussed (2, 3). The results of *in vitro* studies on the influence of citrate on the precipitation of calcium phosphates, however, indicate that this compound might also be one of the factors controlling the morphology and probably the structure of bone mineral. Thus Patterson (4) and Brečević et al. (5) demonstrated habit modification of calcium phosphate crystals when precipitation was carried out in the presence of citrate. It was suggested (4) that this compound might be involved in regulating the crystal size of the apatite in mineralized tissues. Termine and Posner (6) reported that citrate inhibits the formation of amorphous

calcium phosphate (ACP), while Schiffmann (7) presented evidence that it accelerates the precipitation of calcium phosphate from supersaturated solutions if present in low concentrations. Thus it seemed of interest to study the influence of citrate on the formation of ACP and on its subsequent transformation into a crystalline phase.

All experiments were conducted at 25 C. Samples were prepared by direct mixing of calcium chloride solutions with solutions of sodium phosphate previously adjusted to pH, 7.4. From a precipitation diagram (8), such concentrations of the precipitating components were chosen that octacalcium phosphate was always obtained within 24 hr. Citrate was added to the phosphate solutions prior to pH adjustment. The citrate concen-

91

trations used (1×10^{-5} M to 5×10^{-4} M) were at least 10 times lower than those of calcium chloride and comparable to physiological concentrations [the normal range of blood citrate concentrations in man is 4×10^{-5} M to 1.6×10^{-4} M (9)]. Samples containing the same concentrations of calcium chloride and sodium phosphate, but without citrate, were used as controls.

Immediately after formation, the precipitates were amorphous with respect to electron diffraction. The kinetics of the conversion of this phase into octacalcium phosphate (OCP) were followed by recording, simultaneously, changes of the pH, the turbidity and the number of particles (larger than 2 μ) as a function of time. In all experiments, precipitation and crystal growth proceeded similarly in two distinct stages, as shown by Francis et al. (10), in a pH-stat experiment. After an initial drop in the pH and simultaneous increase of the turbidity and particle numbers due to precipitate formation, the pH and turbidity curves show a plateau followed by an inflection of the pH curve and a turbidity maximum. The particle count vs. time curves show in all cases two distinct maximums divided by a broad minimum. The second maximum corresponds in time to the second turbidity maximum. These results indicate the formation of a metastable phase consisting of particles of colloid dimensions which undergo agglomeration processes. In the second, crystallization stage, these particles initiate the deposition of new material. Electron microscopy and electron diffraction indeed revealed the formation of a crystalline material upon the surface of the cryptocrystalline phase.

In the controls, thin, platelet-like crystals of OCP were formed within 24 hr. Low concentrations of citrate delayed the occurrence of the crystallization stage and slowed down the crystallization rate as revealed by electron micrographs. The particle V count

vs. time curves indicate that the effect is due to stabilization of the colloid dispersions. The surface charge of positively charged particles was reversed when the precipitates were formed in the presence of citrate. Infrared spectra of such precipitates exhibit the absorption bands of the symmetrical and antisymmetrical vibrations of the ionized COO^- group at 1,590 cm^{-1} and 1,400 cm^{-1} and the $C=O$ stretching vibration at 1,270 cm^{-1}.

The results indicate that crystalline calcium phosphate was nucleated at the surface of the ACP particles after these had reached a certain size by agglomeration. Negatively charged calcium citrate complexes were adsorbed in the early phases of precipitate formation thus stabilizing to a certain extent the colloid particles, i.e. the amorphous substance. A similar effect might be expected in the course of biological calcification. Thus, citrate might be considered as one of the factors regulating the amount of ACP in the mineral phase of calcified tissues.

Supported by the Public Health Service Research Grants 6X9802 and 1 ROI DEO 2485-01 from the National Institutes of Health, Bethesda, Md.

REFERENCES

1. NEUMAN WF and NEUMAN MW. "The chemical dynamics of bone mineral." Chicago, University of Chicago Press, 1958.
2. HARTLES RL. *Proc 2nd Europ Symp Calcif Tissues.* Liege, Collection des Colloques de l'Université de Liege, 1965, p 93.
3. VAES G. *Calcif Tissue Res* **4**: Suppl, 57, 1970.
4. PATTERSON D. *Nature* (*London*) **173**: 75, 1954.
5. BREČEVIĆ LJ, PETRES J, PEROVIĆ G and FÜREDI-MILHOFER H. *Regional Meeting of Chemists, Zagreb, Croatia, Feb 26-28, 1969.*
6. TERMINE JD and POSNER AS. in: *IADR Program and Abstracts of Papers*, No. 184. Chicago, 1970.
7. SCHIFFMANN E. in: AM Budy (Ed), New York, The New York Academy of Sciences 1967, p 135.
8. FÜREDI-MILHOFER H, PURGARIĆ B, BREČEVIĆ LJ and PAVKOVIĆ N. *Calcif Tissue Res* **4**: (Suppl) 142, 1970.
9. DIXON TF and PERKINS HR. in: Bourne GH (Ed), "The biochemisty and physiology of bone," New York, Academic Press Inc, 1956, p 313.
10. FRANCIS MD, RUSSELL RGG and FLEISCH H. *Science* **165**: 1264, 1969.

STRUCTURE OF CRYSTALLITES IN BONE AND DENTIN

D. STEVE-BOCCIARELLI

Istituto Superiore di Sanità, Rome, Italy

The electron diffraction patterns recorded from pure synthetic octocalciumphosphate (OCP), carbonate octocalciumphosphate (OCPC) and from hydroxyapatite (HA) show that in the first two patterns an intense ring appears, which is absent in the last one. The spectra of OCPC and HA are directly compared in Fig. 1. This fact makes it possible to identify OCP(C) in the presence of HA. Moreover, in the electron diffraction pattern of dicalciumphosphate (DCP), tricalciumphosphate (TCP) and calcium carbonate some intense lines appear which are not found in the patterns of HA and OCP. It is then possible to check whether these crystals are present in the natural mineralized tissue, even if HA or OCP, or a mixture of them, are a large part of the inorganic phase (Fig. 2).

Four types of microscopic structures from bone tissue previously studied by electron microscopy (1–4) were chosen as representing characteristic phases: osteons at the highest (100%) and lowest (70%) degrees of calcification, cementing zone and primary osteon; in addition, follicolinic bone (induced by estrogens in birds) and dentin were studied. No difference was found in the morphology and in the diffraction patterns of air dried specimens (unfixed and unembedded, collected in a drop of pure ethyl alcohol and put on electron microscope grids) and in those of specimens embedded in the traditional ways.

Lattice spacing and intensity measurements were performed by means of a microdensitometer recording the electron patterns made from the plates obtained in the electron microscope, which itself acted as diffraction camera.

The method allows us to draw the following conclusions: 1) OCP(C) is present in every natural mineralized tissue under study; 2) DCP, TCP and CaCO$_3$, as a separate phase, seem to be absent; and 3) HA is present, but in a variable percentage, depending

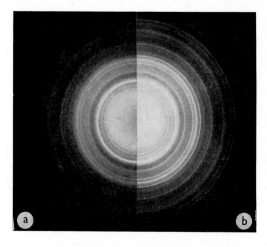

FIG. 1. Direct comparison of the electron diffraction patterns of: a) pure synthetic HA and b) OCPC.

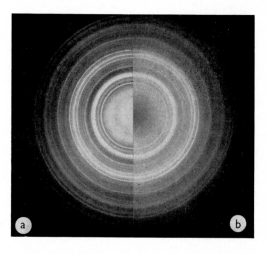

FIG. 2. Direct comparison of the electron diffraction patterns of: a) OCPC and b) osteon 100% calcification.

on the type of tissue. It is mostly found in dentin, secondly in cementing zone and primary osteon and thirdly in the other specimens examined.

Finally, from the selected area diffraction method, it is possible to prove that the material of low density which appears under the electron microscope in some bone tissue zones (more frequently in 70% osteon) does not correspond to an amorphous phase. Therefore, its apparent low density must be explained as the effect of seeing thin flat crystals in a direction normal to their larger side.

All these results are in agreement with the morphological observations on dentin (5) and bone (6) and with some X-ray diffraction results (7), as well as with chemical (8) and spectroscopical (9) analyses.

REFERENCES

1. Ascenzi A, Francois C and Steve-Bocciarelli D. *J Ultrastruct Res* **8**: 491, 1963.
2. Ascenzi A, Bonucci E and Steve-Bocciarelli D. *J Ultrastruct Res* **12**: 287, 1965.
3. Ascenzi A, Bonucci E and Steve-Bocciarelli D. *J Ultrastruct Res* **18**: 605, 1967.
4. Ascenzi A, Bonucci E and Steve-Bocciarelli D. in: *IV European Regional Conference on Electron Microscopy, Rome*, 1968, p 431.
5. Johansen E and Parks F. *J Biophys Biochem Cytol* **7**: 743, 1960.
6. Steve-Bocciarelli D. *Calcif Tissue Res* **5**: 261, 1970.
7. Trautz, OR. *Ann NY Acad Sci* **60**: 696, 1955.
8. Francois P and Herman H. *Bull Soc Chim Biol* **43**: 643, 1961.
9. Hayek E. *Klin Wschr* **45**: 857, 1967.

The samples of pure synthetic crystals were kindly sent by Dr. E. Hayek of the Institut für Anorganische und Analitische Chemie der Universität, Innsbruck, Austria.

STRUCTURAL AND ULTRASTRUCTURAL ORGANIZATION OF BIOLOGICAL HARD AND SOFT TISSUES

A Unified Concept

MARGUERITE F. LITTLE

Eastman Dental Center, Rochester, New York, USA

Organs and tissues with no protein and little or no carbohydrate left, will maintain their morphological entity as long as a structural framework comprising lipid, cations and water is maintained (1). "Anorganic" bone treated with four times the EDTA necessary to decalcify that bone retained its approximate shape and configuration although it had become soft and translucent. After ethylenediamine (ED) extraction 1.25% carbon, 0.067% hydrogen, 0.016% nitrogen and 17.0% of the original citrate remained (2). This study was undertaken to identify the composition of the residual matrix after ED and EDTA extraction. The effect of ED and EDTA treatment of soft tissues known to have a high lipid but low calcium content was also examined.

Formalin-fixed and unfixed rat's heads (skull, mandible and brain), rat and bovine femurs, chicken hearts and commercial bovine "anorganic" bone were used. They were ED (2) and EDTA extracted. Portions of the original and the extracted residue were examined according to standard methods: histochemically with periodic acid-Schiff (PAS) and Sudan B and chemically for N, total saccharides (anthrone and naphtol) and lipids. Chloroform soluble portions of the latter were examined chromatographically for phosphatides and non-phosphatides.

The results are summarized in Tables 1 to 3.

TABLE 1. *Mean composition of original specimens (% dry wt)*

	110 C	Protein (NX 6.25) mean	Citrate	Carbo-hydrate	Lipids[a]	Ash	Ca	P
Hard tissue								
Bovine femur (fresh)	21.3	23.6	1.53	1.3	4.3	72.0	25.8	13.1
Bovine femur ("anorganic")	2.1	0.1	0.43	< 1.0	2.8	97.0	40.8	—
Rat skull bones	—	19.4	—	2.0	4.1	—	ND	ND
Enamel: young	3.2	0.25	.054	ND	0.4	96.4	37.5	15 1
Enamel: precarious	8.1	2.51	.031	ND	1.3	90.1	34.4	15.2
Soft tissue								
Rat brain (fresh)	73.1	43.0	ND	4.0	44.9	6.2	0.04	0.5
Rat brain (fixed[b])	—	43.6	ND	1.5	42.7	—	—	—
Chicken heart	73.4	57.4	ND	—	34.9	3.1	—	—

[a] Some portions undoubtedly as lipoprotein or glycolipid fractions
[b] Formalin.
ND = not done.

TABLE 2. *Matrix after ED[a] and EDTA extraction (% dry wt)*

	Solution	H_2O (25 C)	Dry wt (100 C)	Protein	Carbo-hydrate	Lipid	Ca
Hard tissue							
Bovine femur (fresh)	Alc:Chlor	52	76.2	< .01	< .05	95.2[b]	1.35
Bovine femur ("anorganic")	"	—	77.1	< .04	< .05	91.0	1.32
Rat skull (fixed)	"	—	—	< .001	< .001	85.0	< 0.4
Rat skull (fresh)	"	55	76.8	< .001	< .001	81.3	1.29
Soft tissue							
Rat brain (fixed) A	"	62	83.1	< .001	6.3 ± 3[c]	79.1	< .1
Rat brain (fresh) B	H_2O	(See B)	—	—	1.5 ± 8	81.2	< .1
Chicken heart (fresh) A	H_2O	(See B)	—	—	ND	ND	< .1

[a] ED extracted residue which was soluble in water, either precipitated by acetone (A) or dialyzed and recovered by freeze drying (B).
[b] 3.5% found on ED extracted material.
[c] Into lipid extract; found in residue after final lipids extracted.
ND = not done.

TABLE 3. *Ratio of lipid to water in some hard and soft tissues*

	% lipid	H_2O	Lipid: H_2O	% Ca
Brain	15	83	.18	1
Aorta:				
young	3	80	.04	< 1
old	12	54	.25[a]	8
Human bone	12	24	.5[a]	24
Calculus dental	4.5	8	.5[a]	27
Enamel mature	0.9	2	.5[a]	37
precarious	5.2	12 to 20	.25[a]	26
Crustacean epicuticle:				
early	33	50	.65[a]	—
late	23	23	1.00[a]	30

[a] Smectic mesophase ratios.

The finding of an intact matrix in heart and brain after ED extraction was somewhat unexpected although ED extraction has been used for polysaccharide purification (W. Pigman, personal communication). In brain, the matrix appears to be mainly lipid with a small residual saccharide component. It may well be that the saccharide precludes, blocks or inhibits calcium nucleation, thereby constituting the main difference between the intact matrix of bone and the intact matrix of brain. Brain thus differs from bones and teeth since the matrix of bones and teeth is maintained in the absence of saccharides, and protein, with most of the calcium salts removed, as long as the lipid and H_2O structure remains. The individual lipid components also differ in brain and bone. The lipid to water ratio in fresh human bone is 55% (Table 3). If the lipid is a salt of Na or K this ratio comprises an effective smectic mesophase (3). Smectic systems by their nature are oriented, and orient water or any other molecule present in the interlipid volume (3, 4). Thus they serve as a backbone for proteins or carbohydrates, or both, as well as a framework and template for inorganic crystal formation, and ultimately for the size and shape of the crystals. The affinity of lipids, with their hydroxyl and carboxyl sites, for calcium or phosphoric groups, or both, is well established biologically and synthetically (5, 6).

The role and possible mode of operation of the lipid components in cell structures, calcified and noncalcified, invited the theoretical extension for this study based on known synthetic systems.

REFERENCES

1. Das SK and Harris RS. *J Dent Res* **49**: 126, 1970.
2. Losee F. *US Naval Med Res Inst* Projs NM 0040060901, **14**: 911, 1956.
3. Flautt TJ and Lawson KD. in: "Ordered fluids and liquid crystal"; Advances in chemistry **63**: 26, 1967.
4. DeVries JJ and Berendsen HJC. *Nature (London)* **221**: 1139, 1969.
5. Travis DF. in: "Calcification in biological tissues." 1960, p. 100.
6. Inesi G and Watanabe S. *Fed Proc* **24**: 208, 1965.

BIOCHEMISTRY AND BIOPHYSICS OF EGGSHELL FORMATION

K. SIMKISS

Department of Zoology and Comparative Physiology, Queen Mary College, London, England

The mineralized deposits of vertebrates consist of the calcium salts of the principal inorganic buffers of the body, i.e. the carbonate and phosphate systems. The reasons for this correlation between calcification and the body's buffers is associated with the electron structure and size of the ions involved (1). It will be apparent, however, that the anions exist in most of the body fluids at about pH 7.4 when they are mainly in a monohydrogen form (i.e. HCO_3^- and HPO_4^{2-}). In mineralized structures the anions can be considered to be in a more electronegative form (i.e. CO_3^{2-} and PO_4^{3-}) so that the process of calcification must involve the removal of protons from the site of calcification.

Investigations into these aspects of calcification have been hampered by four types of difficulties. The first is that mineralization usually occurs in some microenvironment that is difficult to sample. Second, the cells involved are often dispersed and embedded in mineral deposits which makes them difficult to collect. Third, there are often great variations in the state of activity of secreting cells which cannot be coordinated. Finally the process of mineralization is often so slow that one would only expect to obtain minute changes in metabolites.

In our work we have been studying the process of eggshell formation, which overcomes some of these difficulties. Shell formation occurs in the "shell gland," or "uterus," of the oviduct in a small volume of uterine fluid. The epithelial and glandular cells of this region are fairly simple histologically and easily collected. The formation of the eggshell occurs with great regularity in the domestic fowl and the rate of calcification is extremely high, i.e. about 2 g calcium in 16 to 20 hr.

During the process of shell formation the oviduct removes calcium ions from the bloodstream and secretes protons. Thus the bird enters a state of metabolic acidosis in which the pH falls from 7.52 to 7.42 and the plasma bicarbonate falls from about 30 to 20 mEq/liter (2). The urine pH also falls from about pH 8.0 to 5.5, bicarbonate virtually disappears and urine ammonia rises from about 20 to 80 mEq/liter during the period of calcification (3). Experiments on whole animals have indicated that during the period before reproductive activity starts the female fowl enters a state of alkalosis which preadapts it to the acidosis associated with eggshell mineralization.

The acidosis associated with shell formation has been connected with the removal of protons from the site of calcification. Measurements have, therefore, been made of intracellular pH of the cells of the shell gland at various stages of calcification. This has been done by the indirect method of Waddell and Butler (4) using the distribution of dimethyl oxazolidinedione between intracellular and extracellular fluids. The results show a rapid fall in pH at the start of calcification followed by a return to normal about halfway through the period of shell secretion (Table 1). A reciprocal relationship has been found in the pH of the shell gland fluid which rises to pH 7.64 at 6 hr and then falls to 7.45 at 10 hr and 7.11 at 16 hr of shell formation (6). This suggests that the shell gland is capable of effectively separating charges and secreting protons to the blood and hydroxyl ions onto

TABLE 1. *Changes in intracellular pH of shell gland during eggshell formation (5)*

	Period of calcification (hr)					
	6	8	10	12	14	16
Intracellular pH	6.55	6.55	6.52	7.07	7.06	7.10

the site of calcification. This provides the basis for the removal of protons which accompanies mineralization and induces the metabolic acidosis in the hen. During this process it is possible to detect a small potential difference of about 5 mv across the shell gland with the lumen negative. This confirms the findings of Hurwitz, Cohen and Bar (7).

The secretion of protons into the blood of the laying bird has been followed by injecting $HC^{14}O_3$ into the plasma and plotting the exponential fall in activity with time. The results obtained obey a time power function or a sum of exponentials, and an analysis of this sort provides evidence for an additional compartment in the calcifying bird. It is hoped that further analyses of this sort will provide additional information on the mechanisms of proton removal associated with calcification.

REFERENCES

1. WILBUR KM and SIMKISS K. in: Florkin M and Stotz EH (Eds), "Comprehensive biochemistry." Amsterdam, Elsevier Publishing Co, 1968 v 26A p 229.
2. MONGIN P and LACASSAGNE L. *CR Acad Sci [D] (Paris)* **258**: 3098, 1964.
3. SIMKISS K. *Comp Biochem Physiol* **34**: 777, 1970.
4. WADDELL WJ and BUTLER TC. *J Clin Invest* **38**: 720, 1959.
5. SIMKISS K. *Biochem J* **111**: 647, 1969.
6. MONGIN P and SAUVEUR B. *CR Acad Sci [D] (Paris)* **270**: 1715, 1970.
7. HURWITZ S, COHEN I and BAR A. *Comp Biochem Physiol* **35**: 873, 1970.

MINERAL METABOLISM OF DIAPHYSEAL BONE *IN VITRO*

P. J. NIJWEIDE

Laboratory for Cell Biology and Histology, University of Leiden, Leiden, The Netherlands

In recent years, much information has been obtained about the behavior of calcium and strontium, concerning intestinal absorption, urinary excretion and incorporation in bone mineral. Most of these findings are based on *in vivo* experiments.

It seemed interesting to study the behavior of calcium and strontium in bone, especially in diaphyseal bone, in an *in vitro* system. For this purpose, a certain number of male, five-week-old, Wistar albino rats were given strontium chloride (3.2 g Sr Cl_2/liter) in their drinking water. After four weeks they were killed by decapitation and the diaphyseal bone of the femora and tibiae was removed and cleaned of surrounding tissue. The bone shafts were divided into pieces of 5 to 10 mm^3 and incubated in an artificial medium (as a rule a Krebs-Ringer solution with CO_2-bicarbonate as buffering system). The metabolism of the diaphyseal bone was studied by measuring the lactate production, the oxygen consumption and the glycine metabolism, using the procedure for metaphyseal bone as described by Nichols and co-workers (1–3). It was found that diaphyseal bone could be kept alive in this system for at least 6 hr without major deviations in the criteria mentioned above.

In addition, the calcium, strontium and phosphate release to the incubation medium were measured. These release phenomena originate partly from cellular processes and partly from the physicochemical processes of solubilization and exchange. The difficulty lies in the estimation of the magnitude of the contribution of each process. Since, in all probability, lactate and citrate play an important role in the solubilization of bone mineral, the influence of these compounds and

of pH changes of the medium on the calcium, strontium and phosphate release of dead bone were studied. Bone incubated for 16 hr at 42 C was considered as dead bone. It was demonstrated (as is shown in Table 1) that lactate had no influence on the equilibrium concentrations of calcium, strontium and phosphate obtained after 12 to 24 hr in a system of bone in contact with medium. Citrate, however, in increasing concentrations, caused a rise of the equilibrium concentrations, although the concentration of calcium increased more than that of strontium.

Variation of the pH also caused a change in the equilibrium concentrations. If the pH decreases, the concentrations of Sr and Ca increase, that of calcium more so than strontium.

TABLE 1. *Effect of the composition of the incubation medium on the ratio (R) of strontium and calcium release to the medium*

Incubation medium	R
Without lactate	2.29
With lactate (1.54 mM)	2.33
Without citrate	2.23
With citrate (1.54 mM)	1.84
pH medium: 7.35	2.71
pH medium: 6.65	2.44
Without Mg^{++}	2.77
With Mg (1.10 mM)	2.39

R is calculated by multiplying the ratio of the strontium and calcium equilibrium concentrations by the ratio of the calcium and strontium amounts in the bone samples used $[(\frac{Sr}{Ca})$ medium $\times (\frac{Ca}{Sr})$ bone]. The Mg^{++} concentration in the incubation medium is normally 1.18 mM. In the case of the measurement of the influence of the pH on R, magnesium was omitted from the medium. Magnesium ions appeared also to have an effect on the value of R.

In conclusion, these data make it highly improbable that strontium is more easily removed from bone than calcium. Lowering the pH and increasing the citrate concentration which may occur at resorption areas by e.g. action of parathyroid hormone, will not stimulate a selective removal of strontium from bone.

Attempts are now being made to compare dead or metabolic inhibited bone with living bone, and to estimate the part of the total bone solubilization caused by cellular in-fluences. In addition the hormonal and other influences on mineral solubilization will be studied.

Sponsored by the Institute of Radiopathology and Radiation Protection, Leiden.

REFERENCES

1. Borle AB, Nichols N and Nichols G. *J Biol Chem* **235**: 1206, 1960.
2. Vaes GM and Nichols G. *Endocrinology* **70**: 890, 1962.
3. Flanagan B and Nichols G. *J Biol Chem* **237**: 3686, 1962.

MECHANISM OF CALCIFICATION OF ELASTIC TISSUE

Induction of a Typical Arteriosclerotic Lesion by Immunization of Rabbits with Purified Elastin

L. ROBERT, Y. GROSGOGEAT, A. M. ROBERT and B. ROBERT

Laboratoire de Biochimie du Tissu Conjonctif, Equipe de Recherche du C.N.R.S. and Laboratoire de Microscopie Electronique, Hôpital Boucicaut, Paris, France

The gradual increase of calcium content in the aging arterial wall is one of the most conspicuous biochemical phenomena observed. Two different phenomena can be considered eparately: a) a gradual, diffuse and continuous increase of calcium in the elastic tissue and b) a localized, massive deposition leading to the development of the atherosclerotic plaques. Neither of these mechanisms is as yet understood at the molecular level.

The presence of antibodies reacting with elastin in the sera of "normal" and pathological individuals (1, 2) suggested an immunological mechanism for arteriosclerosis (3, 4). According to this theory, peptides derived from the degrading arterial wall would initiate the formation of antibodies reacting with elastin and other macromolecules. Such a mechanism is supposed to be able to initiate a continuous degradation process, exposing partially hydrolyzed elastin surfaces to interaction with lipids and other constituents penetrating the arterial wall from the blood stream (5).

To support this theory, the following experiments were performed: Rabbits received biweekly injections of 5 mg purified elastin from human or pig aorta or from beef ligamentum nuchae in complete Freund's adjuvant, or the same amount of structural glycoproteins isolated from human and porcine aorta or a 1 M $CaCl_2$-extract of aorta containing the diffusible macromolecular components. The control groups received Freund's adjuvant alone or a cholesterol rich diet. The animals were sacrificed after two to six months and their aortas examined (6). The chemical composition and the immunochemical properties of these aorta extracts have been described previously (5–9).

Serum cholesterol and β-lipoprotein levels rose continuously in the sera of all the rabbits. The circulating antibody titer was highest in the rabbits immunized with the calcium chloride extract of porcine or human aorta; quite high titers were obtained with structural glycoprotein as immunizing antigen. Lower, but significant, antibody titers were obtained in rabbits immunized with elastin from beef ligamentum nuchae or from human aorta. All antigens produced specific delayed hypersensitivity reactions, detected by intradermal injections of the sensitizing or cross-reacting antigens.

About 70% of the rabbits sensitized with any of the elastin preparations developed macroscopically or microscopically detectable arterial lesions. Only about 50% of the rabbits sensitized with the structural glycoprotein preparations developed similar lesions; about 10 to 25% of the rabbits sensitized with the calcium chloride soluble arterial fractions showed lesions. About 25% of all sensitized rabbits developed macroscopic arterial lesions, in the form of fibrous calcified plaques in the thoracic aorta. Other lesions were only microscopically detectable. It appears from these results that there is an inverse relationship between the frequency and severity of the arteriosclerotic lesions and the circulating antibody titer.

All the lesions were characterized by a marked and early destruction of the elastic fibers accompanied by intensive calcification. The calcium deposits infiltrate the fibrous stroma of the arterial wall frequently imitating egg shell-like formations, which sometimes become confluent and may cause aneurysmal dilatations. Electron microscopic examinations showed the presence of calcium deposits in and around degenerating elastic fibers. Calcium deposits were also seen intracellulary in subendothelial cells.

In the most severe lesions necrotic reactions were seen in the media, the smooth muscle cells showing vacuoles and all the appearances of cytolysis. These lesions were the most conspicuous and the most frequent in the aortas of rabbits immunized with soluble or particulate elastin preparations. These findings confirm the role of specific anti-elastin antibodies in triggering the immunopathological process leading to necrosis and calcification. The observed lesions are very different from those obtained by cholesterol feeding which are much richer in lipids and only calcify after a much longer time. The immunoarteriosclerotic lesions are, on the contrary, characterized by a very early and intensive calcification process mainly localized in degenerating elastic tissue.

The arteriosclerosis induced by prolonged immunization with elastin is, therefore, a good experimental model for the study of the mechanisms of calcium deposition in the arterial wall.

REFERENCES

1. STEIN F, PEZESS MP, ROBERT L and POULLAIN N. *Nature (London)* **207**: 312, 1965.
2. CROUZET J, CAMUS JP and ROBERT L. *Presse Med* **78**: 1185, 1970.
3. ROBERT L, STEIN F, PEZESS MP and POULLAIN N. *Arch Mal Coeur* **9** (Suppl 1): 232, 1967.
4. ROBERT B and ROBERT AM. *Méd et Hyg Genève* **27**: 822, 1969.
5. ROBERT L. in: Jones RJ (Ed) *Atherosclerosis. Proc Second Int Symp.* Berlin, Springer-Verlag, 1970, p 59.
6. ROBERT AM, GROSGOGEAT Y, REVERDY V and ROBERT L. *Atherosclerosis* (in press).
7. MOCZAR M and ROBERT L. *Atherosclerosis* **11**: 7, 1970.
8. MOCZAR M and ROBERT L. *Atherosclerosis* **12**: 31, 1970.
9. ROBERT L, ROBERT M, MOCZAR M and MOCZAR E. in: "Rôle de la paroi artérielle dans l'athérogénèse" (Colloque CNRS 1967) 1968, p. 395.

HETEROTOPIC BONE INDUCED BY SYNTHETIC SPONGE IMPLANTS

GEORGE D. WINTER

Department of Biomedical Engineering, Institute of Orthopaedics,
Royal National Orthopaedic Hospital, Stanmore, Middlesex, England

Bone can be caused to form regularly in the skin of pigs by implanting sponges made of certain synthetic polymers. One such polymer is based on glycolmethacrylate. It is chemically stable, withstands heating to 200 C, is hydrophilic and permeable to metabolites of moderate molecular size. When it is implanted as a solid sheet, calcium salts deposit on the polymer and a fibrous capsule forms around the implant. When implanted in the form of a sponge, having pores of about 40 μm in diameter, the polymeric matrix of the sponge calcifies and true bone appears in the interstices of the sponge.

If the polymer is modified by copolymerizing the glycolmonomethacrylate with 4% of methacrylic acid, it no longer calcifies when implanted in the skin. A sponge made from the copolymer becomes filled with fibrous tissue only and no bone is formed.

Formalized polyvinyl alcohol is another hydrophilic polymer which is available as a sponge with much larger pores, about 0.5 μm in diameter. When implanted, the matrix of the sponge calcifies, but its interstices become filled with fibrous tissue and not bone. However, bone is formed if formalized polyvinyl alcohol sponges with much smaller pores are implanted.

This analysis suggests that the essential factors initiating bone formation are 1) the existence of deposits of calcium phosphate mineral; 2) the growth of connective tissue in contact with the mineral deposits confined in small (approximately 40 μm wide) units of space.

This hypothesis accords well with the published results of some other examples of experimental heterotopic bone formation and with the apparent mode of growth of bone in so-called endochondral ossification in the long bones.

BONE REMODELING AFTER TOOTH EXTRACTION

JAIM PIETROKOVSKI

Department of Oral Rehabilitation, Hebrew University–Hadassah School of Dental Medicine, Jerusalem, Israel

When teeth are removed the supporting tissues collapse and morphological as well as functional changes take place. Bone, as the main supporting tissue, passes through a series of changes from the time of extraction until a stationary period beginning two months after the extraction (1–3).

Materials and methods. One tooth or several adjacent teeth were extracted from albino rats and from rhesus monkeys. The residual ridges were examined from one week to one year after tooth extraction and compared with control specimens without tooth extraction (Fig. 1).

Findings and discussion. At the clinical and microscopic levels the healing rate of the wound was not influenced by the number of teeth extracted. After tooth extraction, blood clot, and later young bone, filled the created socket from its bottom and lower lateral

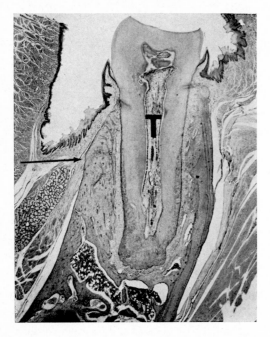

FIG. 1. Control rat specimen. The muscle attachment (arrow) is located at the center of the bone plate which surrounds the root of the tooth (T). Hematoxylin and eosin. × 20.

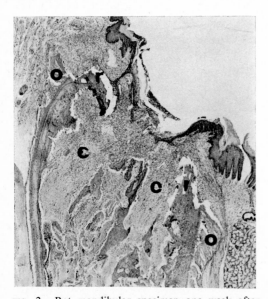

FIG. 2. Rat mandibular specimen one week after tooth extraction. Blood clot (C) fills in the space created by the extraction. Bone resorption is seen at the alveolar crests (r) while new osteophytic bone is seen at the external walls of the socket (O). Hematoxylin and eosin. × 22.

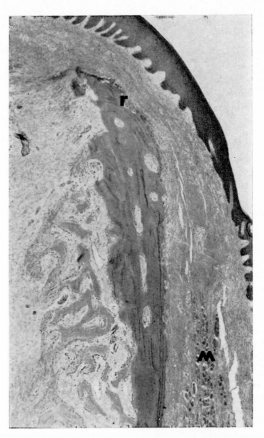

FIG. 3. Monkey specimen two weeks after tooth extraction. The crest of the bone is resorbing (r) down to the level of the muscle attachment (M). Note young bone apposition at the inner wall of the healing socket. Hematoxylin and eosin. × 31.

walls. Active bone resorption occurred simultaneously on the inside and outside of the alveolar crests. Simultaneously bone apposition was seen in the middle and lower third of the socket (Fig. 2).

In those regions of the jaw where muscle fibers were attached to the external bone walls, there was a clear demarcation between the bone that filled in the socket at the fundic and middle part and the bone tissue which resorbed at the alveolar crests. The demarcating factor seemed to be the level of the muscular attachment to the bony plates. Bone located occlusal to the muscle fibers showed

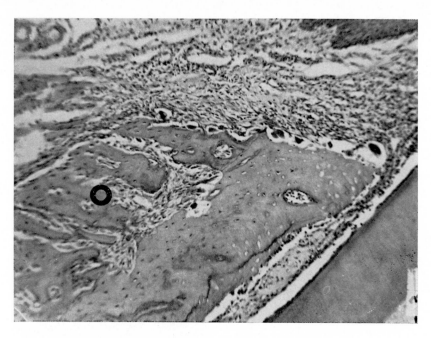

FIG. 4. Rat mandibular specimen six weeks after tooth extraction. Note osteophitic bone (O) attached to the external wall of the socket. Hematoxylin and eosin. × 130.

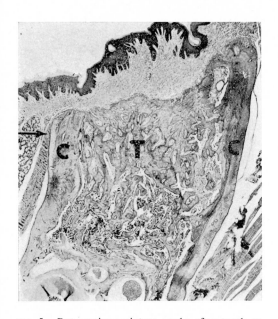

FIG. 5. Rat specimen sixteen weeks after tooth extraction. The trabecular bone (T) which fills in the space formerly occupied by the tooth is well differentiated from the cortical bony walls (C). Note the muscle attached at the lateral walls of the top of the ridge (arrow). Hematoxylin and eosin. × 19.

resorption bays along its surfaces whereas the bony part located apical to the muscle attachment showed new bone apposition (Fig. 2, 3).

In the early stages of healing it was also noted that osteophytic bone appeared at the external bony surface in some of the rat mandibular specimens (Figs. 2, 4). This finding was seen in neither the rat maxillary specimens nor in the monkey specimens. The appearance of this osteophytic bone seems to be caused by unintentional trauma during the extraction procedures, which employ sharp elevators and forceps on the periosteum, and does not form part of the normal remodeling process of bone which follows tooth extraction.

Unintentional trauma occurred in the rat mandibular specimens where the small size of the molar teeth and the large and mobile tongue made a clean extraction difficult. Such trauma was easily avoided in the monkey

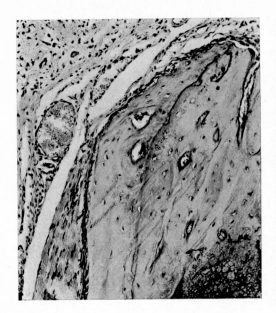

FIG. 6. Increased magnification of Fig. 5 showing the muscle fiber attachment to the top of the bony crest.

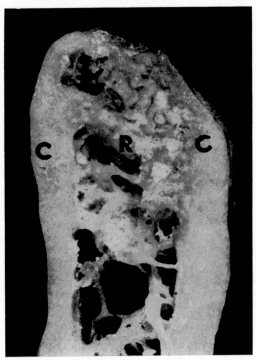

FIG. 7. Human mandibular dry specimen. Note the clear demarcation between the trabecular edentulous ridge (R) and the cortical bone plates C. × 4.

specimens where the mouth opening and the size of the teeth were large enough to allow the extraction of teeth without laceration of the periosteum.

From eight weeks after the extractions, the edentulous ridge acquired a defined stable morphology characterized by an even bone surface covered by a thick layer of connective tissue and a keratinized stratified squamous epithelium (Fig. 5). In most of the specimens, muscle fibers were attached at the buccal and lingual sides of the top of the residual bony ridge. These findings are almost identical with those seen in human specimens (4) suggesting that the muscle attachment is the limiting factor of bone resorption after tooth extraction—that is, the resorption of bony ridge after extraction has its normal limit at the site of the attachment of the adjacent muscles (Fig. 5, 6). Obviously bone resorption of the residual ridge may continue beyond the muscle attachment limit due to other intrinsic factors such as long-term denture wearing, systemic diseases, age or improperly fitted dentures.

The residual bone was always formed by trabecular bone, even in specimens examined one year after extractions. These findings agree well with results of a parallel series of experiments on adult human dry specimens several years after tooth extraction (Pietrokovski and Sorin, in preparation), in which trabecular type of bone was always found at the region where the teeth were extracted. In the human mandibular specimens the trabecular pattern at the edentulous crest was clearly differentiated from the lamellated cortical type of bone located at the buccal and lingual plates (Fig. 7).

REFERENCES

1. SIMPSON HE. *Brit Dent J* **126**: 550, 1969.
2. PIETROKOVSKI J and MASSLER M. *J Dent Res* **46**: 222, 1967.
3. PIETROKOVSKI J and MASSLER M. *J Prosth Dent* (in press).
4. PENDLETON EC. *J Amer Dent Ass* **42**: 1, 1951.

STUDY ON OSSIFICATION IN RATS RECEIVING A DIET RICH IN LACTOSE

MAURICE GOURVITCH

Ecole Pratique des Hautes Etudes (3ème Section) and Départment d'Histologie,
C. Hu. Cochin-St Vincent de Paul, Paris, France

Male Wistar rats received diets balanced with respect to their mineral content. For some groups 30% of the starch was replaced by lactose.

Mature rats which had always received lactose showed generalized skeletal thickening (1). The medullary canals of their long bones were filled with large ossified beads formed by apposition of fine lamellae around the rest of the endochondrium. The remaining non-absorbed cartilage was plentiful in the shaft of the bone, up to the diaphyseal region (2). Fibrous tissue of amorphous appearance formed a general connecting bridge between intramedullary beads.

Animals raised on such a diet, at the same age, had elevated blood calcium levels (1). Nevertheless, in microradiographs of the transverse canals of the tibias and femurs, the existence of large nondense areas was noted mainly at the periosteal origins of the bone and in the large intramedullary osseous inclusions (Fig. 1). Particularly in the latter the osteocyte cells were not very wide and not outlined very well in the weakly mineralized areas (Fig. 2). After toluidine O blue staining, the bone canals showed metachromatic zones corresponding to the regions of weak mineralization. The osteocytes were frequently enlarged with irregular outlines, the canals were wider and shorter, and a metachromatic halo was visible around some of them.

Densitometry was carried out on the microradiographs of these bones and of those of control animals. One or two tetracycline injections facilitated the marking of the sites and the study of the thickness of the bone.

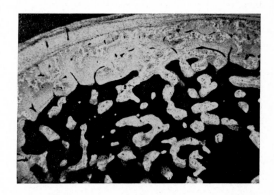

FIG. 1. Microradiograph of femur of a 17-month-old rat fed on a diet rich in lactose. Diaphysis region. Thickness of section: 70 μ.

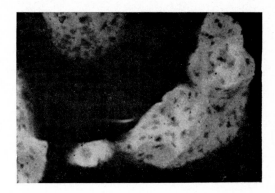

FIG. 2. Same microradiograph. Osteocyte cells lying in the intramedullary osseous body.

In six-month-old animals on a lactose diet, the mean quantity of bone formed in ten days between two fluorescent bands was less than in controls receiving vitamin D. In mature rats, tetracycline treatment revealed that rapidly growing bony masses resembling large bumps were formed. These were mainly situated around the medullary canal, within the periosteum and the edge of the large bony inclusions of the marrow. In the bumps the osteocytes were enlarged, as already described.

Good functioning of the osteoblasts or the cells produced is an indispensable condition for the development of an organic matrix and an enzyme system suited for making perfectly bound hydroxyapatite crystals.

The cytological factor is indispensable, as is an adequate mineral supply and a normal blood calcium level for good mineralization of the bone.

REFERENCES

1. FOURNIER P and DUPUIS Y. *CR Acad Sci [D] (Paris)* **258**: 3090, 1964.
2. GOURVITCH M. *CR Acad Sci [D] (Paris)* **264**: 2929, 1967.

BIOMECHANICAL ASPECTS OF CALCIFIED TISSUE

ELASTIC PROPERTIES OF CALCIFIED TISSUES

J. LAWRENCE KATZ

Laboratory for Crystallographic Research, Department of Physics and Astronomy, Rensselaer Polytechnic Institute, Troy, New York, USA

Ultrasonic techniques have been used to measure the isotropic elastic properties of several natural and synthetic apatites, "bone mineral" and whole bone from various species as well as ivory, dentin and enamel. In addition, similar measurements have been made on oriented samples of bone, ivory, dentin and enamel.

The data from these experiments have been used in calculations directed towards understanding the elastic behavior of calcified tissues as multiphase composite materials at both the ultrastructural and microstructural levels of organization. Initial calculations involved finding the bounds on the elastic properties as would be obtained for a two phase system, i.e., all organic components were assumed to behave as collagen, whose properties were taken from the literature, and all mineral components were assumed to behave as hydroxyapatite, measured in these experiments. These calculations of the elastic bounds for various models have been compared with the results of other investigations of the elastic properties of whole bone (Fig. 1).

The elastic moduli of "bone mineral" (deorganified bone) from various calcified tissues and different species are always significantly lower than the corresponding values for hydroxyapatite. This fact has also been used in the composite calculations and results in tighter bounds on the elastic behavior (Fig. 2).

Preliminary measurements of longitudinal ultrasonic velocities in bulk specimens of reconstituted collagen, indicate that collagen may have properties close to that of an ideally plastic (incompressible) material. This also significantly alters the composite behavior (Fig. 3). In addition, assuming that the hydroxyapatite crystallites provide stiffening through

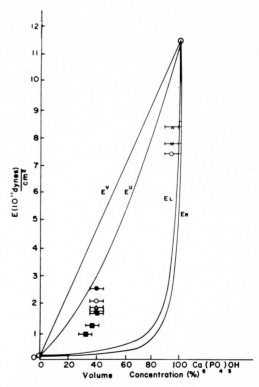

FIG. 1. Voigt, Reuss, and Hashin-Shtrikman bounds on the elastic moduli for a collagen-hydroxyapatite composite; experimental points as taken from various experiments in the literature.

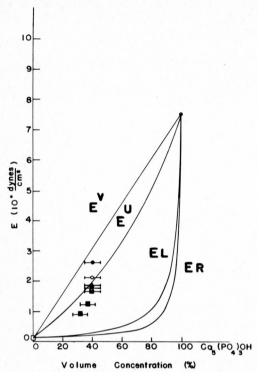

FIG. 2. Voigt, Reuss, and Hashin-Shtrikman bounds on the elastic moduli for a collagen-"bone mineral" composite; experimental points as taken from various experiments in the literature.

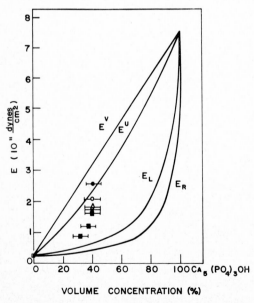

FIG. 3. Voigt, Reuss, and Hashin-Shtrikman bounds on the elastic moduli for a collagen (incompressible)-"bone mineral" composite; experimental points as taken from various experiments in the literature.

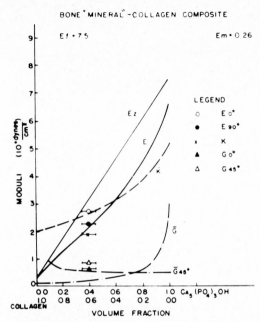

FIG. 4. Anisotropic elastic moduli for a collagen (incompressible)-"bone mineral" composite using Whitney and Riley Fiber Reinforced Composite Model; experimental points as taken from various experiments in the literature.

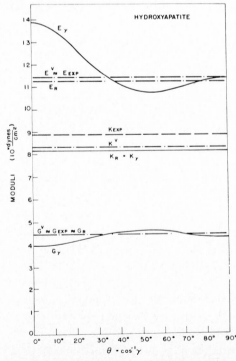

FIG. 5. Computed anisotropic moduli for hydroxyapatite (based on calculated elastic constants) vs. angle with respect to hexad axis, along with computed and experimental isotropic moduli.

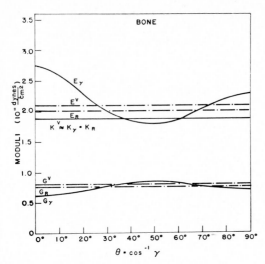

FIG. 6. Anisotropic moduli computed from a modified set of calculated compliances for bone vs. angle with respect to hexad axis.

the mode of fiber reinforcement, a better understanding of the anisotropic elastic properties results.

Further consideration of the effects of anisotropy have been made possible by calculation of a set of pseudo-single crystal stiffness coefficients for hydroxyapatite (Fig. 4). These coefficients are then used to obtain isotropic elastic properties for comparison with experiment as well as anisotropic elastic properties (Fig. 5) for comparison with calcified tissue studies. Data from a number of other studies of elastic properties of various calcified tissues have been used to derive a set of elastic compliances for a hypothetical bone specimen. The isotropic and anisotropic properties calculated from this model (Fig. 6) can be compared with corresponding properties of hydroxyapatite.

Although no fundamental treatment of the effects of porosity on the elastic properties has been developed as yet, corrections for porosity have been made in these calculations, based on phenomenological considerations.

Finally, preliminary calculations show that a microstructural composite model of osteones and interstitial lamellae as fiber reinforcing entities in a weak matrix, the cement line, holds great promise. However, much more detailed information is required about the elastic properties of single osteons, interstitial lamellae, and the cement line substance. In addition, more detailed information is necessary regarding the orientation of the collagen and hydroxyapatite within the osteon lamellae, as well as regarding the direct experimental determination of the elastic properties of the amorphous mineral component of bone and mucopolysaccharides.

Supported by USPHS Training Grant 5TI DE 0117-08 and Research Grant 5POI DE 2336-04 from the National Institute of Dental Research, NIH, and by the National Aeronautics and Space Administration through Rensselaer's Interdisciplinary Materials Research Center.

A METHOD FOR QUANTITATION OF THE AMOUNT OF BONE AND OSTEOID IN UNDECALCIFIED SECTIONS

BIRTE MELSEN and KAI NIELSEN

Department of Oral Pathology, The Royal Dental College, Århus, Denmark

In recent years there has been an increasing need for quantitation in histology for a comparison of normal and pathological findings. This has been equally important in bone pathology where methods for quantitative determination of bone mass as well as bone activity have been necessary for evaluation of slight deviations from normal conditions and of changes following treatment.

Several methods have been described such

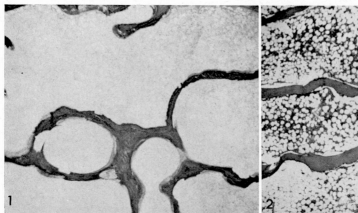

FIG. 1.   Undecalcified 8 μ thick section of trabecular bone showing osteoid borders. Soluchrome. × 41.

FIG. 2.   Decalcified section from the same bone area. Hematoxylin and eosin. × 41.

as counting of osteoblasts and osteoclasts (1, 2), measurements on microradiograms of growth and resorption zones within certain areas of bone (3), and estimation of bone mass through counting of points of intersection between bone surfaces and a grid of definite size (4). Densitometry on radiograms and ash weight determination have been used by Nordin (5). Within certain fields of bone pathology, however, quantitative estimation of bone mass as well as surface length and activity would be desirable, and it would be of interest to determine the part of the bone surface covered by osteoid and to know the quantity of osteoid.

Differentiation of osteoid and mineralized bone is more precise in undecalcified sections of bone than in conventional preparations of decalcified tissue. It is the purpose of this paper to describe a technique which is developed for evaluation of quantity, structure and activity of bone, particularly in chronic renal osteodystrophy.

Material and methods. The material for examination consisted of blocks of bone from the body of the third lumbar vertebra and the iliac crest obtained at autopsy from five patients who had suffered for at least one year from clinically pronounced renal insufficiency.

The blocks were embedded in methyl metacrylate by the method of Jowsey et al. (3) and cut in serial sections of 8μ on a Jung microtome model K.

Every tenth section was stained alternately with Cole hematoxylin and eosin (HE) and soluchrome. The last named stain allows an accurate distinction of mineralized (blue) and nonmineralized (pink) bone (6). That the pink zone corresponded to what would otherwise be considered osteoid was controlled on comparable HE stained sections in which the borderline between osteoid and mineralized bone was less well defined (Fig. 1, 2). This was also the case in decalcified HE stained sections made for comparison.

A microscopic field of 4 × 4 mm was magnified 90 times by microprojection and, on a special type of paper characterized by its uniform thickness (7), the outline of mineralized bone and osteoid was drawn in two different colors, with the use of sharp pointed pencils.

The surfaces of bone and osteoid were then measured with a chartometer. Following perimetry the weights of the projected field and of the areas of bone and osteoid respectively

TABLE 1. *Error of method*

Variables	$s(i) = \sqrt{\dfrac{E(x_1 - x_2)^2}{2N}}$	$\dfrac{s(i) \times 100}{x}$ %
Length of bone surface	0.565	0.97
Length of osteoid surface	0.498	2.93
Total paper weight	0.126	1.05
Bone paper weight	0.146	5.30
Osteoid paper weight	0.078	8.93

TABLE 2. *Calculations based on surface and area measurements*

No. of individual	Bone sample	1 $\dfrac{Bone\ area \times 100}{Total\ area}$ % Mean	Range	2 $\dfrac{Osteoid\ surface \times 100}{Bone\ surface}$ % Mean	Range	3 $\dfrac{Bone\ surface}{Bone\ area}$ Mean	Range	4 $\dfrac{Osteoid\ surface}{Osteoid\ area}$ Mean	Range
1	Iliac crest	40.31	38.9 to 41.3	22.65	18.3 to 24.7	1.64	1.57 to 1.71	6.83	6.01 to 7.43
	Vertebral body	11.16	10.5 to 11.8	21.83	17.5 to 24.9	3.72	2.90 to 4.20	5.81	4.89 to 6.31
2	Iliac crest	30.98	29.7 to 33.4	28.93	26.5 to 29.9	1.77	1.63 to 1.94	4.92	4.73 to 5.21
	Vertebral body	16.15	15.3 to 17.6	27.35	26.2 to 29.3	2.78	2.40 to 3.01	5.33	4.81 to 6.02
3	Iliac crest	40.91	39.1 to 42.8	28.88	23.6 to 34.1	1.48	1.45 to 1.52	5.51	5.50 to 5.56
	Vertebral body	21.74	21.2 to 22.2	26.95	23.8 to 30.3	2.57	2.36 to 2.79	5.22	4.83 to 5.61
4	Iliac crest	24.87	21.9 to 25.5	20.22	20.1 to 20.2	2.97	2.48 to 3.17	9.32	9.12 to 9.47
	Vertebral body	9.94	8.9 to 11.1	18.35	16.3 to 19.9	3.88	3.18 to 4.09	6.35	5.90 to 6.93
5	Iliac crest	42.82	38.7 to 45.0	46.53	43.8 to 50.1	1.58	1.55 to 1.69	7.94	7.78 to 8.29
	Vertebral body	20.41	20.4 to 20.7	42.73	41.9 to 44.2	2.77	2.68 to 2.99	8.17	7.89 to 8.31

was determined after these had been cut out with a razor blade.

The error of the method, s(i), was calculated after 10 double determinations on the same section, and the variation within each individual was determined through measurements on sections from the same block separated by 1 mm.

Results. The results of the methodological studies are presented in Table 1, expressed as s(i) and as the percentage of the average of the real values, which s(i) represents.

The following calculations were then made, as stated in Table 2: 1) relation between bone area and total area which gives an expression of the amount of bone; 2) osteoid surface/bone surface as an expression of growth activity; 3) bone surface/bone area indicating the coarseness of the bone trabeculae and 4) osteoid surface/osteoid area as a measure of mineralization rate. In Table 2 the variation within each individual is expressed as the range (x_{min} to x_{max}) for each of the investigated areas of the iliac crest and the body of the third lumbar vertebra.

Discussion. The error of the measurements and of the weighing method is small, as also is the variation between different sections from the same block of bone. Accordingly, the methods may be considered suitable for evaluation of the conditions in which one is interested.

From the figures in column 1, Table 2, it appears that there is always a greater amount of bone in the iliac crest than in the vertebral body, but there is no constant relationship between these amounts. The proportion of crest/vertebra varies from about 4/1 to about 2/1. This may indicate that iliac crest biopsy is not representative of the skeleton as a whole.

The figures in column 3 of Table 2 are smaller the more coarse the bone trabeculae. Comparison of the results in column 1 with column 3 indicates that the total bone area depends upon the coarseness of the trabeculae.

A comparison of columns 1 and 2 of Table 2 shows no correlation between bone mass and growth activity concerning either vertebral body or iliac crest or when these are mutually compared.

Column 2 compared to column 4 shows no relationship at all between growth activity and the mineralization of osteoid tissue, which may be explained by the fact that the specimens were taken from patients with prolonged renal insufficiency. No attempt has been made to correlate these results with the clinical and biochemical data.

The method described above has been found suitable for estimation of structure and certain growth activities of bone, but it will be necessary to collect considerable normal material as a basis for evaluation of pathological conditions.

REFERENCES

1. FROST HM and VILLANEUVA AR. *Stain Techn* **35**: 179, 1960.
2. FROST HM ET AL. *Anat Rec* **146**: 209, 1963.
3. JOWSEY J ET AL. *J Bone Joint Surg (Amer)* **47A**: 785, 1965.
4. HENNING A. *A Zeiss-Werk Z* **30**: 78, 1960.
5. NORDIN BEC. in: Rodahl K, Nicholson JT and Brown EM (Eds), "Bone as a tissue." New York, McGraw-Hill Book Co Inc, 1960, p 46.
6. SISSONS H. *Roy Nat Orthop Hosp Intern Comm,* 1968.
7. BIRN H. *J Periodont Res* **1**: 51, 1966.

EFFECT OF REDUCED AIR PRESSURE ON FRACTURE HEALING

A BIOCHEMICAL STUDY ON RATS IN VIVO

R. PENTTINEN, J. RANTANEN and E. KULONEN

Department of Medical Chemistry, University of Turku, Turku, Finland

In an earlier study (1, 2), we demonstrated that intermittent hyperbaric oxygen treatment of fractured rat bone promoted the development of callus. On the other hand, bone healing in hypoxia at 0.5 atm was retarded, as reported by others (3) from histological

TABLE 1. *The effect of reduced air pressure on the packed cell volume, hemoglobin concentration and composition of tibial fracture calluses in the rat. (n = 10)*

Variable	7 days Control	7 days Change %	14 days Control	14 days Change %	$P <$
Blood					
PCV, %	44	+34[c]	44	+46[c]	0.001
Hb, mg/100 ml	12.9	+29[c]	13.7	+43[c]	0.001
Callus					
Diameter, mm	7.53	− 8	8.31	−14	0.001
Tensile strength, kg	1.65	−19	2.25	−12	0.05
Wet weight, mg	231	−11	271	−29[b]	0.01
Dry weight, mg	39.7	+7	70.6	−29[b]	0.01
Nitrogen, mg	5.35	− 7	7.44	−29[a]	0.05
Hydroxyproline, mg	1.39	− 6	2.41	−25[a]	0.02
Calcium, mg	2.45	−41	8.78	−46[c]	0.001
Phosphorus, mg	1.50	−32	4.85	−45[c]	0.001
Magnesium, µg	62.7	−26[a]	189.8	−44[c]	0.001
Zinc, µg	3.92	− 4	7.68	−46[c]	0.001
Sodium, µg	214	+6	391	−33	NS
Potassium, µg	124	+17	229	−23	NS
Uronic acids, µg	485	− 5	1,008	−13	NS
Hexosamines, µg	523	− 9	1,070	−23	NS
Neutral sugars, µg	491	+14	775	−23	NS
DNA, µg[d]	746	−37[b]	859	−38[c]	0.001
RNA-ribose, µg[d]	387	−43[c]	377	−29[b]	0.005

[a] $P < 0.005$; [a] $P < 0.01$; [c] $P < 0.001$ ("t"-test); [d] separate series.
NS = not significant.

studies. In the following study, we have analyzed the composition of tibial fracture calluses in unacclimatized rats, subjected to 0.5 atm air pressure for seven days (cartilage proliferation phase) and for 14 days (ossification phase), and compared the results with the findings in calluses of control rats subjected to normal barometric conditions.

Methods. Bilateral tibial fractures were produced in male Wistar rats weighing 121 to 149 g. Two groups, each of 10 animals, were studied. During the first night after the induction of the fracture, the experimental rats were kept in a normal atmosphere; they were then placed into a low-pressure chamber and the air pressure was decreased to 0.5 atm. Recompression of the chamber for 20 to 30 min was made once each day for purposes of weighing and feeding. The control rats were housed in similar cages but at normal barometric pressure. Half the rats in each group were killed seven days and the other

half 14 days after the fractures. The calluses were dissected, the diameters and the tensile strengths measured, and the chemical composition of the samples determined as previously described. For quantitative determination of nucleic acids, a separate series of experiments was carried out with a different group of animals under identical conditions. The isolation and separation of nucleic acids was carried out by the Schmidt-Thannhauser method (4) as modified by Munro and Fleck (5); and RNA-ribose and DNA were determined as described by Ceriotti (6) and Burton (7). The statistical significance of the results was determined by an analysis of variance on an IBM 1130 computer or by the "t" test, as indicated in Table 1.

Results. The results are summarized in Table 1. The experimental rats weighed 19% less at seven days and 12% less at 14 days postfracture than did the controls ($P < 0.001$ both at seven and 14 days). Due to adapta-

113

tion to hypoxia, the packed cell volume of the blood increased by 34% at seven days and by 46% at 14 days ($P < 0.001$ at both days, "t" test) and the hemoglobin concentration of the blood increased by 29% at seven days and by 43% at 14 days ($P < 0.001$ at both days).

The rats of the hypoxic group produced less callus than the controls, as shown from the mean diameters and weights of the calluses indicated in Table 1. The differences were statistically significant at both seven and 14 days. The hypoxic calluses were less resistant to breaking, as judged from the tensile strengths of the hypoxic calluses. The differences were −19% at seven days and −12% at 14 days ($P < 0.05$).

Statistically insignificant changes were found in the amounts of uronic acids, hexosamines and neutral sugars at seven and 14 days, as well as in the content of nitrogen or hydroxyproline at seven days; but at 14 days the hypoxic calluses contained 29% less nitrogen and 25% less collagen than did the controls ($P < 0.02$ for nitrogen and hydroxyproline).

The greatest quantitative changes were found in the mineral content. At seven days, the hypoxic calluses contained 41% less calcium, 32% less phosphorous, 26% less magnesium and 4% less zinc than the controls. At 14 days the content of these minerals was still lower, 46% less calcium, 45% less phosphorus, 44% less magnesium and 46% less zinc than in the controls ($P < 0.001$).

Statistically insignificant changes were found in the potassium content and almost significant changes in sodium at 14 days ($P < 0.05$).

The experimental calluses contained less cells than the controls as judged from the amount of DNA, which was 37% less at seven days ($P < 0.01$) and 38% less ($P < 0.001$) at 14 days than that of the controls. Under conditions of hypoxia, the amounts of RNA-ribose were 43% less at seven days ($P < 0.001$) and 29% less at 14 days ($P < 0.01$) than in the controls.

The above results indicate that decreased air pressure disturbed bone formation and especially the accumulation of minerals during fracture healing, but had a minor effect on the synthesis of polysaccharides typical of cartilage.

Supported in part by The Emil Aaltonen Foundation, The Finnish Cultural Foundation and The Sigrid Juselius Foundation.

REFERENCES

1. NIINIKOSKI J, PENTTINEN R and KULONEN E. *Calcif Tissue Res* **4**: (Suppl) 115, 1970.
2. PENTTINEN R, NIINIKOSKI J and KULONEN E. *Acta Chir Scand* (in press).
3. MAKLEY JT, HEIPLE KG, CHASE SW and HERNDON CH. *J Bone Joint Surg* **49**A: 903, 1967.
4. SCHMIDT G and THANNHAUSER SJ. *J Biol Chem* **161**: 83, 1945.
5. MUNRO HN and FLECK A. in: Glick D (Ed), "Methods of biochemical analysis." New York, Interscience, 1966, v 14, p 113.
6. CERIOTTI GJ. *J Biol Chem* **214**: 59, 1955.
7. BURTON K. *Biochem J* **62**: 315, 1956.

THE CELLULAR RESPONSE OF THE PERIOSTEUM TO TRAUMA
AN AUTORADIOGRAPHIC STUDY OF PERIOSTEAL AUTOGRAFTS

D. PIATIER-PIKETTY and J. ZUCMAN

Clinique Chirurgical Orthopédique et Réparatrice, Hôpital Cochin and Faculté de Médecine de Paris, France

In studies on the healing of recent diaphyseal fractures in animals, it seemed to us that certain local factors play an important role. Among these factors, the periosteum has a special role in the initiation of osteogenesis and the development of bone callus. Under normal conditions the periosteum of the adult animal has only little osteogenic activity. We have attempted to determine which activating factors are operative when there is a perifracture of the periosteum.

In preliminary experiments we tried to show that the association of free autografts of periosteal tissue with bone marrow around the diaphysis induces ossification in the adult animal. We demonstrated that free periosteal grafts retain their osteogenic characteristics, even after several hours in culture media.

The present investigation aimed at studying the progress of free periosteal grafts by cell labeling, using tritiated thymidine *in vitro*. In this way we evaluated the cellular response of the periosteum to trauma and have followed the progress of the labeled traumatized periosteum grafted to a donor animal.

Methods. The animals used were adult rabbits aged 17 to 20 weeks. Standard periosteal trauma was produced by circular scraping of the tibial diaphysis at a height of about 4 cm and by circumferential peeling-off of the periosteum.

Samples of the damaged periosteum were obtained 0, 6, 12, 18, 24 and 48 hr after the first operation and placed in tissue culture for 4 hr at 37 C in a biological medium containing tritiated thymidine in such a quantity that the activity of the medium was 1 μ/ml. At the end of this period, it was assumed that all the dividing cells had absorbed a small amount of thymidine. Historadioautography of the periosteum as well as classic histological methods were used in the study.

The periosteum was removed 24 hr after the trauma labeled in the tissue culture as described above, and immediately grafted on the tibial diaphysis of the donor animal. To this labeled periosteal autograft was added a marrow autograft, removed from the animal's opposite tibia, so as to induce optimal conditions for intense osteogenesis. The animals were sacrificed at various time intervals and historadioautographs prepared.

Results. 1) The cellular response of the periosteum to the trauma: Normally the periosteum is divided into two layers, a deep paraosseous layer (Ollier's osteogenic layer) and a peripheral fibrous layer. Historadioautographs showed that the normal periosteum, when undamaged, is "at rest," and labeled cells, are very rarely found, sometimes in the deep layer, sometimes in the fibrous layer, according to the rate of cell division due to regular physiological renewal of the periosteum. Six and 12 hr after the trauma, the degree of labeling was hardly changed and remained extremely weak. The first signs of cell-division activity become noticeable 18 hr after the trauma. In the deep layer, groups of three to five labeled cells could be seen.

Twenty-four hours after the trauma there was a veritable explosion of cell division. The labeled cells, which were seen in great numbers, were practically all in the deep periosteal layer.

Forty-eight hours after the trauma the cell division activity was not further increased.

115

The amount of labeling was noticeably the same as at 24 hr but the deep layer of the periosteum tended to thicken. Similarly no labeled cells were found in the peripheral fibrous layer.

2) Radioautography of periosteal autografts: In view of the above results, it seemed of interest to examine the changes in the active periosteal cells, grafted in the donor animal (after *in vitro* labeling with tritiated thymidine) 24 hr after the initial trauma. This time lag was chosen because the first series of experiments showed that the periosteal cell-division activity was greatest at this time. The historadioautographs of animals killed at various intervals after the grafting enabled us to confirm not only that the grafted periosteal cells survived but also that a certain uumber of labeled cells preserved their perios-

teal nature inside the tissue even up to about the fourth day. Furthermore, these cells were probably capable of further differentiation into osseous and cartilaginous cells. Six days after the graft, a small number of radioactive cells, different from the periosteal graft cells and corresponding perhaps to preosteoblasts could, in fact, be recovered in the tibial diaphysis region.

Conclusions. 1) When the peridiaphyseal periosteum is traumatically separated from the bone, the deep-layer cells start to divide very actively after a delay of 18 to 24 hr. 2) Free periosteal grafts containing dormant labeled cells remain alive, the cells continuing to divide. 3) The deep-layer cells of a periosteal graft have a tendency to change into chondrocytes.

THE MECHANICAL PROPERTIES AND THE POROSITY OF FEMORAL CORTICAL BONE IN PATIENTS WITH FRACTURED NECK OF FEMUR

ARIEL SIMKIN, MYER MAKIN, JACOB MENCZEL, GORDON ROBIN and ELLEN NAOR

Hadassah University Hospital, Shaare Zedek Hospital and Hebrew University–Hadassah Medical School, Jerusalem, Israel

The purpose of this study was to investigate whether the morphological changes which cortical bone undergoes in osteoporosis influence its mechanical properties as measured by standard tension and compression tests.

Bone biopsies were taken at the time of surgical fixation from 28 patients with fractures of the neck of the femur. Biopsies from an additional five patients with osteoarthritis of the hip joint were obtained during operations for osteotomy. The biopsies, 10 mm in diameter, were taken with a trephine from the lateral aspect of the proximal femur, below the greater trochanter and above the site of insertion of the Smith-Petersen nail.

Four specimens were prepared from each biopsy, two for tensile and two for compressive tests. The tensile test specimens were about 10 mm long and had a cross section of about 0.5×1.0 mm. Compression specimens were $1.0 \times 1.0 \times 2.0$ mm. Each compression specimen was weighed with an accuracy of 0.05 mg and its density calculated.

Loading the specimens was performed in an apparatus designed for testing of such miniature specimens. Special care was taken in the centering of the specimens and exerting the load in a way that ensured pure tensile or compressive load with minimal bending moment. The load was increased gradually

TABLE 1. *Mean relative space area and mean number of spaces per mm² for patients with femoral neck fractures and for those with osteoarthritis*

Variable		Fractures (n = 28)	Osteoarthritis (n = 5)
Relative space area (%)	Mean	4.60	7.77
	SE	0.405	1.90
	Range	1.50 to 8.61	4.41 to 11.02
	No.	22	3
No. of spaces per mm²	Mean	13.2	17.8
	SE	0.680	2.17
	Range	4.6 to 18.5	14.7 to 22
	No.	22	3

TABLE 2. *Mean values of physical properties for patients with femoral neck fractures*

Variable	No.	Mean	SE	Range
Cortical thickness (mm)	28	1.7	0.214	0.3 to 4.0
Ultimate tensile stress (kg/mm²)	15	11.1	1.07	4.1 to 18.5
Ultimate compressive stress (kg/mm²)	21	14.0	0.938	4.2 to 21.4
Tensile strain (%)	10	1.1	0.164	0.26 to 1.83
Compressive strain (%)	17	3.7	0.392	0.79 to 6.15
Modulus of elasticity in tension (kg/mm²)	10	2,555	400.7	700 to 4,050
Modulus of elasticity in compression (kg/mm²)	17	1,116	107.3	630 to 2,000
Energy absorbed to failure, tension (kg mm/mm³)	10	0.087	0.015	0.013 to 0.201
Energy absorbed to failure, compression (kg mm/mm³)	17	0.375	0.048	0.029 to 0.650
Density (g/mm³)	19	1.9	0.021	1.67 to 1.99
Relative space area (%)	22	4.6	0.405	1.5 to 8.61
No. of spaces/mm²	22	13.2	0.680	4.6 to 18.5

with a simple weight-lever mechanism while the elongation (or shortening) was measured by repeatedly photographing the specimen under increasing load. The distance between two selected points on the specimen was then measured on the film with a comparator. A detailed description of the technique may be found elsewhere (1). Stress-strain curves based on these measurements were prepared for each specimen. From these curves the ultimate stress, ultimate strain, modulus of elasticity and energy absorbed to failure were calculated for both tension and compression.

Undecalcified histological cross sections were prepared from each specimen as close as possible to the fracture site. After projection at a magnification of × 700, the relative area of resorption and vascular spaces was measured, using a planimeter. The relative area of the spaces and their number/mm² were recorded for each section.

The means of all the variables studied were calculated for the group with the fractures and for the osteoarthritis group. Differences between the groups were statistically significant* ($P < 0.05$) for two variables only: relative space area and number of spaces. Data on these variables are compared in Table 1. The means for the osteoarthritis group were higher in both cases, indicating that at the examined site, the bones of these patients were more osteoporotic than those

---

* In analyzing the data collected, nonparametric techniques (2) were used exclusively. Assumptions required for the use of parametric tests, especially that of normality, are unrealistic for these data; in addition, such nonparametric tests are especially useful for small samples such as those treated here.

117

TABLE 3. *Correlation coefficients for those variables for which correlation between A and B samples was significant (all patients)*

Variable	No. of specimens	Correlation coefficient[a]	P
Energy absorbed to failure, compression	7	0.809	0.006
Compressive strain	6	0.733	0.02
Specific weight	16	0.384	0.02
No. of spaces/mm^2 in compression specimens	6	0.621	0.05

[a] Kendall rank correlation coefficient.

TABLE 4. *Coefficients of correlation between pairs of variables for which a significant association was found for at least one group (A or B) (all patients)*

Variable pairs	No. of specimens	Correlation coefficient[a]		P	
		A	B	A	B
Ultimate tensile stress/relative space area	15	−0.258	−0.467	0.20	0.016
Compressive strain/number of spaces	17	−0.338	−0.449	0.06	0.012
Energy absorbed to failure compression/no. of spaces	17	−0.323	−0.396	0.08	0.04
Cortical thickness/ultimate compressive stress	25	+0.428[b]		0.004	
Cortical thickness/energy to failure, compression	19	+0.356[b]		0.04	

[a] Kendall rank correlation coefficient.
[b] Mean of A and B.

of the fracture patients. Means for the remaining variables are listed in Table 2 for the fracture patients only. These results are comparable with those obtained by other investigators (3–8) on femoral shaft specimens from adult, nonfracture populations.

In studying the correlation of the mechanical properties to the morphology of the compact bone, it was necessary to take into consideration the fact that two tension or compression specimens (A and B) were prepared from most of the biopsies. Correlation between A and B for each variable was tested for significance. A significant positive correlation was found for four variables only, as summarized in Table 3. For all the other variables, no statistically significant correlation was demonstrable. This may be due to either the small number of specimens involved or the nonhomogeneity of compact bone in the tested area, or both.

In studying the associations between different variables, correlation coefficients were computed separately for the A specimens and B specimens. Only in the case of cortical thickness were correlations computed using the mean of the A and B specimens for each patient. In cases in which there was only one tension or compression specimen, it was entered into both groups, i.e., it was considered once as A and once as B.

Pairs of variables for which a significant correlation coefficient was demonstrated for at least one group (A or B) are listed in Table 4.

As correlation with tensile variables was statistically significant in only one case, it was suspected that the small size of the tensile specimen cross section, which is about half of the compressive specimen, may have led to misleading results. Therefore, three additional parameters were tested for association with the tensile and compressive ultimate stress: the relative eccentricity of the load (caused by the uneven distribution of spaces on the cross section) to the specimens' center; the ratio of the mean space diameter to the length of the shorter side of the cross section, and the ratio of the length (or diameter) of the largest space found on the cross section to the length of the latter's shorter side.

A significant ($P = 0.02$) negative association (correlation-coefficient $- 0.475$) was found between the second parameter and the ultimate tensile stress for the A specimens; a similar correlation coefficient for B specimens was not statistically significant. No association was found between this parameter and the ultimate compressive strength. It may be concluded that the ratio of the average size of the spaces to the specimen's cross section dimension may affect the results of the mechanical tests. It would appear that this influence becomes appreciable at ratios of about 0.1 and over; for most compression specimens the ratio is below 0.1, whereas for most tension specimens, it is above this value.

Supported by Foreign Research Agreement BSS-ACP-IS-1, Public Health Service—Bureau of State Services, U.S. Department of Health, Education and Welfare.

REFERENCES

1. SIMKIN A. Master's thesis. Technion–Israel Institute of Technology, Haifa, 1971.
2. SIEGEL S. "Non parametric statistics for the behavioral sciences." New York, McGraw Hill, 1956.
3. ASCENZI A and BONNUCCI E. *Anat Rec* **158**: 375, 1967.
4. ASCENZI A and BONNUCCI E. *Anat Rec* **161**: 377, 1969.
5. EVANS FG and BANG S. in: Evans FG (Ed), "Studies on the anatomy and function of bone and joints." Berlin, Springer Verlag, 1966 p 142.
6. LINDAHL O and LINDGREN AGH. *Acta Orthop Scand* **38**: 133, 141, 1967; **39**: 125, 1968.
7. MCELHANEY JH. *J Appl Physiol* **21**: 1231, 1966.
8. SEDLIN ED and HIRSCH C. *Acta Orthop Scand* **37**: 29, 1966.

THE CONNECTION BETWEEN THE MORPHOLOGY OF BONE AND MECHANICAL STIMULI

CH. H. LERCHENTHAL

Department of Mechanics, Technion–Israel Institute of Technology, Haifa, Israel

The induction of oriented structure in developing bone tissue through the action of external forces is easily understandable on the basis of the principle of minimum energy, as long as the orientation follows extensional strains. The induction of bone structure along compressive trajectories is far more difficult to conceive since it appears to violate the above principle. The intermediate stage of chondrogenesis assists our understanding since chondrocytes, though built of nonrigid material, represent structures capable of resisting compression by means of osmotically regulated hydrostatic pressure. However, the columnar stacking of the flattened chondrocytes still appears to violate the principle quoted, unless it can be shown that the existing compressive stress pattern creates forces capable of aligning the chondrocytes along its principal thrust axis and of stabilizing the structure thus created against failure through squeezing-out of its elements. An attempt is made to demonstrate that such forces can indeed be created by the following mechanism: Under the action of predominantly compressive stress originally spherical chondrocytes adopt the shape of oblate ellipsoids of revolution. The polar regions of the cell membranes are, under these circumstances, the only sites where the membrane stress (and strain) is isotropic and hence free of a change in electric (or rather ionic) polarization induced through mechanicochemical effects in the membrane material (essentially collagen), whereas all other portions of the cell membrane undergo changes in the level of their polarization through the existence of anisotropic (shear-induced) strain. The difference in ionic polarization thus produced causes an alteration in the hydrotacity of the equatorial zones as compared with the polar caps, thus creating strong attractive forces between the poles of cells in a row and also between their equatorial zones. These forces both align the chondrocytes along the thrust trajectories as well as stabilize the columns thus formed against lateral yield, thus encouraging the growth of trabeculae between the columns parallel to their axes. Prevalent shear forces, on the other hand, deform spherical cells into tri-axial ellipsoids whose membranes are under anisotropic strain throughout the entire surface. Hence, for lack of orientation, the cartilage remains without specific structure (i.e. amorphous) and thus prevents the formation of oriented bone. This explains the generation of the hyaline cartilage encountered in arthrogenesis and pseudo-arthrosis, wherever shear stress prevails during regenerative growth.

The theory is supported by reference to papers on the mechanical, mechanochemical and piezo-electrical, physiological and clinical aspects of the subject.

STRUCTURE AND BIOCHEMISTRY OF COLLAGEN

CHEMISTRY OF COLLAGEN AND ITS CROSS-LINKS

KARL A. PIEZ

Laboratory of Biochemistry, National Institute of Dental Research,
National Institutes of Health, Bethesda, Maryland, USA

The collagen molecule from skin, tendon and bone of vertebrates contains three chains of about 1,000 amino acid residues each. Two (the α_1 chains) are identical and the third (the α_2 chain) is different but homologous. The chains are helical throughout most of their length. There is a region of 10 to 20 residues at the amino-terminal end that is not helical and contains a lysyl or hydroxylysyl residue that is a precursor of cross-links. Cross-linking occurs by the enzymatic conversion of the lysyl or hydroxylysyl residue in peptide linkage to an aldehyde (allysine or hydroxyallysine) which condenses with aldehyde or ε-amino groups on adjacent chains. The Schiff base and aldol products formed may be involved in further reactions.

Species comparisons show that the amino acid sequence in the helical region of the collagen molecule is highly conserved, suggesting a high degree of specificity for the molecular interactions that produce fibrils. The amino-terminal region of the α_1 is also highly conserved. In contrast, there is a great deal of species variability in the amino-terminal region of the α_2 chain explaining the antigenicity of this site.

Tissue comparisons within a single species show that skin, tendon and bone collagens derive from the same structural genes. Minor modifications, such as in the degree of hydroxylation, occur after assembly of amino acids into the α_1 and α_2 chains. However, cartilage contains another collagen in which all three chains are identical. This chain is homologous to the α_1 chain of skin, tendon and bone collagen but must be derived from a separate structural gene. These results demonstrate two methods of controlling function—one at the level of the structural gene and another at the metabolic level.

HETEROGENEITY OF COLLAGEN MOLECULES

JEROME GROSS, ROBERT TRELSTAD, ANDREW KANG,
BRYAN TOOLE and SHOGO IGARASHI

Developmental Biology Laboratory, Massachusetts General Hospital, Boston, Massachusetts, USA

Classical histologists have always accepted the idea that there are different collagens in the tissues of a single animal in terms of staining properties and locations, i.e. basement membranes, special structures such as the fibers of the vitreous and the zonula in

121

the eye, lens capsule, reticulin in the skin of embryos and in mature organs such as spleen and kidney, but with increasing knowledge concerning chemistry and molecular structure we have tended more toward a unitary viewpoint. Although the gross analysis of extractable collagens from a variety of animal tissues has indicated a polypeptide chain distribution of two α-chains and one α_2 $[(\alpha_1)_2 (\alpha_2)_1]$ with a fairly constant amino acid composition for these components, Miller and Matukas (1) have recently shown that cartilage collagen from the chick sternum and certain articular cartilages have a different chain distribution, namely three α-chains $(\alpha_1)_3$ and have also noted that the amino acid composition and therefore the sequence of this chain, designated α_1-type II, is different from that previously described (α_1-type I). Thus the old question of heterogeneity has been vigorously revived and has led us to search further for it at the molecular level in other tissues during development and in physiological transformations such as calcification of bone. In our laboratory we have examined a number of tissue collagens for further evidence of heterogeneity in skin, bones, the eye and in parenchymal organs. We are also extending this search to include various connective tissue abnormalities such as rickets, scurvy, scleroderma and the hereditary connective tissue diseases in humans.

A method was devised for separating quantitatively different species of collagen molecules which did not require prior dissociation into separate random α-chains. Several procedures have been worked out using lathyritic chick xiphoid cartilage as a model. Successive extractions permitted us to obtain the collagen $(\alpha_1 II)_3$ enriched more than 30-fold in the later extracts, with little or no $(\alpha_1 I)_2$ (α_2) present (2). We devised a method which permits separation of the two types of macromolecules from a mixture by intramolecular cross-linking with formaldehyde in solutions of collagen dilute enough to prevent formation of intermolecular cross-links (3). The protein could now be chromatographed on carboxymethyl cellulose after denaturing without chain separation. Clean separation of the two types of collagen in the denatured form was now possible and amino acid analysis of the isolated peaks from cartilage collagen demonstrated that one consisted of the well known $(\alpha_1 I)_2$ (α_2) and the second was $(\alpha_1 II)_3$ of Miller and Matukas. The isolated molecules could now be renatured and examined in a variety of ways, including electron microscopy of segment long spacings. Data have been obtained on the molecular weight, axial ratio, helical conformation, renaturation and denaturation characteristics of the cartilage collagen.

The study of embryonic chick skin collagen has revealed the presence of yet a third α_1-chain differing in amino acid composition from both the other two.

REFERENCES

1. Miller EJ and Matukas VJ. *Proc Nat Acad Sci USA* **64**: 1264, 1969.
2. Trelstad R, Kang A, Igarashi S and Gross J. *Biochemistry* (*Wash*) (in press).
3. Nold J, Kang A and Gross J. *Science* **170**; 1096, 1970.

ANTIGENICITY OF COLLAGEN

K. KÜHN

Max-Planck-Institut für Eiweiss- und Lederforschung, Munich, German Federal Republic

The collagen molecule contains two different kinds of antigenic determinants: the protease labile determinants, which can be split off by treatment with proteases like pepsin and pronase, and the protease stable determinants. This applies to all collagens from different species which have been investigated so far, e.g. calf, rat, human, carp and sea anemone. Most of these determinants are of a sequential nature and can therefore be studied on separated α-chains and even smaller fragments obtained by cyanogen bromide-cleavage.

The protease labile combining sites in human and calf collagen reside in the α_1-chain and are found mainly at the C-terminal end (CNBr peptide α_1-CB6) but sometimes also on the N-terminal peptide α_1-CB1. In early antisera to rat collagen two main antigenic determinants are recognized on the C-terminal end of the α_1 chain as well as of the α_2 chain. In later stages of immunization the antibodies are primarily directed against the N-terminal peptide α_2-CB1.

Antibodies directed against the protease stable antigenic determinants are present in all antisera in low concentrations only. They are located in the triple helical region of the collagen molecule.

Structural studies of the antigenic determinants present in the N-terminal and C-terminal CNBr-peptides of the α_1-chain demonstrated that the main determinants are located in nonhelical sequences and emphasize the participation of aromatic amino acids. Comparison of sequences from collagen of different species revealed the basis of cross-reactions and explained features responsible for the immunologic recognition of a foreign structure.

COLLAGEN SYNTHESIS BY CULTURED HUMAN FIBROBLASTS

GEORGE R. MARTIN, DON LEE LAYMAN, A. SAMPATH NARAYANAN, THOMAS P. NIGRA and ROBERT C. SIEGEL

Laboratory of Biochemistry, National Institute of Dental Research and Dermatology Branch, National Cancer Institute, National Institutes of Health, Bethesda, Maryland, USA

We are studying the nature of the collagenous proteins produced by human skin fibroblasts in culture to determine their relationship to the collagen found in connective tissue. In addition, we have begun the study of collagen produced by cells from patients with inherited diseases affecting connective tissue. Cells were obtained by subculturing the outgrowth from small fragments of human skin in tissue culture media fortified with fetal calf serum and ascorbic acid. Under these conditions, about half of the peptide-bound hydroxyproline produced by the cells was precipitated; the rest was found in the media. The precipitated collagen did not dissolve in cold aqueous solvents. Presumably, the low solubility was the result of cross-linking, since collagen synthesized in the presence of β-aminopropionitrile, a specific inhibitor of cross-linking, did dissolve. Lysyl oxidase, the enzyme catalyzing the initial reaction in the cross-linking of collagen, was found to be secreted into the media by the fibroblasts. The cross-linking of collagen is known to be a necessary step in the development of normal connective tissues and the cells in culture retain this activity.

Collagen extracted from cultures treated with β-aminopropionitrile was found to be similar to the collagen prepared from human skin in its solubility, resistance to proteolytic digestion and in the ratio of hydroxyproline to proline. A chain composition of $(\alpha_1)_2\alpha_2$ was observed in the denatured protein. Cyanogen bromide digests of the chains contained peptides with chromatographic properties identical to those found with human skin collagen. These results indicated that the precipitated collagen produced by the fibroblasts is identical to that found *in vivo*.

The collagenous proteins isolated from the media were different. About 20% of the peptide-bound hydroxyproline in the media was found in randomly coiled α chains. Usually there were more α_2 than α_1 chains. The remaining hydroxyproline was present in an unusual form which unlike typical collagen was soluble under physiological conditions. This protein did not yield α chains when denatured and contained material which had a molecular weight greater than α chains. Following incubation with pepsin, α_1 and α_2 chains were obtained from the protein in a 2:1 ratio.

Since the media protein is soluble and has other properties distinct from those of the typical collagen molecule, it may be a modified form which functions in the transport of collagen from the site of synthesis to the extracellular fiber.

Collagen produced by cells obtained from patients with the Marfan syndrome did not differ from the collagen produced by the control cells. While it has been suggested that the cross-linking of collagen may be defective in this condition, normal levels of lysyl oxidase were synthesized by the cells and the collagen was cross-linked and insoluble. Others have reported that large quantities of hyaluronic acid accumulate in cultured fibroblasts from patients with this condition and any effects on collagen may be the result of this defect.

Cells obtained from six patients with osteogenesis imperfecta were found to synthesize only one-third to one-half as much collagen as did normal cells. Since the collagens from skin and bone are identical, it is possible that the lowered synthetic rate observed in the skin fibroblasts occurs in bone cells also and accounts for the major disabilities in this condition.

SOME ASPECTS OF THE REGULATION OF α-CHAIN SYNTHESIS DURING COLLAGEN BIOSYNTHESIS IN TISSUE CULTURE

B. N. BACHRA and D. BROUWER

Laboratory for Physiological Chemistry, State University at Leiden, Leiden, The Netherlands

With the recent advances in the study of collagen structure and biosynthesis, this protein has become an interesting object for molecular biological investigations.

In view of the peculiar composition and amino acid sequence of collagen it is to be expected that its messenger RNA (m-RNA) must have an extreme composition and nucleotide sequence. We are attempting to characterize this m-RNA in RNA extracts of collagen synthesizing material and to study its properties and biosynthesis.

Two collagens, from the rat and chick, have now been sequenced in part, so that primary amino acid sequences can be compared. Considerable differences occur between these collagens with respect to the N-terminal cyanogen bromine (CNBr)-peptide, although generally, homologous regions seem to occur around the lysine residue involved in cross-linking in α_1 and α_2 of both collagens (1, 2). The second CNBr-peptide of the α_1 of both collagens (α_1 CB2) shows almost complete identity of sequence, except for one serine residue in the rat which has been replaced by alanine in the chick (2, 3). Reasons for this amazingly strict maintenance of primary structure are unknown. This constancy of structure is quite surprising in view of the considerable variations which are known to occur in enzymes, like cytochrome C, and in immunoglobulins having the same specificity. One could suggest that mutations in the specific collagenous amino acid sequences usually are lethal due to the structural requirements of the collagen fold and of cross-linking, but the molecular basis of such strict structural requirements is poorly understood. In this context, it is of interest that only a few genetic diseases are known in which the defect seems to be localized in the collagen itself or its cross-linking. One such disease is the Ehlers-Danlos syndrome in which a defect in cross-linking has been implicated (4). This problem is being studied in our laboratory.

In order to obtain information on the distribution of α-chains and β-components in recently synthesized collagen present in normal and pathological material, it was decided to try and grow, in tissue culture, skin fibroblasts from normal human subjects and from patients with the above disease. Since even pure cultures of fibroblasts synthesize many other proteins besides collagen, ways had to be found to obtain collagenous material from such cultures in a relatively pure form. To this end various extraction and purification methods for collagenous material were tested and evaluated with cultures of 3T6 mouse fibroblasts, an established cell line known for its abundant collagen synthesis under tissue culture conditions (5). In previous work we have shown that, based on radioactive proline and hydroxyproline incorporation, about 5 to 10% of total protein synthesis in these cells represents collagen biosynthesis (6).

Starting with cellular material, we obtained a five- to 10-fold purification, yielding material containing 25 to 50% of its total radioactive protein in the form of collagen. The procedure consisted of an extraction during 2 hr with cold 6 M guanidine chloride, followed after dialysis by chromatography on BioGel A 1.5 m according to the procedure of Piez (7). Polyacrylamide electrophoresis of such purified material showed that radioactivity was present only in the β- and α-bands and that the radioactivity in the β-bands (cross-linking) could be suppressed by adding β-aminopropionitrile during the labeling period. The overall yield of the collagenous material originally present in the cultures was still too low, however, to be truly representative, 5 to 10%; while the chromatographic pattern of peptide-bound radioactive hydroxyproline showed that sizable breakdown of the collagen had occurred during extraction and purification. Efforts are being made to improve both yield and quality of the procedures and preliminary results on this will be presented. In further experiments these improved extraction and purification procedures are used to obtain information on the rate of α_1- and α_2-chain synthesis.

Since, according to present concepts, the tropocollagen molecule in mammals consists of two α_1 chains and one α_2 chain, some regulation of the biosynthesis of these subunits

125

seems required to result in the manufacture of identical tropocollagen molecules. Preliminary results of work on this problem with 3T6 mouse fibroblasts in tissue culture will be presented.

REFERENCES

1. Bornstein P. *Biochemistry* (*Wash*) **8**: 63, 1969.
2. Kang AH and Gross J. *Biochemistry* (*Wash*) **9**: 796, 1970.
3. Bornstein P. *Biochemistry* (*Wash*) **6**: 3082, 1967.
4. Hegreberg GA and Page RC. *Fed. Proc.* **29**: 357, 1970.
5. Goldberg B, Green H and Todaro GJ. *Exp Cell Res* **31**: 444, 1963.
6. Bachra BN and van der Eb AJ. *Biochemistry* (*Wash*) **9**: 3001, 1970.
7. Piez KA. *Anal Biochem* **26**: 305, 1968.

THE INTERMOLECULAR CROSS-LINK PRECURSORS IN COLLAGENS AS RELATED TO FUNCTION

Identification of γ-Hydroxy α-Amino Adipic Semialdehyde in Tendon Collagen

GERALD L. MECHANIC

Dental Research Center, University of North Carolina School of Dentistry, Chapel Hill, North Carolina, USA

Collagen is a protein that self-assembles under physiological conditions to form a polymolecular fibrilar matrix. This matrix is the supporting structure of the tissue in the body and serves as the main organic component in mineralized systems. The specificity of the 640 Å fibril to nucleate and mineralize hydroxyapatite has been documented in papers by many authors. The covalent linkages which determine the structure of the collagen molecule and its subsequent forms are of obvious prime interest.

Materials and methods. a) Analytical cross-link determination. Soluble collagen from various tissues was obtained by extraction to be reduced as molecules or as fibrils with sodium borotritide. The collagen was exhaustively extracted from the tissue until no more collagen was soluble in 5% acetic acid. This residue is arbitrarily called insoluble collagen. The soluble collagen was reconstituted twice and dissolved in 1% acetic acid to make a 0.2% protein solution. The solution was dialyzed successively against 0.11 M NaCl, 0.05 M sodium acetate buffer, pH 5.1, and 0.4 M sodium phosphate buffer, pH 7.4, when collagen molecules were desired. If fibril formation by heat gelling was desired, 0.11 M NaCl, 0.05 M Tris pH 7.4 buffer was substituted for the phosphate buffer. The collagen was reduced at 5-min intervals with 100-fold molar excesses until a total of a 300-fold molar excess was used. The reaction mixture was then exhaustively dialyzed against H_2O and lyophilized. The reduced collagen was hydrolyzed with 3 N HCl at 110 C for 24 hr. The hydrolysate was then chromatographed on an amino acid column using a variable gradient. Two ml fractions were collected and 5 to 10% of the sample was taken for scintillation counting. Hydrolysates were also treated with periodate and chromatographed. Insoluble collagen was also reduced, hydrolyzed and chromatographed.

b) Preparation of cross-links. Twenty grams of insoluble tendon collagen were reduced, hydrolyzed in 3 N HCl and chromatographed in four equal parts on a 5 S × 1.8 cm column using potassium formate, potassium acetate gradients at 200 ml/hr. Ten ml fractions were collected and a 2% sample was taken for counting.

After desalting with perchloric acid by adjusting to pH 3.0, the material was rechroma-

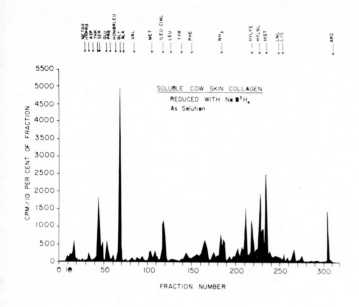

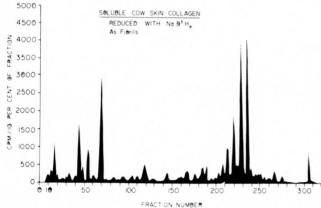

FIG. 1. Soluble cow skin collagen reduced with sodium borohydride as molecules in 0.4 M phosphate buffer, pH 7.4, at 0 C. This material was dialyzed until free of excess radioactivity, hydrolyzed and run on an amino acid analyzer. Ten percent of the sample was counted. This was compared with soluble cow skin collagen reduced as fibrils.

tographed on a 63 × 0.9 cm column using a linear gradient of pyridine acetate. Impure samples were reseparated on paper using CHCl$_3$/MeOH/NH$_3$ 40:40:10. The paper was monitored on a strip scanner and the radioactive spot eluted. Homogeneity was assayed using thin layer chromatography.

Results. a) Analytical: Fig. 1 is an elution pattern of soluble mature tendon collagen, its hydrolysate treated with periodate and fibrils made from the molecules. Note the prominent peak falling before amino acid threonine and its subsequent reduction on periodate treatment of fibril formation. This amino acid was

hypothesized to be 5,6-dihydroxynorleucine which would be derived as a reduction product of α-hydroxy α-amino adipic semialdehyde. The natural compound was isolated and subjected to mass spectrometry as the iboc permethylated derivative. Its mass spectrum was consistent with the structure of dihydroxynorleucine and identical to the spectrum of a synthetic sample. The most prominent cross-link peak appearing in the insoluble tendon collagen elutes between fraction 205 and 210. This material was isolated and subjected to mass spectrometry as the iboc permethylated derivative. The spectrum was consistent

127

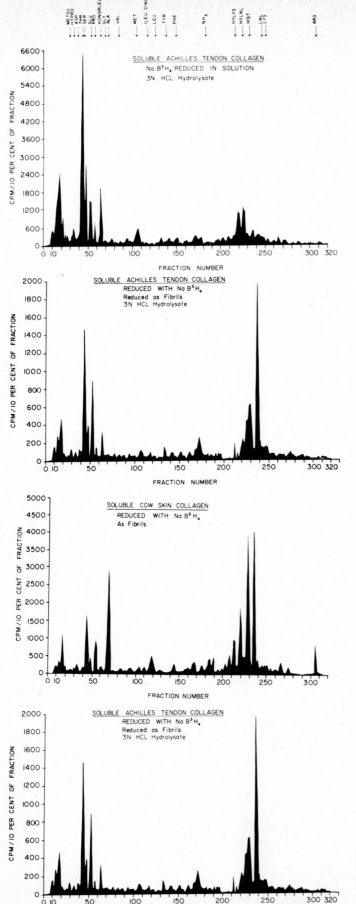

FIG. 2. Soluble Achilles tendon collagen reduced as molecules and as fibrils.

FIG. 3. Soluble mature skin collagen reduced as fibrils compared with soluble mature tendon collagen reduced as fibrils.

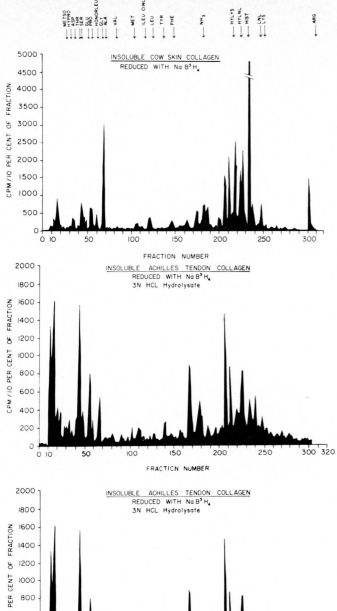

FIG. 4. Insoluble mature skin collagen compared with insoluble tendon collagen.

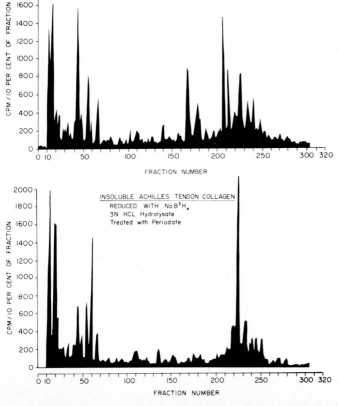

FIG. 5. Insoluble mature tendon collagen compared with its hydrolyzate treated with periodate.

with δ, δ' dihydroxylysinonorleucine which would represent a condensation product involving α-amino, α-hydroxy adipic δ-semialdehyde and hydroxylysine.

δ, δ' dihydroxylysinonorleucine does not appear in young soluble tendon collagen but in older collagen. It also does not appear in insoluble dentin from mature animals. The results of the radiochromatograms shown clearly depict changes in the distribution of cross-link precursors and intermolecular cross-links. The distribution varies with age of the collagen and with the tissue collagen examined (Fig. 2–5).

b) Synthesis of dihydroxynorleucine: The dihydroxynorleucine was synthesized by condensing acrolein with diethylacetamino malonate. This product was then coupled to nitromethane. Upon subjecting the sodium salt of the hydroxynitro compound to acidification, the aldehyde that was obtained was reduced with sodium borohydride. The product was hydrolyzed and isolated. Mass spectrometry of the iboc permethylated derivative gave a spectrum corresponding to dihydroxynorleucine. The material behaved on an amino acid analyzer analytical column, the potassium column and the pyridine acetate column as did the natural compound. Thin layer chromatography also showed identical behavior. A pure sample of the natural amino acid is being isolated and will be subjected to mass spectrometry.

ISOLATION AND IDENTIFICATION OF THE ANTIGENIC DETERMINANTS OF HUMAN COLLAGEN

D. MICHAELI and E. H. EPSTEIN, JR.

Departments of Biochemistry and Surgery, University of California, San Francisco, California and Laboratory of Biochemistry, National Institute of Dental Research, Bethesda, Maryland, USA

The antigenic determinants of guinea pig skin collagen have been isolated and identified (1). It was found that the major determinant was at the NH$_2$-terminal of the α$_2$ chain. On the other hand, the antigenic determinants of rat skin collagen were found both on the α$_1$ and α$_2$ chains (2). Recently, the peptides derived from soluble human collagen after cyanogen bromide (CNBr) cleavage were isolated and characterized (3). We report here on the identification of the α- and β-chains that carry the antigenic activity of collagen and on the antigenic activity of the peptides obtained by CNBr cleavage of these chains.

Human skin was obtained *post mortem* from infants with respiratory failure who died soon after birth. Collagen was extracted with 0.5 M acetic acid and was purified as previously described (2). α and β chains, and peptides obtained from CNBr cleavage thereof, were obtained as described by Epstein et al. (3). Antibodies to human collagen were produced in rabbits by three s.c. and i.m. injections of 20 mg collagen dissolved in 4 ml of 0.05 % acetic acid and mixed with an equal volume of complete Freund's adjuvant. Hemagglutination experiments were performed as previously described (1). Hemagglutination inhibition experiments were performed by 1 hr incubation of serial twofold dilutions of inhibitor with four agglutinating units of antiserum, prior to addition of antigen-coated red blood cells.

Both hemagglutination and hemagglutination inhibition experiments indicate that the major antigenic activity of human collagen resides in α$_2$, either in the single chain form or cross-linked to an α$_2$ chain. By titration of the appropriate α and β chains with anti-

TABLE 1. *Hemagglutination of anticollagen serum with human α and β chains*

	Titer[a] (Serial twofold dilution of serum)											
Inhibitor	1	2	3	4	5	6	7	8	9	10	11	12
α_1	+	+	+	+	+	+	+	++	++	++	+++	+++
α_2	0	0	0	0	0	0	0	+	+	++	++	+++
β_{11}	0	0	+	+	+	+	+	++	++	++	++	+++
β_{12}	0	0	0	0	0	0	0	0	0	0	0	+

[a] Agglutination was scored on a 0 to + + + + scale.

TABLE 2. *Inhibition of the hemagglutination reaction between human collagen, α and β chains and anticollagen serum*

	Titer reduction				
Inhibitor	Collagen	α_1	α_2	β_{11}	β_{12}
—	0	0	0	0	0
α_1	0	5	0	9	9
α_1CBO,1	0	12	0	12	12
α_1CBO,1A	0	12	0	12	12
α_1CB2	0	1	0	0	0
α_1CB3, CB4, CB5, CB6	0	0	0	0	0
α_1CB7	0	0	0	0	2
α_1CB8	0	0	1	0	4
α_2	7	1	7	1	3
α_2CB1		ND[a]			
α_2CB1A	0	6	ND[a]	4	6
α_2CB2	0	ND[a]	0	1	0
α_2CB3	0	1	10	1	7
α_2CB4	0	0	5	1	4
α_2CB5	0	1	5	1	6
β_{11}	2	3	0	4	4
β_{12}	11	3	6	5	7
"β_{22}"	ND[a]	3	8	5	7

[a] Not done because of inadequate supply of peptide.

collagen serum, the following titers were obtained: α_1, 1:2, α_2, 1:128, β_{11}, 1:2, β_{12}, 1:64. The titer to human collagen was 1:2,000. These results were confirmed by hemagglutination-inhibition experiments (Table 1) which showed that α_2 and β_{12} had strong inhibitory activity when incubated with anticollagen serum, whereas β_{11} demonstrated weak activity, and α_1 gave only marginal inhibition. The marked reduction in titer to α_2, as compared to the titer to the native molecule, might be due to a weaker binding with the chain that had lost the conformation it had in the native molecule, or to loss of antigenic determinants composed of residues originating from more than one chain.

To identify the CNBr peptides that contain the antigenic activity, anticollagen was preincubated with these peptides and then tested with native collagen, β_{11}, β_{12}, α_1 and α_2 (Table 2). It is evident that the major antigenic determinants in the α_2 chain are located within the helical portion of the molecule (CB3, CB4 and CB5) as well as at the non-helical NH_2-terminal end (CB1 and CB1A). By contrast the antigenic determinant on the α_1-chain is confined at the NH_2-terminal end (CBO, 1 and CBO, 1A). The fact that the major antigenic activity is located in the helical region of the collagen molecule (CB3, CB4 and CB5) supports the assumption that antibodies to human collagen recognize, in addition to certain sequences, a helical conformation, the loss of which may result in a marked reduction in binding.

Epstein et al. (3) isolated on CM-cellulose a peak which they tentatively indentified as β_{22}, on the basis of amino acid composition. The fact that this fraction inhibited the reaction between anticollagen and α_2 lends immunochemical support to this conclusion, since neither α_1 nor β_{11} inhibited this reaction.

The identification of the antigenic determinants of human collagen may facilitate the elucidation of the role of collagen in various human pathologic conditions involving connective tissue.

REFERENCES

1. MICHAELI D, MARTIN GR, KETTMAN J, BENJAMINI E, LEUNG DYK and BLATT BA. *Science* 166: 1522, 1969.
2. MICHAELI D, BENJAMINI E, LEUNG DYK and MARTIN GR. *Immunochemistry* (in press).
3. EPSTEIN EH JR, SCOTT RD, MILLER EY and PIEZ KA. *J Biol Chem* (in press).

BONE COLLAGEN METABOLISM IN AGING RATS

B. NUSGENS and CH. M. LAPIERE

Service de Dermatologie, Hôpital de Bavière, Université de Liège, Belgium

We have investigated some of the mechanisms which could control collagen deposition in bone during growth and aging in rats. Five groups of a total of 20 Wistar female rats (ages $1\frac{1}{2}$, 3, 6, 12 and 24 months), were injected i.v. with 50 µc of 3,4 H^3-L-proline and killed in groups of two, 1, 3, 6, 24, 48, 72, 120, 240, 480 and 720 hr after injection. The blood serum was collected and the specific radioactivity of the free proline was determined. The long bones on both sides (humerus, radius, ulna, femur and tibia) were collected, defatted, dissected into diaphyses and epiphyses, cleaned of tendons and bone marrow, homogenized and the diaphyseal bone separated into fractions of increasing specific gravity in a continuous gradient of density (1). The hydroxyproline was measured and its specific radioactivity determined.

The accretion of collagen in the epiphyses was found to be around 2 mg per day at the age of six weeks. It diminished rapidly with increasing age (350 µg at three months, 30 µg at six months, 3 µg at 12 months and 0 µg at 24 months). In the diaphyses, the accretion at six weeks was of the same order but the reduction in aging rats was slower. Even at 24 months the deposition of collagen was still about 50 µg per day.

The isotope dilution curve of the blood free proline followed a similar time function in all the groups of animals and there was little delay in the labeling of the proteins. Bone collagen synthesis can be evaluated by dividing the radioactivity accumulated in the sample by the proline precursor specific radioactivity during the same period of time (2). To minimize the effect of an early removal of newly synthesized collagen, this calculation is only valid at the shortest time period after injection of the labeled proline and is rendered more accurate by taking degradation into account (Nusgens, Onkelinx and Lapiere, unpublished data). Such a calculation shows that synthesis was eightfold higher in epiphyses than in diaphyses in all age groups. In both calcified tissues, the rate of synthesis decreased with increasing age. The overall degradation of bone collagen can be estimated by subtracting from the amount of synthesized collagen, the value of the collagen deposited in the tissue. This collagen catabolism was higher in the epiphyses in which it accounted for 90% of the synthesis in the youngest animals and rose progressively to 100% with increasing age. It was close to 50% at six weeks in the diaphyses and increased up to 90% at 24 months. The proportion of the newly synthesized collagen removed in the eldest animal bone was larger than in the youngest one. This is probably related to the larger rate of remodeling in the bone of growing animals.

Density fractionation of the diaphyseal bone shows this calcified tissue as a heterogenous population of units of an increasing degree of mineralization. The fractional distribution is related to the age of the animal (3). As a function of age, there is a constant accumulation of the most calcified matrix and some reduction of the less mineralized one.

The protein composition of the fractions is related to their degree of mineralization. Per unit volume, the amount of collagen remains constant but associated polypeptides rich in dicarboxylic amino acids, serine, leucine, tyrosine and phenylalanine diminish with increasing mineralization (1). These maturational changes of the protein matrix are identical in the various age groups.

The rate of calcification of the collagen matrix of the diaphyses which increased by following the evolution of the radioactivity in fractionated bone, is not basically modified by aging.

Bone can therefore be considered an organ accumulating fully calcified matrix in an amount regulated through coordinated variations of the rate of synthesis and degradation. The process and the rate of maturation of the newly formed protein matrix does not seem to be modified by aging.

REFERENCES

1. LAPIERE ChM and NUSGENS B. in: Balazs EA (Ed), "Chemistry and molecular biology of the intercellular matrix." New York, Academic Press v 1, 1970, p 55.
2. LAPIERE ChM, ONKELINX C and RICHELLE LJ. in: Comte P (Ed.), "Biochimie et physiologie du tissu conjonctif." Sté Ormeco et Imprimerie du Sud-Est à Lyon, Publ, 1966, p 505.
3. RICHELLE LJ, ONKELINX C and AUBERT JP. in: Fleisch H, Blackwood JJ and Owen M (Eds), *3rd European Symposium on Calcified Tissues* Berlin, Springer Verlag, 1966, p 123.

COLLAGEN DEVELOPMENT IN TISSUE CULTURES *IN VITRO* UNDER STATIC MAGNETIC FIELDS

E. ISRAELI, Z. KARNI*, Z. SCHUR and D. BARZILAI

Department of Mechanics*, Technion–Israel Institute of Technolgy and Endocrinological Laboratory, Rambam Government Hospital, Haifa, Israel

It is claimed (1), rather vaguely, that in experiments *in vivo* with living mice, the amount of collagen, as one measure for the healing of wounds, tends to decrease under the influence of a magnetic field. The present investigation was carried out in order to determine whether a static magnetic field affects the *in vitro* development of collagen in a tissue culture, in respect of volume and texture.

Materials and methods. In our study of the magnetic effect *in vitro*, chick embryo fibroblasts were used. Nine-day-old chick embryos were minced and dispersed to a single cell suspension with the aid of 0.25% trypsin solution. These cell suspensions were suspended in the culture medium in a concentration of 1×10^6/ml and plated into a 100 mm plastic petri dish (Falcon) to form primary cultures. To obtain a better homogeneity of the cultures, the formed monolayers (confluency of the monolayers was usually obtained 48 to 72 hr after seeding) were again dispersed with 0.25% trypsin to a single cell suspension and plated at 2 to 4×10^5 cells in 35 mm plastic petri dishes. The majority of the cells developing at this second passage were fibroblasts. The cultures were then incubated in a 37 C humidified incubator with a constant inflow of 10% CO_2 in air.

The nutritional medium used was basal Eagle's medium (2) with $\times 4$ concentration of vitamins and amino acids, and containing 15% calf serum and 80 µg/ml vitamin C. The medium was changed every two to three days. The overall period of incubation was six seven days. The cultures were then fixed with formalin and stained by the reticulum stain using the silver impregnation technique (3). With this method, the reticulum fibers, which represented early stages of collagen aggregation were stained brown to purple black, depending on their stage of aggregation.

Magnets. The magnets used were alnico

magnets of three types. The first, was a horn-shaped magnet with a gap of 38 mm between the two pole faces. The intensity of the magnetic field measured between the poles amounted to 1,060 Gauss at mid-distance, with an average variation of –240 Gauss/cm across the pole axis. Near the two poles, the field reached the values of 1,920 Gauss and 1,650 Gauss respectively. Two such magnets were used separately.

The second type was a horseshoe magnet with a pole face of 2.5 cm. Here, two such magnets were placed antisymmetrically at a distance of 38 mm. This allowed for the placing of a petri dish between the two magnets on each side—two dishes one on top of the other, i.e. a total of four dishes. The magnets were screwed to a 2-cm thick wooden shelf with as many ventilation holes as on the metal shelves of the incubator. The magnetic field between the opposite poles of the two magnets amounted to 1,120 Gauss at mid-distance, with an average variation of –200 Gauss/cm across the pole axes.

The third type was again a pair of horseshoe magnets similar to the former, but larger and stronger. They too were placed antisymmetrically 38 mm apart and screwed to a 2-cm thick wooden shelf. This time, however, the magnetic field intensity at mid-distance between the opposite poles of the two magnets reached the value of 5,020 Gauss, with an average variation of –2,000 Gauss/cm across the pole axes. The width of these magnets allowed for four dishes one on top of the other, i.e. a total of eight dishes.

The magnets were arranged on three shelves inside a separate incubator. Additional wooden shelves were used for the controls which were placed as far as possible from the magnets. Altogether, in each experiment 10 dishes could be placed inside the different magnetic fields with other scattered dishes other, serving as controls.

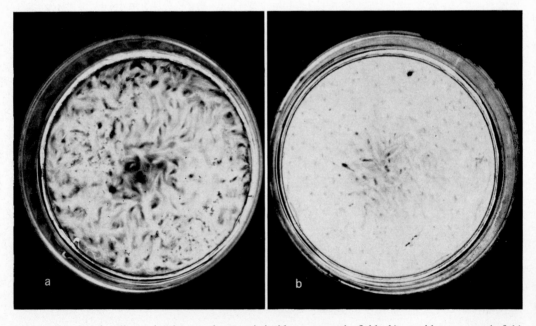

FIG. 1. Developed collagen in tissue cultures: a) inside a magnetic field; b) outside a magnetic field.

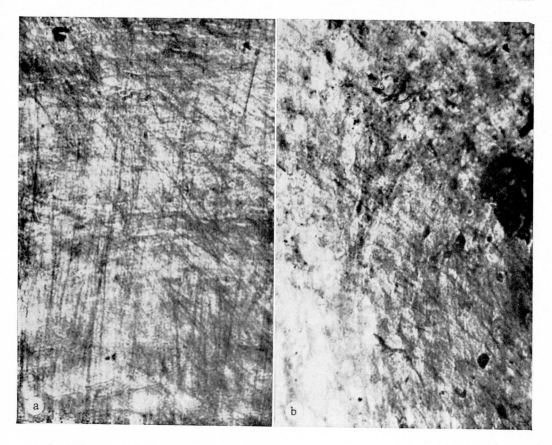

FIG. 2.   Enlargement of collagen in tissue cultures: a) inside a magnetic field; b) outside a magnetic field.

Results. The purpose of the experiments in the first stage was to get an overall visual impression of the difference—if any—which exists between collagenous tissues cultivated inside and outside a static magnetic field. At the end of each successful experiment, the cultures were fixed and stained histologically. Photographs, both colored and black and white, were then taken of the gross cultures and of random sections of the cultures under various microscopic enlargements. Fig. 1 shows gross cultures: a) in a dish placed inside the magnetic field and b) in that of the control outside the field. Fig. 2a shows an enlargement of a tissue culture (approx. × 450) typical of a development in the magnetic field. This is contrasted with Fig. 2b which shows

a tissue culture developed outside the field. Both cultures are from the same batch. The difference between the two may be noticed. All these results refer to the magnetic field intensities in the range of 1,000 Gauss.

From the experiments conducted so far, mostly in the 1,000 Gauss range, it seems as though the magnetic field causes an intensification of the entire tissue, a thickening of the collagen fibers and as a result of this, an over-all increase in the collagen density. At present, however, the experimental data are still insufficient to draw definite conclusions as to the effect of static magnetic fields on collagen development in tissue cultures.

We have recently introduced quantitative analysis and varied the field intensity. These

135

results and the effect of other parameters, will be reported at a later date.

Sponsored in part by the Julius Silver Institute of Bio-Medical Engineering Sciences under Research Project 140–097.

REFERENCES

1. BARNOTHY MF. "Biological effects of magnetic fields." New York, Plenum Press, 1964.
2. EAGLE HS. *Science* **22**: 501, 1955.
3. MALLORY FB. "Pathological technique." Philadelphia, WB Saunders Co, 1944.

IN VITRO MATURATION OF BONE COLLAGEN

ROBERT C. SIEGEL, HERBERT KAGANT,
CARL FRANZBLAU and GEORGE R. MARTIN

National Institute of Dental Research, Bethesda, Maryland, and
Boston University School of Medicine, Boston, Massachusetts, USA

Recently, it has been suggested that the formation of the intramolecularly cross-linked β components from α chains is not an intermediate step in the biosynthesis of insoluble collagen fibrils (1). Instead, β chains are postulated to arise during the extraction of collagen with acetic acid. Cross-links in collagen are known to form by the condensation of aldehydes derived from lysyl and hydroxylysyl groups. Formation of these aldehydes is catalyzed by lysyl oxidase (2). We have previously demonstrated the formation of β components and insoluble collagen during the incubation of lathyritic chick bone collagen with a partially purified preparation of lysyl oxidase (3, 4). The present work concerns both the rate at which cross-linked components are produced by the enzyme and the nature of the cross-links. With time, purified bone collagen incubated with lysyl oxidase becomes progressively insoluable. After 8 hr incubation only 75% of the material would dissolve, and after 24 hr, less than 10%. Whereas the original sample contained only 3 to 4% of the β components, β components comprised about half of the soluble protein after 8 hr incubation. These β components were found to contain both the aldol intramolecular cross-link and the hydroxylysino-norleucine intermolecular cross-link when examined by amino acid analysis after alkaline hydrolysis. The collagen that was insoluble after 24 hr incubation with lysyl oxidase also contained both types of cross-link. These observations suggest that the enzyme dependent maturation of bone collagen proceeds in an orderly fashion with products such as β components forming at an early stage and more highly cross-linked and insoluble products later. The β component itself is utilized for the formation of more highly cross-linked products since it reaches a peak concentration at 8 to 12 hr in this *in vitro* system and then decreases to barely detectable levels. Thus, intramolecular and intermolecular cross-links form by similar reactions.

1. FRANZBLAU C, KANG AH and FARIS B *Biochem Biophys Res Commun* **40**: 437, 1970.
2. SIEGEL RC, PINNELL SR and MARTIN GR. *Biochemistry (Wash)* **9**: 4486, 1970.
3. SIEGEL RC and MARTIN GR *J Biol Chem* **245**: 1653, 1970.
4. SIEGEL RC and MARTIN GR *Calcif Tissue Res* **4** (Suppl): 42, 1970.

BIOPHYSICAL ASPECTS OF THE CALCIFICATION OF COLLAGEN *IN VITRO*

ELTON P. KATZ

Department of Oral Biology, School of Dental Medicine and Institute of Materials Science,
University of Connecticut, Storrs, Connecticut, USA

It is now well documented (1) that the collagen of bone and teeth is impregnated with mineral salt. In this paper I will report the initial findings of an *in vitro* study of the biophysical mechanisms involved in this phenomenon.

The time course of calcification of purified, reconstituted collagen, having the native type 640 Å X-ray reflections, was obtained by determining the mineral ion content of uniform aliquots of the protein after incubation at 25 C for varying periods of time in a large excess of calcifying solution (2, 3). The dependency of the kinetics of calcification on mineral ion concentration (C_o) was determined over the calcium concentration range 2.075 to 2.312 mM, at a constant molar calcium to phosphate ratio of 0.775.

It was found that the time course of calcification and its dependency on initial concentration could be adequately represented by the empirical relation

$$P(t) \simeq \text{constant } C_o{}^{14} t^{2.25 \pm 0.05} \qquad (1)$$

where $P(t)$ is the g of phosphorus per g of collagen at the time t. This result was entirely consistent with a mechanism of calcification involving two distinct steps: one of nucleation and one of crystal growth. Moreover, the 14th order dependency of the kinetics of calcification on concentration indicated a way by which these two steps could be resolved experimentally, as shown in Fig. 1.

In this Fig. the uptake of mineral by collagen, as measured by its phosphorus content, is plotted against hr of incubation at 25 C for two different experimental procedures. The solid circle points (●) show the initial kinetics of calcification. The dotted line

through these points follows the empirical equation 1. The values represented by the squares (□), each the average of six experiments, were obtained in the following way: after incubation for the time designated on the plot the mineralizing solution was diluted 25 to 30%, and the samples were then re-incubated at 25 C for approximately 100 hr. The square point at zero time shows that mineralization cannot be initiated at 25 C in the diluted mineralizing solution. Any uptake of mineral that does occur upon reincubation can, therefore, only be due to the growth of crystals that had been already initiated before the diluting procedure. This result demonstrates directly that the mechanism of mineralization involves a nucleation step and a crystal growth step. The solid circle points (●) represent the net kinetics of both of these

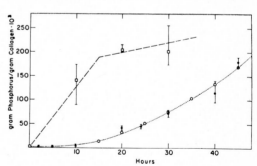

FIG. 1. The initial kinetics of mineralization of steer-skin collagen in its 640-Å aggregation state. The phosphorus content per g of collagen is plotted against hr of incubation at 25 C ± 0.02. The mineralizing solution initially contained 0.142 M KCl; 0.02 M sodium veronal (pH 7.4), 2.984 mM KH_2PO_4; and 2.312 mM $CaCl_2$. □, the kinetics of nucleation; ●, the kinetics of nucleation and growth; O, theoretical model. ....., empirical time dependence of $2.97 \times 10^{-6} t^{2.21}$.

processes: the square points reflect essentially only the time course of nucleation.

An *a priori* expression of the time course of mineralization based on this two-step mechanism, assuming that the growth of the crystals is controlled by the diffusion of ions to the crystal surface, is

$$P(t) = k \int J(\tau) (t-\tau)^{3/2} \, d\tau \qquad (2)$$

(4, 5) where $J(\tau)$ is the nucleation frequency at the time τ. When this expression is evaluated using the time course of nucleation represented by the dashed curve in the figure to take account of the time dependency of $J(\tau)$, one obtains the values represented by the open circles (o). This is to say then that the kinetics of calcification can be predicted quite well on the basis of the *a priori* equation 2 and the kinetics of nucleation.

The size of the nucleus can be calculated from the nucleation theory (3, 5) employing either the data of equation 1 or the (independent) data represented by the squares in Fig. 1. A value of 12 to 13 ions per nucleus is obtained from the former, and in very good agreement, a value of 11 ions per nucleus from the latter. These values are approximately a factor of two smaller than the nucleus size predicted under these solution conditions in the absence of reconstituted collagen (3).

Another parameter evaluated from the data of these experiments is the diffusion constant of the phosphate ion; approximately (10^{-8} cm^2sec^{-1}. This value is approximately a thousand times smaller than a diffusion constant for an ion in water, and indicates that the collagen matrix not only initiates the formation of crystals, but controls their subsequent development as well.

The author is grateful to Miss Shirley McCann for her technical assistance. This study was aided by grants from the National Institutes of Health (No. AM-06375) and The John A. Hartford Foundation. Reconstituted steer-skin collagen was kindly provided by Ethicon Co., Emeryville, N. J.

REFERENCES

1. GLIMCHER MJ and KRANE SM. in: Gould BS (Ed) "Treatise on collagen." New York, Academic Press, 1968, v 2, p 68.
2. STRATES BG, NEUMAN WF and LEVINSKAS GJ. *J Phys Chem* **61**: 279, 1957.
3. KATZ EP. *Biochim Biophys Acta* **194**: 121, 1969.
4. HAM FS. *Phys Chem Solids* **6**: 335, 1958.
5. NIELSEN AE. "Kinetics of precipitation." Oxford, Pergamon Press, 1964, pp 14, 72.

A MICROMECHANIC INVESTIGATION ON SINGLE OSTEONS USING A SHEARING STRENGTH TEST

A. ASCENZI and E. BONUCCI

1° Istituto di Anatomia Patologica, Università di Roma, Rome, Italy

The aim of the research reported in this paper is to record the stress-strain interactions in osteons loaded according to their axis, using a technique which can be considered a double shearing strength test.

Cross sections about 300 μ in thickness were prepared by grinding from femoral compact bone of human subjects aged 25 years. Osteons oriented perpendicularly to the upper and lower surfaces of these sections were selected. Each section was placed on a rigid plane bearing a central cylindrical hole, whose diameter was a little greater than that of the osteon. The section was fixed firmly to this plane in such a way that the selected osteon coincided and was in line with the cylindrical hole. A steel cylinder, with a diameter a little smaller than that of the hole, was placed on the upper surface of the selected osteon. This cylinder, whose axis was in line with the axis of the osteon, functioned as a punch. Little by little, as this punch was loaded, it pressed on the osteon, inducing first a deformation and then a break in the connections at the

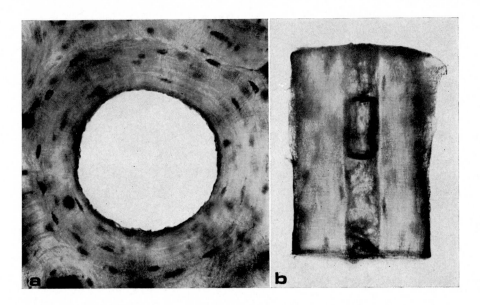

FIG. 1. a) Upper surface of a tested osteon, showing the hole which remains in the center of the osteon after its axial portion has been pushed out. b) Osteonic cylinder pushed out from the osteon shown in (a). × 300.

level of the lamellae situated at the immediate periphery of the osteon, i.e. the lamellae coincident with the circumference of the punch. Consequently, as soon as the connection was interrupted, an osteonic cylinder, having the diameter of the punch, slipped from the section in the hole of the supporting plane (Fig. 1).

The progressive advance of the punch to the point of ultimate strength was measured using a micrometer based on cavity and pulse technique (1, 2).

A careful selection of the osteons was made in order to test osteonic units having a known degree of calcification and a known orientation of the collagen bundles. The degree of calcification was determined by microradiographic technique in order to select osteonic units either at the initial stage of calcification or when fully calcified. Among the different arrangements produced by differences in fiber bundle direction in successive lamellae, those characteristic of three types of osteons were chosen using a polarizing microscope. In the first type the fibers have a marked transverse spiral course in successive lamellae. Under the polarizing microscope the osteons belonging to this type appear homogeneously bright in cross section. In the second type the fibers in one lamella have a marked longitudinal spiral course, while in the next the fibers have an almost transverse spiral course so that the fibers in two successive lamellae make an angle of nearly 90°. Under the

polarizing microscope the osteons of this second type reveal an alternation of dark and bright lamellae in cross section. In the third type the fibers have a marked longitudinal spiral course with the pitch of the spiral changing so slightly that the angle of the fibers in one lamella was practically the same as that of the fibers of the next lamella. Under the polarizing microscope the osteons belonging to this type appear homogeneously dark in cross section. The total number of tested osteons was 40. They were kept and tested wet using a saline solution.

The main preliminary conclusions which can be drawn from this investigation are: 1) The ultimate shearing strength is greatest for osteons having transversly oriented fiber bundles and lowest for osteons having longitudinally oriented fiber bundles. 2) The stress-strain curves for fully calcified osteons are markedly different from those of osteons with low calcium content, the modulus of elasticity being much lower in osteons of the latter type. 3) The expansion of the punch was limited to the interval corresponding to the elastic deformation of the osteon samples and hardly reaches 1 % of the initial length.

REFERENCES

1. Ascenzi A and Bonucci E. *Anat Rec* **158**: 375, 1967.
2. Ascenzi A, Bonucci E and Checcuci, A. in: Evans FG (Ed), "Studies on the anatomy and function of bone and joints." Heidelberg, Springer-Verlag, 1966, p 121.

THE ULTRASTRUCTURE OF THE HYPERTROPHIC CHONDROCYTE

MARIJKE E. HOLTROP*

Laboratory for Cellbiology and Histology, State University, Leiden, Netherlands

It is generally accepted that hypertrophic cells of the epiphyseal plate degenerate at the site of calcification and ultimately die. Several studies, however, suggest at least some cell activity. There is even good evidence that hypertrophic chondrocytes have the potential to become bone cells (1). From this it was

* Present address: Orthopedic Research Laboratories, Massachusetts General Hospital, Boston, Massachusetts, USA.

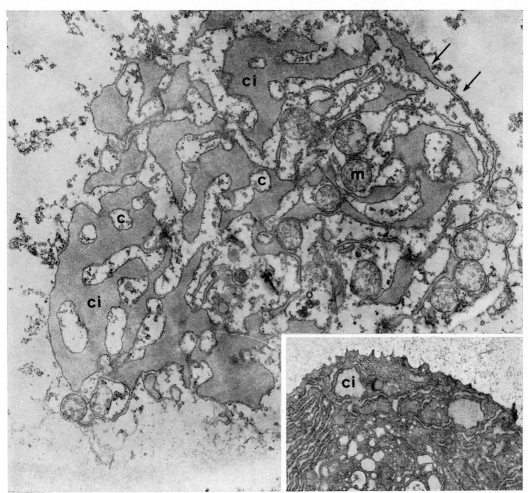

FIG. 1. Rough endoplasmic reticulum in early hypertrophy. The flat cisternae have become more filled. Arrows indicate where this process has only partly taken place. Many cisternae have interconnected, forming large irregularly shaped cisternae with entrapped islands of ground cytoplasm. The contents of the cisternae are as electrondense as the cisternae of the flattened cartilage cell (compare with inset), indicating that the increase of volume is due to increase of contents and not to uptake of water. ci = dilated cisterna; m = mitochondrion; c = cytoplasm. × 9,400.

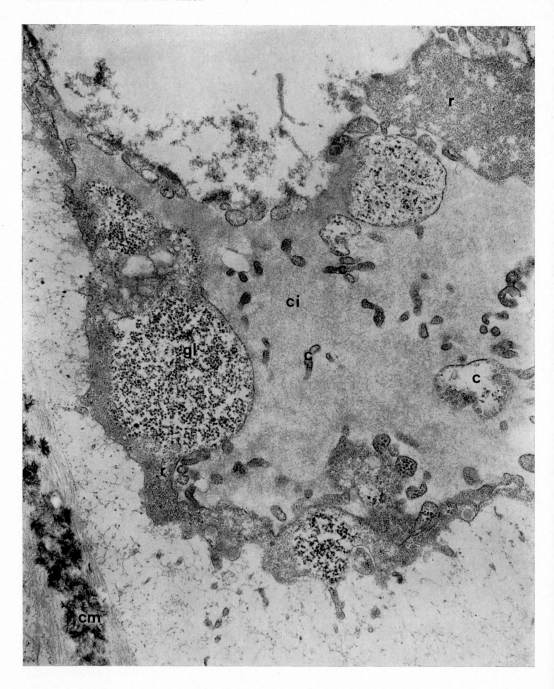

FIG. 2. Rough endoplasmic reticulum in a later stage of hypertrophy. A large cisterna has formed. Little islands of ground cytoplasm with membrane bound ribosomes lie in the large cisterna. Fields of free ribosomes can be seen. ci = dilated cisterna; c = cytoplasm; r = free ribosomes; gl = glycogen; cm = calcified matrix. × 18,200.

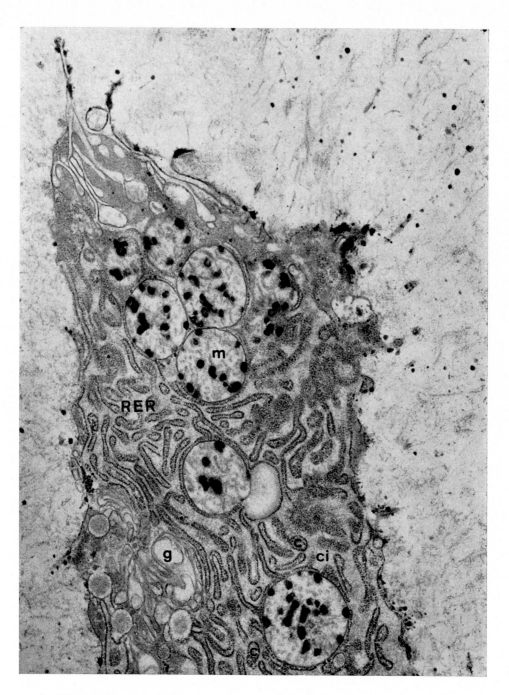

FIG. 3.   Electron dense granules in mitochondria of a hypertrophic chondrocyte. The granules are always found in association with the membranes of the mitochondria. m = mitochondrion; RER = rough endoplasmic reticulum; ci = dilated cisterna; c = islands of cytoplasm in RER cisterna, containing membrane bound ribosomes; g = Golgi area.   × 20,000.

presumed that the morphological appearance, as seen so far by light and electron microscopy, may not be representative of the state of the cell *in vivo*, and may be due to bad preservation. This has led to a study on improving fixation techniques for hypertrophic chondrocytes, using the epiphyseal plates of ribs from young mice. The results showed ultrastructural preservation of the cells that strongly suggests cell activity from the beginning of enlargement of the cell up to the stage where the lacuna breaks open.

In successive stages of hypertrophy different organelles change their aspect considerably. The cisternae of the rough endoplasmic reticulum (RER) continually enlarge. At the same time the flat cisternae become more filled and form many connections (Fig. 1). This process goes on to the extent that eventually so much space is taken up by the RER contents that the ground cytoplasm and the membrane bound ribosomes become entrapped and form little islands in the middle of the RER cisternae (Fig. 2). One can find only a few of these islands in a large amount of RER contents (Fig. 2), or many islands close together leaving less space for the RER contents (Fig. 3). When the alterations in the RER start, there seems to be no difference in electrondensity between the RER contents in hypertrophic cells and those in flattened cartilage cells (Fig. 2). This would suggest an increase of contents rather than an increase in volume by water uptake. In later stages the aspect changes and the RER contents become less homogeneous. In addition to the RER, fields of free ribosomes are seen, even to the extent of taking up rather large areas in the cell (Fig. 2).

The mitochondria of some cells show a prominent change. Starting just before or at the onset of calcification of the matrix, they accumulate an electrondense material in the form of granules of 500 to 1,000 Å (Fig. 3). These are similar to the granules described by Martin and Matthews in rat and mouse epiphyseal plates (2). They are found in mitochondria all through the hypertrophic zone, even in some of the very last hypertrophic cells, just before the lacuna breaks open.

The hypertrophic chondrocyte lies in a wide lacuna which is filled with fine fibrillar, loosely distributed material. Long and slender processes extend through the lacuna towards the cartilage matrix.

These morphological features do not conform with the long accepted view of degeneration and cell death. Through all stages the cell shows a morphological aspect that strongly suggests cell activity. Several investigators have suggested that the cell in early stages of hypertrophy plays a role in the calcification of the matrix. This could not, however, explain the alterations in the cell beyond the area where the matrix calcifies. Previous autoradiographic studies seem significant in this respect in which good evidence was given that hypertrophic chondrocytes have the potential to become osteoblasts and osteocytes (1). In the light of those experiments the increase of contents in the cisternae of the RER could be seen as preliminary steps in the transformation of these cells into bone cells. Also, the presence of granules in the mitochondria could represent stored material needed by the future bone cells.

REFERENCES
1. HOLTROP M E. in: Fleisch H, Blackwood HJJ and Owen M (Eds), *3rd Europ Symp Calcif Tissues*. Berlin, Springer-Verlag, 1966, p 32.
2. MARTIN J H and MATTHEWS J L. *Calcif Tissue Res* **3**: 184, 1969.

INVESTIGATIONS OF HIGH DENSITY AREAS IN METABOLIC BONE DISEASES

F. HEUCK

Department of Radiology, Laboratory of Microradiography, Katharinenhospital, Stuttgart, German Federal Republic

Microradiography of undecalcified bone ground sections shows differences of the mineral concentration in osseous tissue. The microradiographic picture of normal osseous tissue of different age groups is well known (1–4). The high resolving power of microradiography gives evidence of the mineral concentration of small areas as cement lines. High density areas are observed only sporadically in normal osseous tissue.

Commonly known are the cement lines which border the osteons, the lines of high density inside the haversian systems (the resting line) and also the high mineralized lines in some osteons, so-called cockade osteons. In the interstitial lamellae of normal bone of men and animals highly mineralized areas are, however, seldom found (Fig. 1, 2).

The absorption of dyes is usually, but not invariably, diminished in highly mineralized areas. These areas are probably formed during bone transformation and demonstrate a certain phase of mineral deposition in Tela ossae. The hypothesis seems justified, that high density areas are an indicator of this phase of bone transformation when destruction and osteolysis are followed by apposition. The pattern of highly mineralized lines and areas seems to reflect the map-like outlines of sites of destruction (scalloping). This does not hold for the cockade osteons with their cement lines nor for the resting lines of the haversian systems. The mode of origin of the highly mineralized areas in the interstitial lamellae of normal bone tissue is unknown.

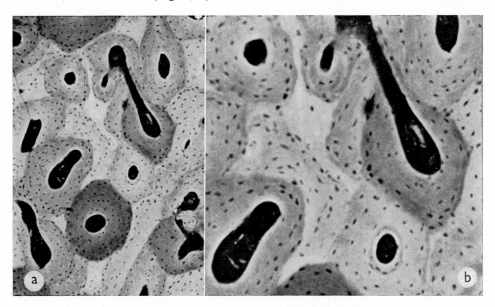

FIG. 1. Highly mineralized resting lines in areas of interstitial lamellae (a 36-year-old man, who died in an accident). a) × 75; b) × 150.

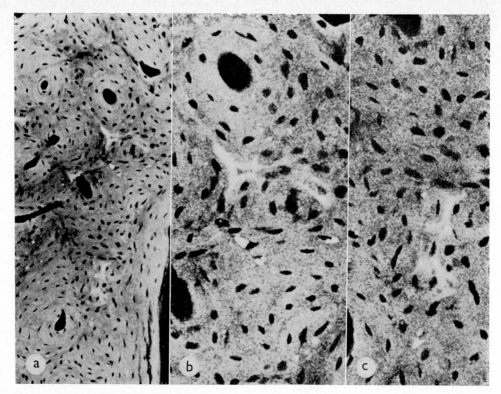

FIG. 2. Map-like shaped, highly mineralized areas in interstitial lamellae of the compact bone of a rabbit. a) × 25; b) × 100; c) ×100.

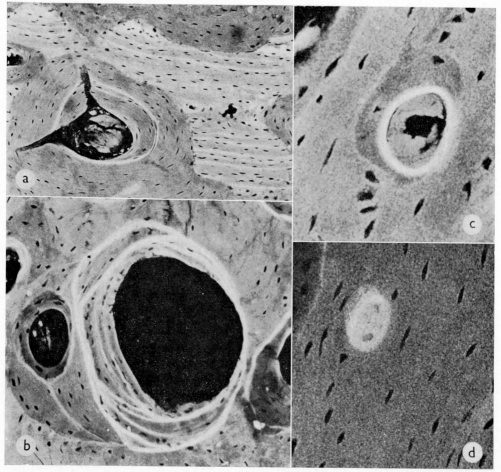

FIG. 3. Numerous cement lines, cockade osteons and highly mineralized osteocyte halos in marble bone disease in a 35-year-old woman. a) × 65; b) × 100; c) × 250; d) × 250.

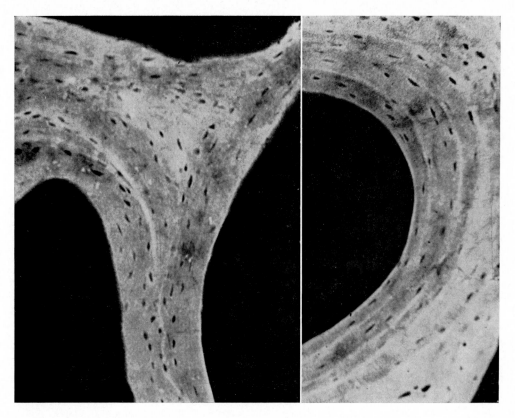

FIG. 4. Small cement lines in spongy bone (left) and in haversian system (right) in bone, due to gastro-intestinal disease in a 57-year-old man. × 250.

Microradiography of congenital and acquired systemic diseases of osseous tissue revealed quite a number of cement lines. In addition to the borderlines of osteons, numerous ribbon-shaped highly mineralized areas in the interstitial lamellae could be demonstrated. They could be seen in compact bone as well as in large numbers in the lamellae of spongy bone, and were ribbon-shaped, map-like and occurred as spots. In the course of very turbulent transformation processes of osseous tissue in secondary hyperparathyroidism in chronic renal disease (renal osteodystrophy), highly mineralized areas could be demonstrated in a marginal area around the destruction zone.

In congenital and acquired bone diseases highly mineralized areas occur near the osteocyte lacunae as high density halo.

An example of increased development of highly mineralized areas in a congenital metabolic bone disease is osteopetrosis or marble bone disease. Here they occur in compact as well as in spongy bones (Fig. 3).

We have observed differences in the type and frequency of highly mineralized areas in metabolic bone diseases: 1) Bone tissue with a small number of osteoid seams and transformation areas (Howship's lacunae) had numerous mineralized areas and lines in the haversian systems and interstitial lamellae of compact and spongy bone. The border between bone tissue and surrounding connective tissue was not uniform but showed different density (Fig. 4). 2) In systemic bone diseases with an increase in the number of osteoid seams adjacent to highly mineralized cement lines, low density and mineral-deficient areas could be seen. There were large highly mineralized zones between the osteoid seams and the normal mineralized osseous tissue (so called "demarcation line" of Lacroix) where very scattered highly mineralized osteocyte halos could be found. 3) The very rapid transformation rate of osseous tissue in hyperparathyroidism, especially in secondary hyperparathyroidism, led to a considerable change of the bone structure and the microradiographic picture of mineral concentration. There was striking evidence of high mineralization of the cement lines, the borders of Howship's lacunae and the marginal areas of osteocytic osteolysis. The cement lines formed map-like figures in the compact and spongy bone and there was an increase

of the periosteocytic mineralization. In secondary hyperparathyroidism sclerotic areas could also be demonstrated macroscopically by X-ray.

The highly mineralized areas are a remarkable phenomenon of the healthy bone, and even more so in the osseous tissue in metabolic bone disease. It is presumed that these areas develop by sudden precipitation of calcium salts, depending on the ion concentration in bone tissue. Further study should give better information on the dynamics of bone transformation and mineral metabolism.

REFERENCES

1. ENGSTRÖM A. Handbuch d Med Radiol, 1970.
2. BOHATIRCHUK FP. *Amer J Anat* **113**: 117, 1963.
3. JOWSEY J. *Amer J Med* **40**: 485, 1966.
4. HEUCK F. *Radiologe* **9**: 142, 1969.

MICROSCOPIC AND ELECTRON MICROPROBE CHARACTERIZATION OF THE SCLEROTIC LAMELLAE IN HUMAN OSTEONS

DONALD J. ORTNER and DAVID W. VON ENDT

Division of Physical Anthropology, Department of Anthropology,
National Museum of Natural History, Smithsonian Institution, Washington, D.C., USA

One hypothesis on the function of osteons is that incompletely mineralized osteons contribute to mineral homeostasis, whereas more highly mineralized osteons are primarily structural (1). Rowland's research (2), based on uptake of radioactive calcium, suggests that mineral exchange is not related to the degree of mineralization of the osteon but rather is a function of the proximity of bone mineral to circulatory fluids. In the osteon he associates mineral exchange with the bone immediately surrounding the haversian canal.

In addition to the problem of where mineral exchange occurs there is the question of the nature of the exchangeable mineral. Hydroxyapatite, because of its crystalline structure, requires relatively high energy for solubiliza-

tion. In view of this it would be desirable to have a noncrystalline calcium phosphate at the exchange site in osteons.

Posner (3) and Termine and Posner (4) have presented evidence supporting the existence of an amorphous calcium phosphate in bone. Posner (3) suggests that the amorphous mineral is tricalcium phosphate which is distributed evenly throughout bone and comprises about 40% of bone mineral. He also indicates that the amount of amorphous mineral is higher in young bone and decreases with age.

In our laboratory we have been studying the morphology of the osteon and noticed that a high percentage (38%) of osteons have one or more lamellae adjacent to the haversian canal which are morphologically differ-

TABLE 1. *Average composition of Ca, P and Mg with the Ca/P molar ratio for three types of bone in human osteons*

| | Ca (%) | | P (%) | | Mg (%) | | Ca/P | Points analyzed |
	Mean	SD	Mean	SD	Mean	SD		
Mature bone	36.77	5.64	17.13	2.66	0.47	0.12	1.66	45
Forming bone	32.06	5.65	15.00	2.60	0.58	0.13	1.66	36
Sclerotic bone	39.32	7.43	18.79	3.55	0.78	0.17	1.62	30

TABLE 2. *Ca/P molar ratios for three types of bone in two mineral phases. Ca in $CaCO_3$ has been subtracted from the total Ca value*

| | Total mineral | | Hydroxyapatite | Tricalcium phosphate |
	Theoretical	Observed		
Mature bone	1.61	1.57	1.64 (60%)	1.48 (40%)
Forming bone	1.55	1.55	1.66 (31%)	1.50 (69%)
Sclerotic bone	1.50	1.54	——	1.54 (100%)

ent from the rest of the osteon. From a study of undecalcified cross sections of the tibiae from over eighty human individuals we reached the following conclusions. First, in darkfield light these inner lamellae were much darker than the rest of the osteon, suggesting an amorphous mineral rather than a more highly refractive crystalline mineral. Second, in microradiographs the same lamellae were much denser than the remainder of the osteon. Third, these amorphous, sclerotic lamellae tend to be associated with more highly mineralized osteons although they occasionally occur in incompletely mineralized osteons.

Posner's suggestion that the amorphous mineral in bone is tricalcium phosphate, which has a Ca/P molar ratio of 1.50 in contrast with a Ca/P molar ratio of 1.67 for hydroxyapatite, offers a testable hypothesis for clarifying the nature of the mineral phase in the amorphous, sclerotic, inner lamellae. Using an electron microprobe we determined the concentration of calcium, phosphorus and magnesium in four osteons which had a sclerotic ring, and for comparative purposes, two osteons which microradiographs showed to

be incompletely mineralized. All of these determinations were done on a single thin section.

Using a step-scanning drive on the mechanical specimen stage of the probe we analyzed a total of 111 spots distributed in: 1) the normal portion of osteons having a sclerotic zone, 2) the sclerotic zone itself and 3) forming osteons. The results of this analysis are given in Table 1. Our microprobe data have been corrected for mass absorption, atomic number, and fluorescence.

It is apparent that the Ca/P ratio decreases in the amorphous, sclerotic zone while the magnesium concentration increases. Eanes and Posner (5) have suggested that magnesium stabilizes the relatively unstable amorphous calcium phosphate and thus would be expected to be more highly concentrated in an amorphous mineral phase. It is also possible that carbonate is involved in stabilizing amorphous mineral (6). There are two problems in interpreting the data in Table 1. First, calcium carbonate is reported to constitute approximately 5.2% of the mineral in human bone (7). Second, the amorphous phase in bone is reported to be at least 40%, and even higher in incompletely mineralized bone (3). Both these factors must be considered before Ca/P molar ratios can have meaning.

In Table 2 we have assumed that the calcium carbonate fraction is evenly distributed throughout the osteon and have subtracted the weight percent of calcium in calcium carbonate from the total calcium value. On the basis of Posner's report (3) we determined the molar concentrations of both calcium and phosphorus by assuming that the percentage of mineral in the amorphous phase (tricalcium phosphate) for mature and forming bone was 40 and 69%, respectively. On the basis of our microscopic studies we assumed that the sclerotic lamellae were entirely amorphous and, except for calcium carbonate, composed of tricalcium phosphate.

Given our assumptions, the Ca/P molar ratios for both mature and forming bone appear reasonable. It is also clear that the molar ratios in hydroxyapatite are much higher than the molar ratio found in the sclerotic ring. However, this observation depends on the validity of our assumption that the sclerotic lamellae are, in fact, primarily tricalcium phosphate. The basis for this assumption is the microscopic appearance of the lamellae and the slightly lower calcium phosphorus ratio (1.54) in the sclerotic lamellae. In our opinion the difference in the molar ratios between mature bone and sclerotic bone is less than convincing without the microscopic evidence to support our assumption that it is in fact amorphous. It remains to be determined whether the calcium carbonate concentration in the sclerotic ring is the same as in the rest of the osteon. Certainly the fact that the Ca/P molar ratio in sclerotic bone is higher than expected suggests that calcium carbonate may be more highly concentrated in this type of bone.

In conclusion, our evidence supports the possibility of an amorphous calcium phosphate being localized in the lamellae immediately surrounding the haversian canal of some osteons. By inference we would expect this mineral to be more labile and more active in mineral homeostasis.

Supported in part by National Institute of Child Health and Human Development Grant HD03861.

REFERENCES

1. AMPRINO R. in: Bargmann W (Ed), "Aus der Werkstatt der Anatomen." Stuttgart, Georg Thiem Verlag, 1965, p 1.
2. ROWLAND RE. *Clin Orthop* **49**: 233, 1966.
3. POSNER AS. *Physiol Rev* **49**: 760, 1969.
4. TERMINE JD and POSNER AS. *Calcif Tissue Res* **1**: 8, 1967.
5. EANES ED and POSNER AS. *Calcif Tissue Res* **2**: 38, 1968.
6. BACHRA B. *Ann NY Acad Sci* **109**: 251, 1963.
7. BILTZ RM and PELLEGRINO ED. *J Bone Joint Surg* [*Amer*] **51**: 456, 1969.

THE MEASUREMENT OF PERIOSTEOCYTIC ENLARGEMENT IN PRIMARY AND SECONDARY HYPERPARATHYROIDISM

P. MEUNIER, J. BERNARD and G. VIGNON

Laboratoire de Recherches sur l'Histodynamique Osseuse, Faculté de Médecine, Lyon, France

The stimulating effect of parathormone on periosteocytic osteolysis has been demonstrated on the basis of results obtained from many experiments on animals. However few histological and microradiographic observations have been made on human bone tissue (1–7).

Experimentally, in animals, parathormone

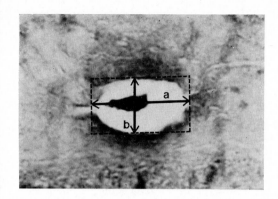

FIG. 1. Measurement of surface area of periosteocytic lacunae. a × b = lacunar area.

is a powerful stimulant of proteolytic activity of osteocytes, inducing an enlargement of periosteocytic lacunae (6, 8–11). There have been very few observations of this phenomenon in human bone tissue: Jowsey et al. (7) noted enlarged lacunae in 27 out of 32 cases of hyperparathyroidism, and Bélanger et al. (5) reported dilated and confluent lacunae in a case of adenomatous hyperparathyroidism.

Such a contrast between the abundance of experimental data and the scarcity of bone morphometric observations in patients with hyperparathyroidism induced us to study quantitatively the existence and importance of periosteocytic osteolysis in human hyperparathyroidism. We felt that the measuring of lacunae in bone samples could be a useful diagnostic tool.

Materials and methods. One hundred and ten iliac crest samples were obtained by biopsy or from autopsy specimens and were partially decalcified in nitric acid. In all cases, 32 serial sections 5 μ thick were cut and analyzed quantitatively using micrometric and integrating eyepieces.

The mean volume of periosteocytic lacunae was estimated by measuring the area of the pericellular cavity. These cavities were ellipsoidal and appeared to be well delimited oval lacunae. The surface of each lacuna was

estimated by measuring the length (a) and the width (b) of the ellipse with a micrometric eyepiece. We considered the product a × b, i.e. the surface of the rectangle containing the lacuna, as an indication of lacunar area (Fig. 1). In all cases, 50 lacunae, selected at random, were measured and the mean surface was calculated.

The measurement of trabecular bone osteoclastic resorption surfaces was done using a Zeiss II integrating eyepiece according to a method previously described (12). It was expressed as the percentage of the total trabecular surface.

The above two measurements were carried out on: a) 35 cases of accidental death in

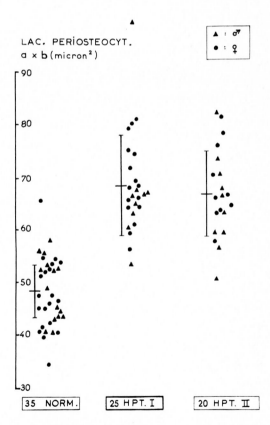

FIG. 2. Periosteocytic lacunar area in normal subjects and patients with hyperparathyroidism. HPT I, primary hyperparathyroidism; HPT II, secondary hyperparathyroidism.

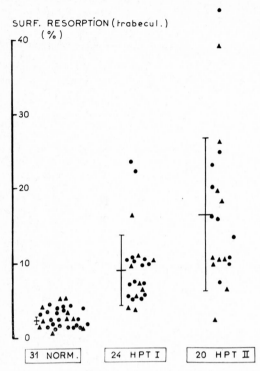

SURF. RESORPTION (trabecul.) (%)

FIG. 3. Osteoclastic resorption surface in normal subjects and in patients with hyperparathyroidism.

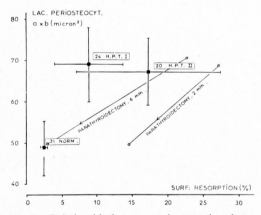

LAC. PERIOSTEOCYT.
a x b (micron²)

FIG. 4. Relationship between periosteocytic enlargement and trabecular osteoclastic resorption areas in normal subjects and in patients with hyperparathyroidism.

previously normal subjects (mean age: 41 years); b) 25 patients with primary hyperparathyroidism which was proven by the surgical detection of parathyroid adenoma in

22 cases, of parathyroid hyperplasia in two cases and of parathyroid carcinoma in one case (mean age: 51 years); c) 20 patients on maintenance hemodialysis and having chronic kidney failure with histological signs of secondary hyperparathyroidism i.e. increased resorption surfaces (above 4.6%) (mean age: 28 years); d) 20 patients with osteoporosis which was proven by the fact that the trabecular bone volume was consistently less than 12%, regardless of age. These patients demonstrated the clinical symptoms of osteoporosis and their X-rays showed thin, biconcave vertebrae or crushed vertebrae (mean age: 59 years); e) 10 patients with osteomalacia which was proved by the presence of Looser-Milkman fractures in four cases and in all cases by thick and numerous osteoid seams (mean age: 53 years).

Results. Fig. 2 compares the surfaces of periosteocytic lacunae sections in 35 normal subjects (48.3 $\mu^2 \pm$ 4.8) with 25 cases of primary hyperparathyroidism (68.3 $\mu^2 \pm$ 9.5) and with 20 cases of secondary hyperparathyroidism (67 $\mu^2 \pm$ 8.1). These means were statistically compared using Student's "t" test. This comparison shows the existence of a significant periosteocytic enlargement in hyperparathyroidism ($P < 0.001$).

Fig. 3 compares the trabecular surface areas of osteoclastic resorption in 31 normal subjects (2.4% $\pm$ 0.4) with 24 cases of primary hyperparathyroidism (9% $\pm$ 4.9) and with 20 cases of secondary hyperparathyroidism (17.4% $\pm$ 10.2). As previously observed in a smaller group of cases (12), there is a significant increase in the resorption surface areas in primary hyperparathyroidism ($P < 0.001$) as well as in secondary renal hyperparathyroidism ($P < 0.001$).

A relationship between the values indicating periosteocytic enlargement and the values expressing the extent of trabecular osteoclastic resorption areas was sought. Fig. 4 shows the mean values and standard deviation of the two parameters in each group. Our results show the presence of wider resorption surfaces in secondary hyperparathyroidism than in primary hyperparathyroidism. The degree of periosteocytic enlargement is the same in both groups. In two cases where 7/8 of the parathyroid mass was removed to correct accentuated secondary renal hyperparathyroidism, both parameters decreased after surgery.

The volume of periosteocytic lacunae is not significantly increased in osteoporosis (20 cases; 51.2 $\mu^2 \pm 4.7$) or osteomalacia (50.5 $\mu^2 \pm 7$), compared with 35 normal cases ($P > 0.05$).

Measurements of periosteocytic enlargement appears to be an accurate and useful method for confirming a positive diagnosis of hyperparathyroidism on iliac bone biopsies. This measurement is possible on decalcified sections and on very small specimens where trabecular resorption surfaces cannot be determined.

REFERENCES

1. BAUD CA. *Acta Anat (Basel)* **51**: 209, 1962.
2. BAUD CA and DUPONT DH. *Coll Colloq Univ Liège* 1965, p 31.
3. BELANGER LF, SEMBA T, TOLANI S, COPP DH, KROOK L and GRIES C. in: *3rd Europ Symp Calcif Tissues, 1965.* Berlin, Springer Verlag, 1966, p 1.
4. BELANGER LF. *Calcif Tissue Res* **4**: 1, 1969.
5. BELANGER LF, ROBICHON J, MIGICOVSKY BB, COPP DH and VINCENT J. in: Sognnaes (Ed), "Mechanisms of hard tissue destruction." Washington, American Association for the Advancement of Science, 1963, p 531.
6. DURIEZ J and CAUCHOIX J. *Presse Med* **73**: 1,297, 1967.
7. JOWSEY J, RIGGS BL and KELLY PJ. *Mayo Clin Proc* **39**: 480, 1964.
8. BELANGER LF. in: Gaillard PJ, Talmage RV and Dudy AM (Eds), "The parathyroid glands: Ultrastructure, secretion and function." Chicago, University of Chicago Press, 1965.
9. BROWN WR, KROOK L and POND WG. *Cornell Vet* **56** (suppl 1) : 1, 1966.
10. HENRIKSON PA. *Acta Odont Scand* **26** (suppl 50) : 1, 1968.
11. KROOK L and LOWE JE. *Path Vet (Basel)* **1** : suppl 1, 1964.
12. MEUNIER P, VIGNON G, VAUZELLE JL and ZECH P. *Path Biol (Paris)* **17**: 927, 1969.

ULTRASTRUCTURAL ASPECTS OF DISINTEGRATING COLLAGEN FIBRILS IN OSTEOPOROTIC BONES

CARL D. SALOMON and GERSHON VOLPIN

Department of Anatomy, Hebrew University–Hadassah Medical School, Jerusalem, Israel

Young rats on a calcium-deficient diet develop osteoporosis. The first signs of bone resorption in the metatarsals are observed after seven days and reach a peak after thirty days. The loss of bone mass is manifested by thinning of the compacta, and by the appearance of resorption cavities therein. In our light microscope and electron microscope studies (1, 2) it was noted that bone resorption takes place in two stages. In the first stage calcium disappears from the perilacunar areas, leaving organic matrix consisting mainly of collagen (Fig. 1b), which is resorbed in the second stage. In both stages an active part is played by hypertrophied bone cells, which contain abundant rough-surfaced endoplasmic reticulum with large cisternae (Fig. 1b). In comparison with these hypertrophied cells, normal osteocytes are small with relatively few cytoplasmic organelles (Fig. 1a, decalcified with EDTA).

The specific aim of the present study was to follow the disintegrating collagen fibrils until their total disappearance. Young female rats weighing 40 to 50 g were fed on a calcium-deficient diet containing 0.02 to

153

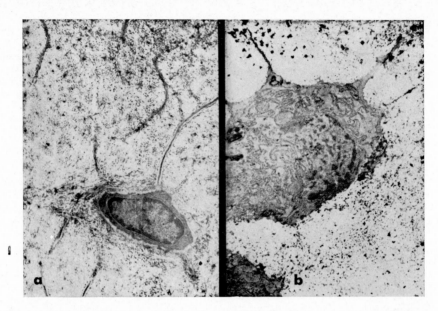

FIG. 1.   a) Normal osteocyte, poor in cytoplasmic organelles, decalcified with EDTA. × 5,000. b) Hypertrophied osteocyte from calcium-deficient bone, showing large amounts of rough-surfaced endoplasmic reticulum with large cisterns. The area around the cell is calcium-free, as a result of the process of bone resorption, and contains organic matrix. × 5,000.

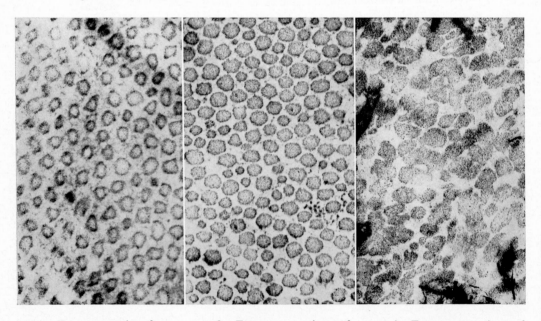

FIG. 2.   Transverse section of normal collagen fibrils showing dense outer shell and less dense inner core. × 63,000.

FIG. 3.   Transverse sections of collagen fibrils from calcium-deficient bone showing first phase of collagen disintegration, with thinner outer shell and coarser granulation of inner core. × 63,000.

FIG. 4.   Transverse sections of collagen fibrils from calcium-deficient bone showing almost uniform density. No differentiation between outer shell and inner core. × 63,000.

154

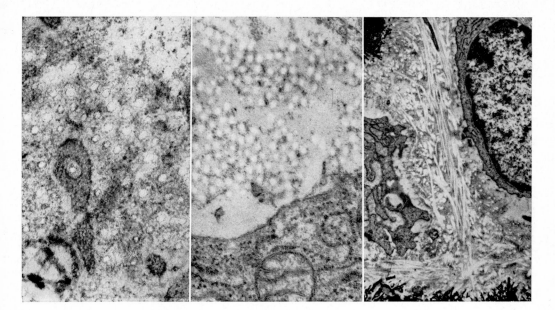

FIG. 5. Transverse sections of collagen fibrils from calcium-deficient bone showing that collagen fibrils became less electron-dense than the ground substance. The central parts of the collagen fibrils are almost completely dissolved. × 50,000.

FIG. 6. Transverse sections of collagen fibrils from calcium-deficient bone showing hole-like images of former collagen fibrils in electron-dense ground substance. × 42,000. Note denser parts in ground substance in Fig. 2 to 6.

FIG. 7. Longitudinal sections of collagen fibrils from calcium-deficient bone showing negative images of fibrils. Note last traces of periodicity in some fibrils. × 6,700.

0.03 % calcium. Metatarsals were examined two, three and four weeks after the start of the diet. In transverse section, normal collagen fibrils had an electron dense outer shell, and a less dense finely granular inner core (Fig. 2), as previously noted in connective tissues other than bone (3–5). The average diameter of these fibrils is around 500 Å. With the onset of disintegration, the outer shell became progressively thinner and less electron dense, while the granulation of the inner core became coarser (Fig. 3).

In the next phase the changes became more prominent. On transverse section, the distinction between outer shell and inner core disappeared, and the collagen fibrils showed a uniform coarse granulation (Fig. 4); at this stage the fibrils varied considerably both in shape and size. The largest fibrils appeared swollen and reached a diameter of 660 Å, as compared with the normal average diameter of 500 Å. Throughout all these early stages of degeneration, the collagen fibrils were more electron dense than the ground substance in which they were embedded. As degeneration progressed, however, the fibrils gradually lost density, and they finally became less dense than the surrounding ground substance (Fig. 5–7).

At a later stage, the fibrils became less granular, but the granulation disappeared more rapidly in the central part of the fibril than in the outer rim, and was also much finer (Fig. 5). Ultimately, even the last remnants of granulation disappeared, and the spaces formerly occupied by the collagen fibrils resembled holes in the ground substance (Fig. 6). It is difficult to account for

155

these holes on any other basis than that they are spaces formerly occupied by collagen fibrils in the ground substance (Fig. 6). In longitudinal section, too, the fibrils appeared as empty spaces (Fig. 7), some of them still showing traces of periodicity.

The greater density of the ground substance at a time when the collagen fibrils have lost much of their density suggests the possibility that the degeneration of collagen may perhaps precede that of the ground substance. The ground substance is usually described as amorphous but even in the normal animal it shows areas of varying electron density. This phenomenon merits further investigation. The mechanism of the disintegration of collagen fibrils is not yet known, but one obvious pos-

sibility is that it is due to proteolytic enzymes. This view is supported by the presence of large amounts of rough-surfaced endoplasmic reticulum with conspicuous cisternae in the hypertrophied bone cells. This presumably indicates an increase in the synthesis of proteins, among which there might well be proteolytic enzymes.

REFERENCES

1. SALOMON CD and VOLPIN G. *Calcif Tissue Res* **4** (Suppl): 80, 1970.
2. SALOMON CD and VOLPIN G. in: "Microscopie electronique." 1970, pp 867–868.
3. FERNANDO NVP, VAN ERKEL GA and MOVAT HZ. *Exp Molec Path* **3**: 529, 1964.
4. DADOUNE JP and ABELANET R. *Path Biol (Paris)* **16**: 1053, 1968.
5. BEN-ISHAY Z, DAVIES AM and LAUFER A. *Exp Molec Path* **8**: 358, 1968.

FINE STRUCTURAL LOCALIZATION OF ALKALINE PHOSPHOMONOESTERASE IN THE FRACTURE CALLUS OF THE RAT

GUSTAV GÖTHLIN and JAN L. E. ERICSSON

Department of Pathology, Sabbatsberg Hospital, and Department of Orthopedic Surgery, Norrbackainstitutet, Karolinska Institutet Medical School, Stockholm, Sweden

Biochemical and light microscopic histochemical evidence indicates that the occurrence of high activity of "alkaline phosphatase" [nonspecific *alkaline phosphomonoesterase,* (E.C. 3.1.3.1.)] in bone forming cells coincides with the start of precipitation of calcium salts in the extracellular medium (1–3). Robinson's theory (4) that alkaline phosphatase in bone tissue is directly responsible for the hydrolysis of phosphatase esters, resulting in local increase in the concentration of phosphate ions followed by deposition of calcium phosphate salts from a supersaturated solution, has now been abandoned by most authorities. Although the precise role of alkaline phosphatase and its mechanism of action during the

process of calcification has remained obscure, the enzyme appears to govern this process—directly or indirectly (5–7). It is therefore of interest to identify the cellular and subcellular localization of alkaline phosphatase activity in osteogenic tissues.

Several light microscopic investigations have attempted to elucidate the distribution of alkaline phosphatase in different types of osteogenic tissues (1, 8). However, the results have been partly contradictory and have failed to identify the precise localization of the final product. So far, electron microscopic studies have—to the best of our knowledge—not been published.

We have previously studied the fine structure of the fracture callus in the rat and tried to follow the histogenesis of the various types of cells occurring in the callus (9 and Göthlin and Ericsson, in preparation). In the present preliminary work electron microscopic histochemical methods have been applied in an attempt to elucidate the fine structural localization of alkaline phosphatase using Gomori-type metal precipitation techniques on undecalcified tissues. Emphasis has been placed on applying methods which minimize structural preparatory artifacts (5). Furthermore, the specificity of the reactions have been

tested by addition of biochemical inhibitors to the incubation media (5).

Calluses of variable age from fractured femora were fixed in 1.5% cacodylate-buffered purified glutaraldehyde (pH 7.3) for 24 hr. After appropriate buffer wash the tissues were impregnated with dimethylsulfoxide (DMSO) to minimize freezing artifacts and facilitate penetration of the substrate (5). Approximately 50 μ thick frozen sections of the tissues were incubated, at pH 9.2, in a medium containing Na-β-glycerophosphate and either lead or calcium as capturing ions. Following

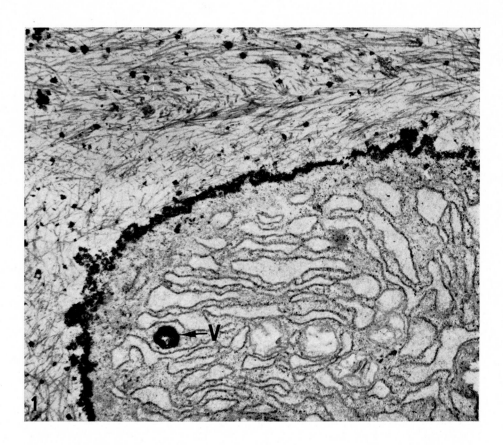

FIG. 1. Callus, 23 days. Electron micrograph showing portion of osteogenic (osteoblast-like) cell and surrounding collagen-containing extracellular matrix substance, from tissue incubated for 20 min in the lead nitrate-glycerophosphate medium. In the cell, reaction product (lead phosphate precipitate) is confined to the plasma membrane and a possible endocytic vesicle (V). There is diffuse deposition of final product in the extracellular matrix. Calcification was noted in adjacent areas of the matrix. Epon; thin section stained with lead citrate and uranyl acetate. × 17,500.

incubation, the sections were washed, post-fixed in OsO₄, and processed for electron microscopy. Histochemical controls included media lacking the substrate. The following inhibitors were utilized in media used for specificity tests: L(+)-cysteine, L(–)-phenyla-nine, 2,3-dimercaptopropanol (BAL), EDTA and parachloromercuribenzoate (BCMB). Incubation of approximately 6 μ thick frozen sections was also performed for light microscopic comparative studies. Visualization of the reaction product in these sections was achieved by immersion in ammonium sulfide (in the case of the calcium method following prior exposure to cobalt ions).

Specific BAL, L-cysteine, EDTA and L-phenylalanine sensitive, PCMB-insensitive, alkaline phosphomonoesterase activity was demonstrated in the eight-day-old callus and at all longer intervals up to 35 days after the fracture. Strongest and most extensive deposition of reaction product was noted at 23 and 27 days; with longer intervals the activity appeared to subside. Activity was confined to the following osteogenic cells: fibroblasts, chondroblasts, hypertrophic chondrocytes and osteoblasts with variable degrees of differentiation (Fig. 1). There was no activity in histiocytic cells or osteoclasts. The lead phosphate and calcium phosphate precipitates occurred on the plasma membrane of all the cells with positive reaction. The precipitates were sparse and inconspicuous on the membranes of fibroblasts, but heavy in the case of osteoblasts (Fig. 1); chondroblasts and chondrocytes took an intermediary position in this respect. Reaction product was also present in small cytoplasmic vesicles, often located immediately below the plasma membrane. These elements may represent endocytic vesicles. Possible slight reaction was also found in the Golgi apparatus of some cells

(mainly osteoblasts). Furthermore, precipitate was also present on the membranes bordering many of the intracellular vacuoles containing collagen (8). These vacuoles probably contain newly synthesized collagen on its way to the extracellular medium (9). In the latter, precipitate was present on the small "globules" described by Bonucci (10) ("vesicles connected with calcification") (11); there was also some diffuse activity.

These results show that there is a true alkaline phosphomonoesterase present in the osteogenic cells of the callus. Enzyme activity is mainly associated with the plasma membrane and with membranes derived from the latter, or destined for fusion with the plasmalemma. Strongest activity is exhibited at times when calcification occurs in the tissue. Lower activity apparently ensues when the process of calcification approaches completion. The findings support the concept that alkaline phosphatase is in some way related to mineralization in bone forming tissue.

The assistance of Miss Silwa Mengarelli and Mrs. Britt-Marie Åkerman is gratefully acknowledged.

Supported in part by grants from the Karolinska Institutet.

REFERENCES

1. BOURNE GH. "The biochemistry and physiology of bone." New York, Academic Press, 1956, p 251.
2. GREENSPAIN JW and BLACKWOOD HJ. *J Anat* **100**: 615, 1966.
3. JIBRIL AO. *Biochim Biophys Acta* **141**: 605, 1967.
4. ROBISON R. *Biochem J* **17**: 286, 1923.
5. COX PC and GRIFFIN MJ. *Lancet* **ii**: 1018, 1955.
6. FLEISCH H, MAERKI J and RUSSELL GG. *Proc Soc Exp Biol Med* **122**: 317, 1966.
7. TEAFORD ME and WHITE AA. *Proc Soc Exp Biol Med* **117**: 541, 1964.
8. PRITCHARD JJ and RUZICKA AJ. *J Anat* **84**: 236, 1950.
9. GÖTHLIN G and ERICSSON JLE. *Virchow Arch (Zellpath)* **6**: 24, 1970.
10. BONUCCI E. *Z Zellforsch* **103**: 192, 1970.
11. ANDERSON HC. *J Cell Biol* **41**: 59, 1969.

SOME MORPHOLOGIC AND DYNAMIC ASPECTS OF REMODELING ON THE ENDOSTEAL-CORTICAL AND TRABECULAR SURFACES

Z. F. JAWORSKI

Ottawa General Hospital and University of Ottawa, Ottawa, Canada

It is established that the usual permanent decrease and rare increase in the mature skeleton mass are due, respectively, to the expansion or contraction of the bone marrow cavity (1). Hence the renewed interest in the behavior of the endosteal envelope covering the internal surfaces of the cortex and the whole spongiosa. The remodeling is a surface phenomenon taking place in discrete sites where osteoclastic resorption occurs first and osteoblastic bone formation follows (2). Because the spongiosa has greater surface to volume ratio than the cortex, the turnover rate of the former exceeds that of the cortex. The configuration, dimensions and distribution of the remodeling centers on the endosteal surfaces have been less systematically studied (3). Acquaintance with these features is a prerequisite for the elucidation of the mechanism through which bone is lost with aging and in osteoporosis, or occasionally gained in other conditions. A study of the endosteal remodeling in various age groups and diseases was therefore undertaken, adopting a new approach. The material obtained at autopsy (vertebrae, ribs and iliac crest) or by biopsy (ribs and iliac crest) was processed in the following manner. After removing the bone marrow, thick (200 to 300 µ), fresh undecalcified sections were stained with Villaneuva tetrachrome and mounted in transparent plastic. Stained endosteal surfaces were inspected under the stereomicroscope. Bone forming centers are identified because of the green color taken up by the non-mineralized osteoid. In conjunction with the study of thick (50 to 70 µ) and thin (5 to 10 µ) undecalcified sections similarly stained, three-dimensional configuration of remodeling centers on the endosteal surfaces could be reconstructed.

The typical center measures approximately 400 to 500 µ by 500 to 2,000 µ on the surface and 60 to 80 µ in thickness. Although the configuration of endosteal and haversian remodeling centers differs, they turn over a comparable volume of lamellar bone, approximately 0.05 mm³ per center. These observations indicate that the distribution and density (number per unit surface area) of the remodeling centers on the endosteal surface vary with their location in a given bone, the age and the disease. On the basis of these observations, it is possible to visualize the mechanism for the continuous bone loss with aging and in osteoporosis.

Bone loss from endosteal surfaces (thinning of the cortex and trabeculae, or their loss) appears to be due basically to the built-in negative bone balance occurring in individual remodeling centers. In the spongiosa (trabeculae and plates) this cumulative negative bone balance is amplified when the thickness of the trabeculae and particularly of the plates becomes less than the depth of the osteoclastic resorptive thrust (approximately 80 µ). Thus, circular defects are produced in remodeling sites which cannot be refilled by the subsequent phase of bone formation. This mechanism accounts for the earlier loss of the horizontal trabeculae or plates in the vertebrae, where more active remodeling was shown to occur (4, 5).

On the cortical endosteal surface, the basic bone loss is amplified by osteoclastic erosion of the innermost haversian systems and their invasion by the bone marrow. Since the subsequent phase of bone formation is much less pronounced, these new large cavities become "endostealized." Thus, as at the periphery of the bone marrow cavity, new trabeculae are formed at the expense of the cortex, and in the center trabecular bone mass diminishes. In osteoporosis these processes appear to be accentuated.

In conclusion, the morphologic and dynamic behavior of remodeling on endosteal surfaces was studied by surface staining of thick human lamellar bone sections of various ages. The physiological bone loss with aging is ascribed to a basic, built-in negative bone

balance in remodeling centers on endosteal surfaces. This basic mechanism is reinforced and accelerated as the trabeculae become thinner, and as the innermost haversion systems in the cortex enlarge and become "endostealized." In osteoporosis these processes are accentuated.

REFERENCES

1. GARN SM, ROHMANN CHG, WAGNER B, DAVILA GH and ASCOLI W. *Clin Orthop* **65**: 51, 1969.
2. FROST HM. *Calcif Tissue Res* **3**: 211, 1969.
3. BROMEY RG, DOCKUM NL, ARNOLD JS and JEE WSS. *J Geront* **21**: 1966.
4. ATKINSON PJ. *Calcif Tissue Res* **1**: 24, 1967.
5. WAKAMATSU E and SISSON HA. *Calcif Tissue Res* **4**: 147, 1969.

VARIATION IN BONE MATRIX VOLUME ASSOCIATED WITH OSTEOCYTE LACUNAE IN MAMMALIAN AND REPTILIAN BONE

M. H. HOBDELL and C. E. HOWE

Department of Anatomy, King's College, London, England

In mammals there are two distinct microscopic arrangements of bone tissue: primary membrane bone and adult lamellar bone. These two types can be distinguished in microradiographs by three principal features: 1) Primary bone is more highly mineralized. 2) There are many more vascular channels in primary bone. 3) In primary bone each osteocyte appears to be associated with a smaller volume of intercellular matrix than in adult lamellar bone.

The microscopic organization of bone in different reptilian species presents an even greater range of patterns of structural organization depending on the individual anatomical and growth characteristics of each particular species.

The present study was designed to quantify the difference in the mean volume of bone

matrix associated with an individual osteocyte in the two types of mammalian bone tissue and in the various types of reptilian bone tissues.

Ground sections of polymethyl methacrylate-embedded fetal and adult mandibular cortical bone were prepared at known thicknesses (which varied from 40 to 200 μm) from the following mammalian species: *Homo sapiens*, *Rattus rattus*, *Loxodonta africana*, *Trichechus manatus*, *Canis familiaris*, and *Manis temmincki*. Similarly, transversly-cut ground sections were made from the diaphysis of the long bones of the following reptiles: *Calotes* sp., *Lacertidae*, *Iguana iguana*, *Agama stellio*, *Stenodactylus stenodactylus*, *Varanus* sp., *Varanus niloticus*, *Anolis*, *Caiman sclerops*, *Lissemys punctata*, *Gopherus berlandieri*, *Testudo pardalis*, *Terapene carolina carolina*,

TABLE 1. *The mean volume of bone matrix associated with one osteocyte lacuna in various mammalian bones*

Species	Type of bone tissue	
	Primary bone	Adult lamellar bone
Homo sapiens	0.000042	0.000077
Rattus rattus		
(young)	0.000030	
(old)	0.000040	
Loxodonta africana	0.000040	
Trichechus manatus	0.000032	
Canis familiaris	0.000032	
Manis temmincki		0.000072

All figures are in mm³.

Pythonidae, and *Sphenodon punctata*. Contact microradiographs were made either on an electrostatically focused X-ray set or an electromagnetically focused X-ray set, using a copper target at 20 kv and with 1 ma tube current on Kodak experimental film V6028.

The number of osteocyte lacunae in a known volume of bone was counted directly by using an eye-piece graticule in the light microscope. Since the whole thickness of the bone section is in focus in the microradiograph, the number of lacunae recorded in the contact microradiographic image is the same as in the bone section. This latter feature was confirmed for adult lamellar bone by comparing optical reconstructions of the lacunar positions in the bone sections with the microradiographic record.

In the adult, human, mandibular cortical

TABLE 2. *The mean volume of bone matrix associated with one osteocyte lacuna in various reptilian bones*

Species	Type of bone tissue	
	Primary bone	Haversian bone
Calotes sp.	0.000020	
Lacertidae	0.000023	
Iguana iguana	0.000022	
Agama stellio	0.000033	
Stenodactylus stenodactylus	0.000027	
Varanus sp.	0.000016	
Varanus niloticus	0.000029	
Anolis	0.000022	
Caimen sclerops	0.000033	
Lissemys punctata	0.000015	
Gopherus berlandieri	0.000025	
Testudo pardalis	0.000019	
Terapene carolina		0.000044
Pythonidae	0.000020	
Sphenodon		0.000047

All figures are in mm³.

bone it was found that the mean volume of bone matrix associated with an individual osteocyte lacuna was 0.000077 mm³, whereas the mean volume of bone matrix associated with an individual osteocyte lacuna in any of the mammalian primary membrane bones examined was never more than 0.000042 mm³ (Table 1). The mean volume of bone matrix associated with an individual osteocyte in the reptilian bones examined varied greatly. (Table 2). This variation did not appear to be related either to the pattern of microscopic organization of the cortical bone or to the order to which the reptile belonged.

METABOLIC BONE DISEASES

BONE REMODELING IN PRIMARY HYPERPARATHYROIDISM
Preoperative and Postoperative Studies

WALTER A. MERZ, ATTILA J. OLAH, ROBERT K. SCHENK, MAXIMILIAN A. DAMBACHER, JAN GUNCAGA and HEINRICH G. HAAS

Department of Anatomy, University of Basel and Division of Metabolism, Department of Medicine, University Hospital (Bürgerspital) of Basel, Basel, Switzerland

Bone turnover was studied in 25 patients with proven primary hyperparathyroidism: Quantitative histological evaluation was performed on 16 preoperative bone biopsies, six pairs of pre- and postoperative bone biopsies, and three postoperative iliac crest specimens obtained at postmortem. The results were compared with clinical and biochemical data.

The preoperative biopsies showed a consistent increase in the number of osteoclasts and osteoblasts but no correlation between these two cell types. The total area of Howship's lacunae was enlarged, but structural changes in the trabecular network were mild in the majority of patients. The osteoid volume was increased, but normal or even subnormal if compared with the number of osteoblasts. Mineralization therefore seems to be normal or slightly accelerated in primary hyperparathyroidism.

After correction of the hyperparathyroid state, striking changes of the remodeling activity were observed: Within a few hours, osteoclasts seemed to disappear almost completely, the few remaining cells showing pyknotic nuclei and abnormal staining of the cytoplasm. The extent of the osteoblast layers and osteoid seams rapidly expanded, reaching a peak about two weeks after operation. At this time the whole trabecular surface was covered by osteoid and osteoblasts. Subsequently, both osteoblastic and osteoclastic remodeling activities returned to the normal state.

Increased bone formation was found to be a consistent feature of hyperparathyroidism. In view of the marked postoperative increase of bone formation ("rebound phenomenon") it cannot, however, be attributed to the action of parathyroid hormone. As the augmentation of the osteoblasts was considerable regardless of any structural or clinical evidence of mechanical failure of bone, a mechanical explanation is also inadequate. We suggest, therefore, that a still unidentified factor may be responsible for the stimulation of the osteoblasts in the hyperparathyroid state.

In addition, a peculiar group of cases can be differentiated clinically and histologically. While the common group shows a proportional increase of osteoblasts and osteoid seams, a minority of subjects reveal an apparent deficiency of mineralization, which is not due to renal insufficiency or malabsorption. Clinically, this latter group is characterized by bone pain, excessively high alkaline phosphatase levels and serum calcium values in the normal or slightly elevated range. In the first group of subjects, usually with recurrent renal stones, frank hypercalcemia is combined with normal or slightly increased alkaline phosphatase. The possible existence of two types of bone disease in primary hyperparathyroidism will be discussed.

EFFECT OF CADMIUM ON SKELETAL TISSUE IN NORMAL AND CALCIUM-DEFICIENT RATS

SVEN-ERIK LARSSON* and MAGNUS PISCATOR

Department of Orthopaedic Surgery, Umeå University, and Department of Environmental Hygiene, Karolinska Instituet, Stockholm, Sweden

In 1942, bone disease was reported in workers exposed to cadmium oxide dust (1). Although no roentgenological evidence of bone disease was obtained in a more recent extensive examination of cadmium poisoned workers (2), a case of osteomalacia was reported in 1969 (3). Since renal tubular damage is a common feature of cadmium workers (1), the development of bone disease could be anticipated, due to disturbances in calcium and phosphorus metabolism.

Recently, attention has been drawn to the so-called Itai-Itai disease in Japan (4), characterized by osteomalacia in women with renal tubular damage, and possibly caused by cadmium in rice. However, these women were also on diets low in calcium and vitamin D. These circumstances initiated the present investigation aimed at providing information regarding the effect of exposure to cadmium for different periods of time, on the skeletal tissue and calcium metabolism in normal and calcium-deficient female rats.

In two experimental series, groups of eight-month-old Sprague Dawley rats were treated for one and two months in the following way: 1) Cd plus Ca, 25 ppm of cadmium in deionized water supplied as drinking water and the low calcium diet of General Biochemical Inc., Ohio, supplemented with 1.0% Ca and 0.8% P. 2) Cd minus Ca, 25 ppm of cadmium in drinking water and a low calcium test diet containing 0.04% Ca and 0.8% P.

3) Minus Ca, no cadmium but otherwise as group 2. 4) Controls, deionized water and the test diet supplemented with calcium. Animals received water and diet ad lib.

Seventy-two hr before sacrifice 15 μc of Ca^{45} in physiological saline solution were injected i.p. into each animal. The composition of the right tibia was examined after determination of the wet weight immediately, the dry weight after incubating the bone at 52 C for 48 hr and the ash weight after ashing the bone at 800 C for 16 hr. The metaphyses (proximal and distal fifths) and the diaphysis of the left tibia were examined similarly for their content of inorganic matter. Plasma and bone Ca^{45} activity were recorded in a Packard Tri-Carb liquid scintillation counter. Calcium accretion rate by bone was calculated according to Bauer et al. (5). Plasma calcium and tissue cadmium were analyzed as described previously (1, 6).

The body weight of the control animals showed no significant change during the experimental period. Cadmium exposure alone for two months resulted in a significant decrease ($P < 0.05$) in body weight by 2%, and in a decrease by 4% when there was a concomitant reduction in the calcium intake. Institution of the low-calcium diet alone resulted in a 2.5% increase in body weight. These findings were considered to demonstrate a toxic effect of cadmium, the storage of cadmium in the liver and the renal cortex being markedly increased after exposure to cadmium (Table 1). A further increase by 60% in tissue cadmium was found when the exposure to cadmium was combined with a

---

* Present address: Department of Orthopedic Surgery, University of Illinois Medical Center, Chicago, Illinois, USA.

TABLE 1. *The concentration of cadmium (μg/g dry weight) in renal cortex and liver in two series of rats, treated for 1 and 2 months, respectively, by cadmium and normal diet (Cd+Ca), cadmium and calcium-deficient diet (Cd–Ca), and normal diet (controls)*

Series	Group	n	Renal cortex	SD	n	Liver	SD
1 month	Cd+Ca	5	72	12	5	18	3
	Cd – Ca	5	115	17	6	29	3
2 months	Cd+Ca	5	129	20	6	29	5
	Cd – Ca	6	205	23	6	49	6
	Controls		⟨ 5			⟨ 1.5	

TABLE 2. *The concentrations of water, organic and inorganic matter in percent of the wet weight of the right tibia in two series of rats, treated for 1 and 2 months, respectively, by cadmium and normal diet (Cd+Ca), cadmium and calcium-deficient diet (Cd–Ca), calcium-deficient diet (–Ca) and normal diet (controls)*

Series	Group	n	Water %	SD	Organic matter %	SD	Inorganic matter %	SD
1 month	a. Cd+Ca	5	26.48	0.69	27.31	0.39	46.21	0.79
	b. Cd – Ca	6	28.45	3.28	28.38	1.18	43.15	2.27
	c. – Ca	6	28.13	1.33	27.89	0.55	43.98	1.38
	d. Controls	6	25.08	0.91	28.14	0.43	46.78	0.58
2 months	e. Cd+Ca	6	24.37	0.30	27.97	0.82	47.67	0.83
	f. Cd – Ca	6	27.34	1.26	28.27	1.36	44.40	0.52
	g. – Ca	6	25.16	0.71	27.73	0.31	47.12	0.58
	h. Controls	6	24.50	1.25	27.49	0.54	48.01	1.20

P	P	P
a–d $<$ 0.05	a–b $<$ 0.05	a–b $<$ 0.025
a–c $<$ 0.05	(nonparam)	a–c $<$ 0.02
b–d $<$ 0.05 (nonparam)	a–d $<$ 0.02	b–d $<$ 0.01
c–d $<$ 0.005		c–d $<$ 0.005
e–f $<$ 0.001		e–f $<$ 0.001
e–g $<$ 0.05		f–g $<$ 0.001
f–g $<$ 0.01		f–h $<$ 0.001
f–h $<$ 0.01		

reduced calcium intake. This important relationship found between calcium intake and storage of cadmium in the tissues was probably due to increased absorption of cadmium analogous to that of calcium.

The content of inorganic matter of the tibia showed a decrease of 5.7% after combined cadmium exposure and a reduced calcium intake for 1 month (Table 2). Corresponding to the decrease in inorganic matter of the bone there was an increase in water content,

the organic matter being unchanged indicating classic osteoporosis. The initial calcium deficiency osteoporosis was reversed after reduced calcium intake, maintained for two months, confirming previous reports (6). Combined cadmium exposure and a low calcium intake for two months resulted in a reduction in inorganic matter of the whole tibia by 7.5%. The metaphyseal bone showed a decrease in inorganic matter of 10.5% while the corresponding figure for the diaphyseal

TABLE 3. *The calcium accretion rate by bone, calculated as mg calcium/hr* $\times$ *10^{-7}, in two series of rats, treated for 1 and 2 months, respectively, by cadmium and normal diet (Cd+Ca), cadmium and calcium-deficient diet (Cd–Ca), calcium-deficient diet (–Ca) and normal diet (controls).*

					Left tibia			
Series	Group	n	Right tibia	SD	Metaphyses	SD	Diaphysis	SD
1 month	a. Cd+Ca	5	1.95	0.28	2.68	0.40	0.83	0.11
	b. Cd–Ca	6	2.19	0.41	3.51	0.73	0.83	0.19
	c. –Ca	6	2.29	0.35	3.46	0.43	0.91	0.15
	d. Controls	6	2.17	0.22	3.12	0.32	0.90	0.06
2 months	e. Cd+Ca	5	2.12	0.26	2.96	0.30	0.90	0.10
	f. Cd–Ca	5	2.40	0.44	3.86	0.64	0.98	0.18
	g. –Ca	5	2.46	0.24	3.62	0.40	1.10	0.10
	h. Controls	6	2.16	0.16	3.18	0.30	0.94	0.14

	P		*P*		*P*
	e–g	0.05 to 0.10	a–b	0.05 to 0.10	e–g $<$ 0.05
	g–h	$<$ 0.05	a–c	$<$ 0.025	g–h 0.05 to 0.10
			a–d	0.05 to 0.10	
			e–f	$<$ 0.05	
			f–h	0.05 to 0.10	
			g–h	0.05 to 0.10	

TABLE 4. *Blood Ca^{45}, specific activity 72 hr after the i.p. administration of the isotope in two series of rats, treated for 1 and 2 months respectively, by cadmium and normal diet (Cd+Ca), cadmium and calcium-deficient diet (Cd–Ca), calcium-deficient (–Ca) and normal diet (controls).*

Series	Group	n	% Ca^{45} of injected dose/mg Ca	SD
1 month	a. Cd+Ca	5	0.0218	0.0041
	b. Cd–Ca	6	0.0228	0.0036
	c. –Ca	6	0.0228	0.0015
	d. Controls	6	0.0194	0.0011
2 months	e. Cd+Ca	5	0.0274	0.0007
	f. Cd–Ca	5	0.0317	0.0022
	g. –Ca	5	0.0332	0.0033
	h. Controls	6	0.0265	0.0040

P
c–d $<$ 0.005
e–f $<$ 0.01
e–g $<$ 0.01
f–h $<$ 0.05
g–h $<$ 0.025

bone was 3.7% compared with that of the normal controls.

The calcium accretion rate by the metaphyseal bone (Table 3) was significantly reduced after exposure to cadmium alone for one month. In view of the observed concom-itant decrease in the amount of organic matter (Table 2) these data indicate an inhibition of new bone formation. After two months of cadmium exposure, no significant change in the amount of organic matter was found but there was a tendency to reduced calcium accretion. As for calcium restriction alone, combined cadmium exposure and a reduced calcium intake was found to give rise to increased calcium accretion by bone. These findings were considered to indicate that the observed inhibitory effect of cadmium exposure alone upon new bone formation was an indirect rather than a direct one.

The retention of blood calcium (Table 4) was apparently not affected by cadmium exposure for 1 and 2 months. After calcium restriction alone, increased retention of calcium was found confirming previous reports (6). When the reduced calcium intake was combined with cadmium exposure, the increase in blood calcium retention was found to reach the same level as that observed after calcium restriction alone. Further studies are in progress to examine the effect of prolonged cadmium exposure upon this mechanism involved during the adaptation to a low calcium intake. It was considered that the observed increase in the storage of cadmium in the liver

and the renal cortex caused by reduced calcium intake during exposure to cadmium was due to increased absorption of cadmium analogous to that of calcium.

It was deduced from the data obtained in the present study that the osteoporosis found after combined cadmium exposure and calcium restriction for 2 months was caused by increased bone resorption which would mobilize skeletal calcium to maintain blood calcium, the parathyroids probably being involved.

REFERENCES

1. NICAUD P, LAFITTE A and GROS A. *Arch Mal Prof* **4**: 192, 1942.
2. FRIBERG L. *Acta Med Scand* **138**: Suppl 240, 1950.
3. ADAMS RG, HARRISON JF and SCOTT P. *Quart J Med* **38**: 425, 1969.
4. TSUCHIYA K. *Keio J Med* **18**: 181, 1969.
5. BAUER GCH, CARLSSON A and LINDQUIST B. *Kungl fysiografiska sällskapets i Lund förhandl* **25**: 1, 1955.
6. LARSSON S-E. *Acta Orthop Scand* Suppl 120, 1969.

QUANTITATION OF BONE AND BONE TURNOVER IN BIOSPY SPECIMENS FROM THE ILIAC CREST IN ACROMEGALY

F. ROELFSEMA, J. VAN DER SLUYS VEER and D. SMEENK

Department of Clinical Endocrinology, University Hospital, Leiden, The Netherlands

Acromegaly is frequently stated to be associated with osteoporosis. This impression is mainly based on the radiological appearance of the vertebral column. However, only a few results of histological investigations of bone in acromegaly are available. Microradiographs of 30 to 40 μ thick ground sections of undecalcified bone were measured according to the method of Merz et al. The criteria of Jowsey for bone formation and resorption were used.

It was found that the average volumetric density (V_v) of trabecular bone of acrome-

galic patients was higher than that of a comparable control group. The specific surface (S/V) was lower, indicating an increased diameter of bone trabeculae. Bone formation and resorption were more active in the cortical and subcortical regions of acromegalic bone compared with control bone. A slight increase in bone formation was found in the trabecular region.

The results of this study do not show evidence of osteoporosis in acromegaly. On the contrary, active remodeling with formation of thicker bone trabeculae was found.

ALKALI THERAPY IN IMMOBILIZATION OSTEOPOROSIS

URIEL S. BARZEL

Metabolic Endocrine Laboratory, Montefiore Hospital and Medical Center and
Albert Einstein College of Medicine, New York, New York, USA

Work previously reported from this laboratory demonstrated that ingestion of sodium and potassium bicarbonate stimulated bone formation and prevented low calcium osteoporosis in normal adult rats (1). The present study was designed to examine the effect of the bicarbonate salt on calcium metabolism of immobilized healthy adult volunteers.

The subjects were studied on the Clinical Center ward. They were given a constant diet containing 220 mg calcium and 890 mg phosphorus, and 78 mEq sodium of which 51 mEq was in the form of sodium chloride. Activity was restricted to bed rest except for 2 hr daily spent in a mechanized wheel chair, during which time the subjects traveled within the ward area.

Balance studies were completed in four subjects receiving sodium and potassium bicarbonate capsules by mouth and two subjects receiving equivalent amounts of placebo capsules. Bicarbonate or placebo administration was started on the sixth immobilization day. In three of the four subjects given the bicarbonate, the negative calcium balance (–257 mg/day) showed an immediate improvement averaging 140 mg/day (such that the balance became –117 mg/day). This effect was due to lower stool calcium content as well as decreased calciuria. This improvement in calcium balance was associated with a slight improvement of the phosphorus balance. Continued salutary effect of bicarbonate salt on calcium metabolism was registered for at least two weeks. The fourth subject, the only Negro studied thus far, was in balance in the first five days of immobilization, and remained in balance during the period of alkali ingestion. The control subjects were in negative balance throughout immobilization and no change was registered in the balance when placebo capsules were added.

REFERENCE

1. BARZEL US and JOWSEY J. *Clin Sci* **36**: 517, 1969.

METABOLIC BONE DISEASES ASSOCIATED WITH MALIGNANCY

GILBERT S. GORDAN, LOUIS LICHTENSTEIN and BETTY S. ROOF

University of California at San Francisco, San Francisco, California, USA

Neoplastic diseases affect the skeleton by direct invasion or by the elaboration of humoral substances. Ectopic secretion of parathyroid hormone (PTH) by "nonendocrine" tumors, first suggested by Albright (1) in a case of renal cell carcinoma with osseous metastasis, has been widely confirmed. It is now clear that PTH is elaborated by many carcinomas of the kidney or lung, and some carcinomas of the cervix, ovary, colon and other organs. While this form of hyperparathyroidism produced histologic evidence of osteitis fibrosa, roentgen evidence of hyperparathyroid bone disease has not so far been reported, presumably because of the condition's relatively short duration. Other reported peculiarities of ectopic hyperparathyroidism are low serum chloride concentrations and response of hypercalcemia to corticoids in about 20% of cases. We now report that the PTH elaborated by cancers differs from normal PTH. Immunologically, some ectopic PTH are recognized only by guinea pig antiserum and others only by chicken antiserum, whereas normal, adenomatous, or uremic PTH is recognized equally well by both. In addition, as pointed out by Berson and Yalow (2), PTH is found in the blood of many cancer patients without hypercalcemia. Since the PTH elaborated by cancers differs from the normal hormone, and the immunologic heterogeneity differs from that found in normal or uremic serum, or in the blood of patients with parathyroid adenomas, it is further suggested that ectopic elaboration of hormones is not merely a manifestation of dedifferentiation and loss of depressors by anaplastic tissue.

A common cause of hypercalcemia is malignancy, and the malignancy responsible for most hypercalcemia is breast carcinoma. Unlike carcinoma of the lung and kidney, the hypercalcemia of breast cancer is not accompanied by the phosphate abnormalities of hyperparathyroidism (3). In fact, the serum phosphate level is statistically elevated and tubular reabsorption of phosphate (TRP) is perfectly normal. The constancy of these phosphate characteristics in the hypercalcemia of breast cancer made possible correct preoperative diagnosis of coincidental parathyroid adenomas in three patients with breast cancer who also showed low TRP and mild hypophosphatemia. More recently, we have found no elevation of PTH levels by direct radioimmunoassay in human breast cancer extracts and in the serum of patients with breast cancer. Recently, Berson et al. (4) have similarly been able to diagnose correctly parathyroid adenomas in breast cancer patients because of elevated blood PTH levels.

Although breast cancer extracts contain no PTH, they do contain a potent osteolytic substance. This material is not vitamin D (5). Chromatography of breast cancer extracts shows that the osteolytic material resides in the sterol and steryl ester fractions. Combined gas-liquid chromatography and mass spectrometry (GLC/MS) of tissue extracts showed the phytosterols compesterol, stigmasterol, sitosterol and Δ^7-sitosterol (6). Combined GLC/MS of serum from breast cancer patients also shows these phytosterols and their short chain esters. Bioassays indicate that stigmasterol and Δ^7-sitosterol have osteolytic activity, but their acetic esters are much more active. In fact, stigmasteryl acetate has greater osteolytic activity than vitamin D_2, vitamin D_3, 25-hydroxycholecalciferol or 25-hydroxyergocalciferol. The potent osteolytic phytosteryl esters of stigmasterol and Δ^7-sitosterol are found uniformly in the blood of women with localized or disseminated breast cancer. They also occur in lactating mothers and in some normal nongravid women, but are not found in the blood of men.

It is suggested that phytosteryl esters may normally mobilize calcium from bone for lactation. Testing of this hypothesis is now under way. If correct, it may explain the presence of phytosteryl esters in the blood of patients with breast cancer and the associated hypercalcemia as an exaggeration of a normal phenomenon. It may also provide an explanation for a skeletal disease described by Stephen (son of Sir James) Paget (7) in 1889 in which "cystic" changes occur in the bones of women with breast cancer but do not contain neoplastic deposits. Two such cases follow:

Case 1. A 51-year-old woman declined mastectomy for a proved breast cancer two and one-half years before study. The mass shrank on radiotherapy but the patient thereafter sustained multiple spontaneous fractures without trauma, involving the wing of the right ilium, two ribs, two vertebrae, both acetabula and both superior and inferior pubic rami. Iliac crest biopsies showed active bone resorption with irregularity and notching of the trabecular surfaces associated with increased cellular activity. No carcinoma was seen. Films showed diffuse osteoporosis and multiple fractures but no Looser zones or subperiosteal resorption. Serum calcium levels were slightly elevated on three occasions, with normal serum phosphate, and TRP was elevated to 93%. Alkaline phosphatase was consistently at upper limit of normal. The patient died of acute glomerulonephritis with uremia of short duration. Autopsy showed carcinoma of the breast but no metastasis. Multiple bone sections showed generalized thinning with substantial reconstruction, focal areas of resorption and numerous Howship's lacunae. Fibrosis was seen only at the sites of fracture.

Case 2. A 70-year-old woman was seen shortly after a simple mastectomy for carcinoma of the breast with negative axillary lymph nodes. She sustained multiple spontaneous fractures involving a patella, humerus, both femurs, tibia and one rib. Five bone biopsies, including fracture sites and two iliac crest trephine biopsies, showed no malignant cells. X-rays showed generalized osteoporosis, thin cortex and no evidence of hyperparathyroid bone disease or fibrous dysplasia. The roentgen changes were stable for eight years; serum calcium, phosphate and TRP were all normal; alkaline phosphatase was repeatedly normal or elevated.

In conclusion, carcinomas can affect the skeleton by: 1) direct invasion, 2) ectopic synthesis of peptide hormones causing hyperparathyroidism with or without hypercalcemia, 3) elaboration of calcitonin and 4) secretion of a substance causing vitamin D resistant rickets and osteomalacia. Breast cancer does not elaborate PTH but is frequently associated with osteolytic phytosteryl esters with action on bones similar to that of vitamin D. These phytosteryl esters may play a normal role in mammary gland function. It is suggested that Stephen Paget's disease of bone (nonneoplastic "cystic" changes) may represent the remote effect of the osteolytic humor from the tumor.

REFERENCES
1. Case records of the Massachusetts General Hospital 27461. *New Eng J Med* **225**: 789, 1941.
2. BERSON SA and YALOW R. *Science* **154**: 907, 1966.
3. GORDAN GS, EISENBERG E and LOKEN HF. *Recent Progr Hormone Res* **18**: 297, 1962.
4. BERSON SA and YALOW R. *Amer J Med* (in press).
5. GORDAN GS and SCHACHTER D. *Proc Soc Exp Biol Med* **113**: 760, 1963.
6. GORDAN GS, FITZPATRICK M and LUBICH W. *Trans Ass Amer Physicians* **80**: 183, 1967.
7. PAGET S. *Lancet* **i**: 571, 1889.

THE EFFECTS OF CORTICOSTEROIDS ON JOINT TISSUE

N. E. SHAW and EVE LACEY

Department of Orthopaedic Surgery, The Royal Infirmary and Manchester University, Manchester, England

From time to time in the past decade reports have appeared on the adverse effects of corticosteroids on joints. Attempts have been made to validate such effects by likening the condition to Charcot's arthropathy, or by suggesting that subchondral microfractures result from osteoporosis.

Modern histochemical techniques have

been used to study the influence of cortico-steroids on joint tissues. Experimental work on young rabbits showed that intramuscular cortisone and intra-articular methyl predni-solone exert similar effects on hyaline carti-lage: the production of acid mucopolysac-charides (glycosamino-glycans) by cartilage cells is inhibited by these drugs and formation of new sulphomucins in cartilage already de-pleted of this material by papain is prevented. The lipoid content of cartilage cells is in-creased. Articular cartilage and epiphysial plate cartilage are similarly affected. The sur-face of articular cartilage shows fibrillation. The rosette formation of cartilage cells of the epiphysial cartilage plate is considered to be an artifact resulting from distortion of the cartilage columns in the depleted and softened matrix.

Intra-articular methyl prednisolone exerts a systemic effect. Corticosteroids have an adverse effect on the underlying cancellous bone, either from diminished osteoblastic ac-tivity or indirectly by impaired conversion of cartilage matrix into cartilage cores of can-cellous bone.

The formation of bone or cartilage of im-paired biochemical and mechanical quality in normal animals under the influence of corti-costeroids and the adverse effects on cartilage already degraded by papain account for the accelerated degenerative changes that have been described when these drugs are adminis-tered in joint disease. These studies, in con-junction with the use of radioactive tracer techniques, shed much light on the response of the cellular components of joint tissues to corticosteroids. The results will be discussed in detail and have far-reaching implications.

THE EFFECTS OF DISODIUM ETHANE-1-HYDROXY-1,1-DIPHOSPHONATE ON ADJUVANT-INDUCED ARTHRITIS IN RATS

MARION D. FRANCIS and LAWRENCE FLORA

The Procter and Gamble Company, Miami Valley Labs, Cincinnati, Ohio, USA

Disodium ethane-1-hydroxy-1,1-diphospho-nate (EHDP^{TM}) has been suggested as a possible therapeutic agent in the treatment of diseases involving disturbed calcium and phosphate metabolism (1–4). Killed *Myco-bacterium butyricum* suspended in mineral oil (adjuvant) given by a single s.c. injection into the footpad of adult female Wistar rats in-duces a disseminated, chronic and crippling type of arthritis which closely resembles rheumatoid arthritis in man (5) and also mimics ankylosing spondylitis in its later stages of development. The course of the inflammatory polyarthritis induced by the adjuvant was followed by macroscopic and histologic examination; the calcific response by whole body X-ray, microradiography and electron probe. The earliest radiologically visible effect noted in the adjuvant-injected paw was a pronounced loss of mineral in the calcaneus, distal tibia and metatarsals, ac-companied by a diffuse deposition of mineral in the soft tissue immediately surrounding the articulations of these bones. EHDP^{TM} admi-nistered in a dose of 4 mg/kg per day, s.c., from the time of adjuvant injection prevented the bone loss and totally blocked the adjuvant-induced periarticular calcification while hav-ing no apparent effect on the inflammatory process. It is suggested that the periarticular calcification may be initially nucleated by the rapid loss of mineral locally from these bones during the period of extreme inflammation and permeability of the tissues.

When the EHDP^{TM} injections were discontinued, the calcific response became radiologically visible within two weeks after cessation of treatment indicating that EHDP^{TM} had prevented calcification and its subsequent destructive effects but had little if any effect on the stimulus to calcify. EHDP^{TM} (4 mg/kg per day s.c.) given three weeks after adjuvant injection, when calcification was visible radiologically, reduced the progression of subsequent calcium deposition. These data suggest the possible use of this material in certain forms of human arthritic conditions.

REFERENCES

1. FRANCIS MD.   *Calcif Tissue Res* **3**: 151, 1969.
2. FLEISCH H, RUSSELL RGG, FRANCIS MD. *Science*: **165**: 1262, 1969.
3. FRANCIS MD, RUSSELL RGG, FLEISCH H. *Science*: **165**: 1264, 1969.
4. MICHAEL WR, KING WR and FRANCIS MD. *Clin Orthop* (in press).
5. PEARSON CM, WAKSMAN BH and SHARP JT *J Exp Med* **113**: 485, 1961.

CHONDROCALCINOSIS IN ADULT RABBITS

ZVI YOSIPOVITCH* and MELVIN J. GLIMCHER

Orthopedic Research Laboratories, Massachusetts General Hospital, Boston, Massachusetts, USA

Although chondrocalcinosis, or calcific deposits in articular cartilage and menisci, is encountered in about 7% of adult humans, there are no reports of a similar alteration in other mammalian joints.

Although the etiology and pathogenesis are not understood, chondrocalcinosis may be associated with a large variety of conditions such as degenerative arthritis, trauma to joints, rheumatoid arthritis, pseudogout, gout, hyperparathyroidism, hypercalcemias from other causes, hemochromatosis, ochronosis, radiation damage; or it may be the result of a primary, familial metabolic defect. Therefore, it has been proposed that chondrocalcinosis may be a pathologic manifestation of a variety of disorders of cells and cartilage matrix.

The purpose of this paper is to report the gross and microscopic features of spontaneous chondrocalcinosis in the articular cartilage of the hips and knee joints from a large population of adult rabbits.

The large joints of 170 unselected normal adult New Zealand white rabbits were macroscopically inspected. The age of the rabbits varied from one to three years and their weight from 8 to 12 lb. Calcific deposits, usually involving the hips and the knee joints, were recognized grossly in 21 rabbits (12%). White, hard and gritty deposits, which ranged in size from barely discernible white spots to areas 3 mm in diameter, were scattered on or near the articular surfaces of the acetabulum, the femoral head and the medial plateau of the tibia uncovered by the meniscus. In addition to 21 rabbits with macroscopic chondrocalcinosis, six others which were grossly normal, proved to have the lesion when examined histologically.

Histological examination of mineralized and decalcified sections which included the subchondral bone revealed a variety of

---

* Present address: Department of Orthopedics, Hadassah University Hospital, Jerusalem, Israel.

changes. The early changes noted were localized lesions in the deep and middle layers of the cartilage which were, characteristically, sharply delimited from the surrounding cartilage. The chondrocytes in the affected area showed degenerative changes such as pyknosis, hypertrophy, dissolution and the appearance of cell ghosts. After decalcification, the lesions appeared to have a cystic or honeycomb structure, and contained metachromatic and periodic acid-Schiff-positive material. Mineralized and demineralized sections stained with hematoxylin and eosin revealed an intensified basophilia.

Evidence of mineral in the deposits was provided by the positive staining of frozen sections of articular cartilage with von Kossa's reagent. Early changes appeared as an irregular distribution of granules of silver representing early calcific deposits. Granules of various sizes were packed around the ghost chondrocytes, or scattered irregularly throughout the matrix of the lesion. Microradiography of undecalcified sections confirmed that the lesions were mineralized and that the mineral was restricted to the lesions. Wide-angle X-ray diffraction examination revealed that the mineral phase contained hydroxyapatite. Polarized light microscopy of undecalcified sections showed little evidence of crystal orientation.

In moderate and advanced stages, the smaller lesions appeared to have coalesced and extended throughout the entire thickness of the cartilage. They occasionally bulged and in some instances actually perforated, the surface of the cartilage. The cartilage surrounding the lesion was normal when the involved area was small, and displayed a concentric orientation of cells and matrix when the lesion was larger. The latter suggested that expansion of the lesion had occurred.

In three rabbits that received radioactive inorganic sulfate (S^{35}), radioautography revealed a higher uptake in the chondrocytes surrounding the cystic area, than chondrocytes in other locations, suggesting a response of the cartilage cells surrounding the lesion.

The two possibilities that explain the findings are that mineralization follows tissue damage or, alternately, that mineralization precedes cellular damage.

CALCIUM DEFICIENCY AND HUMAN PERIODONTAL DISEASE

LEO LUTWAK, LENNART KROOK, P. A. HENRIKSON, R. URIS, J. WHALEN, ANN COULSTON and G. LESSER

Cornell University, Ithaca, New York and Cornell University Medical School, New York, New York, USA

The initial lesion in generalized osteopenia due to dietary calcium deficiency in adult dogs has been shown to be excessive resorption of alveolar bone leading to periodontal disease. Bone resorption in the mandible results in recession of alveolar crest bone with consequent tooth mobility and secondary gingivitis. Repletion with added dietary calcium reverses the bone loss with subsequent disappearance of the clinical signs.

The morphology of human periodontal disease is similar to that seen in experimental periodontal disease in dogs. Diet surveys suggest that the nutritional prerequisites exist in man for a similar etiology, i.e., dietary calcium deficiency.

In ten human cases of periodontal disease, treated for six months with an additional 1,000 mg of calcium/day, gingivitis was decreased in all patients and completely absent in one after the treatment period. Pocket depth and tooth mobility were the primary signs which improved. Pre- and postexperimental radiography showed increased alveolar crest bone and partial filling of bony pockets in seven of the 10 patients.

In a second series, 90 patients with periodontal disease were treated with either one of three forms of oral calcium supplements at a dosage of 1,000 mg of calcium/day, or with placebo for six months and subsequently changed to one of the other three treatments for a second six-month period. All subjects were evaluated clinically and radiographically at the start of the study, at six months and at twelve months. In addition, bone density measurements were obtained, at monthly intervals, of the distal radius and ulna and of the mandible. Blood specimens were evaluated monthly for concentrations of calcium, phosphorus, magnesium, alkaline phosphatase and cholesterol; 24-hr urine specimens were analyzed for creatinine, calcium, phosphorus and magnesium. No adverse effects attributable to the calcium supplementation were observed. Urinary calcium increased, but remained within accepted normal ranges.

No significant changes occurred in bone density of the radius in any group; there was a slight increase in bone density of the ulna and a clear increase in bone density of the mandible in the patients on calcium supplements. There was a clear increase in alveolar bone as measured on a roentgenogram in the patients on calcium supplements. There were no significant changes in any of the blood chemistry measurements in any of the groups. Urinary phosphorus and magnesium decreased in the patients receiving supplements.

The mean dietary calcium intake of patients with periodontal disease in this study was 540 ± 280 mg/day, while the dietary phosphorus was 860 ± 250 mg/day. Since there was no direct relationship between the two, dietary Ca/P ratios were also calculated, with a mean of 0.60 ± 0.18, a value similar to that producing secondary hyperparathyroidism in experimental adult animals.

FATIGUE FRACTURES OF THE FEMUR

J. ESCHBERGER

Forschungsabteilung I, Allgemeine Unfallversicherung, Arbeitsunfallkrankenhaus, Vienna, Austria

Fatigue fractures are defined as fractures which occur without previous adequate traumatic insult. The traumatic process involved is that of protracted local bone change which culminates in reduced weight-bearing and insufficiency.

Excluding those cases caused by tumors, we are left with two distinct types of fatigue fractures: 1) fatigue fractures with underlying disease, e.g. Paget's disease, osteodystrophy, deranged calcium balance and 2) fatigue fractures without apparent underlying disease.

Although the pathologic changes present are similar in both groups, the processes in the first group are modified in terms of the underlying disease: in Paget's disease, for instance, there is additional markedly increased osteoclastic activity.

In fatigue fractures of the femur typical

remodeling processes are seen which reduce the quality of the bone substance and ultimately are responsible for the fracture (Fig. 1, 2).

X-rays of the area of remodeling in the femur reveal increased cortical thickness and density, most pronounced at the fracture site on the traction side of the bone affected in the case of the external aspect (Fig. 1).

Histologically, the pathologic changes are seen to be much more extensive than would be expected from the radiological findings. The bone changes are seen to begin at a distance of some centimeters from the fracture site. The proportion of mineralized bone drops to 65% and the cortex is expanded, obviously as a compensatory response. The haversian canals are characterized by a preponderance of dense connective tissue which is, however, normally vascularized so that necrosis in terms of endarterial obliteration is absent. Towards the fracture site the bone structure is often seen to consolidate, the lumen of the haversian canals is smaller and necrotic areas of major extension are present. These usually show signs of remodeling and are, as a rule, embedded in dense connective tissue, which manifests itself in a loss of continuity on the X-ray film.

Remodeling of bone substance may take various forms which are slightly modified by the bone disease present. Usually destructive and remodeling processes are seen side by side. Normal osteoclastic activity is seen particularly in diseases which are generally characterized by increased remodeling, such as Paget's disease. In fatigue fractures part of the tissue removed by osteoclasts is replaced by connective tissue so that the bone structure becomes looser. The second distinctive feature of fatigue fractures is destruction by osteoclastic osteocytes.

As documented by electron microscopic studies, osteocytes and their processes are capable of expanding the surrounding halo volume under normal conditions. In the remodeling area this phenomenon is increased to pathological proportions; part of the tissue is disintegrated, becomes necrotic and is separated from the remaining bone.

These microsequesters accumulate in the lumen of the haversian canals and may occasionally undergo organic incorporation and destruction. The presence of phosphatase, demonstrable histochemically, indicates that this destruction is an active process.

The third and perhaps most interesting phenomenon is the osteolytic disintegration of the osteon in the area of the cement line. The cement line, which is generally assumed to form the boundary between two osteons, also appears to have an active function. On microradiography and on histochemical analysis it can be seen to consist of a dense zone and another less dense zone facing the haversian canal. This is characterized by a network of canaliculae which form some kind of ring conductor and communicate with the neighboring osteons. In young persons and under pathological conditions alkaline phosphatase is increased in this area. In addition, osteolysis occurs and the sequestered bone breaks into the lumen of the canal.

The sequesters may either remain there or be carried to other sites so that microsequesters can be found in apparently normal osteons. Even if they remain at the original site, either being incorporated in the bone structure or sequestered, they may undergo enzymatic change. If so, demineralization is followed by destruction and disintegration of the matrix.

Again, phosphatase activity is found to be positive. The resulting loss of substance is compensated for by the formation of connective tissue; but the bony defect may also be replaced by new bone tissue, just as the connective tissue can be replaced by bone tissue at a later stage. This new bone tissue is, however, fibrous bone and thus a poor

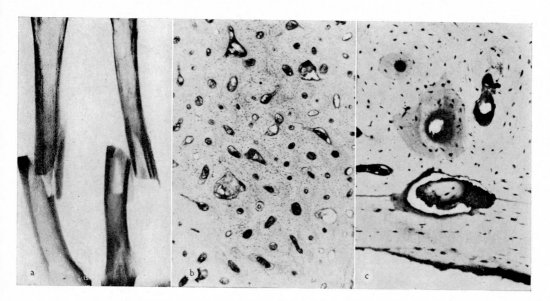

FIG. 1. Fatigue fracture of femur in a 70-year-old female. a) Radiograph showing increased cortical thickness; b) Cross section through the cortical bone bordered on the fracture; infraction of some of the osteons. c) Ground cross section; infracted bone in a haversian canal.

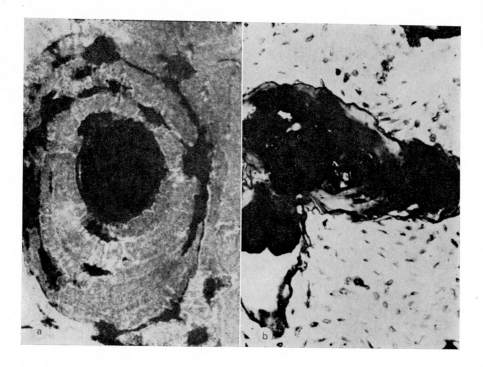

FIG. 2. Fatigue fracture of femur in a 59-year-old female. a) Microradiograph after decalcification in 5% citric acid. Dissolution of bone in the range of osteocytes and the less dense zone of the cement line. b) Cross section stained for alkaline phosphatase. Osteolysis and infraction of an osteon.

substitute. Just prior to the fracture a finely interlacing structure is seen and the site of repair can readily be identified in polarized light.

FIG. 3. Connective tissue between infracted bone and haversian canal as a sign of healing in a 35-year-old female with congenital luxation of the hip-joint.

Hoping to obtain evidence for the early stages of the remodeling process, we performed biopsies on young patients osteotomized for weight-bearing anomalies of the leg. The patients had usually presented with shortening of the leg due to congenital dislocation of the hip. The biopsy material revealed circumscribed foci at the site at which increased tension may be expected to occur. In all patients low-grade insufficiency of the supporting tissue was suggested by the history (congenital dislocation of the hip). In the area of the lamellae the break was seen to follow the cement line and was associated with the formation of microsequesters. These, however, were virtually never disintegrated, but rather incorporated in the haversian system (Fig. 3).

Such incorporated sequesters which completely obstruct a haversian canal and prevent the supply of the corresponding osteon with body fluids are not so infrequently observed. But in the patients seen, the organism was apparently still capable of compensating for this process. Changes other than slight cortical thickening were not seen radiologically.

THE EFFECT OF PHOSPHATE ON FRACTURE HEALING IN RABBITS

AD NOLLEN and OLAV BIJVOET

Departments of Orthopedic Surgery and Internal Medicine, University Hospital, Nijmegen, The Netherlands

Goldsmith et al. (1) suggested that oral phosphate supplements accelerated fracture healing in man. The effect was judged by the time required for clinical union but the criteria for the latter were not quantitative. Their suggestion is an important one since until now it has not been possible to influence the rate of fracture healing by simple therapeutic means. We have studied the effect of phosphate on the rate of fracture healing in the rabbit. The degree of healing was assessed by measurements of the tensile strength and the morphology at the site of the fracture.

A transverse osteotomy of the right radius between the middle and distal third of the bone was performed with a rotating saw in 60 six-month-old male rabbits. All the animals were fed with alfalfa; phosphate was

TABLE 1. *Tensile strength at osteotomy site in control phosphate-treated rabbits*

| Weeks | Controls | | | Phosphate-treated | | | P |
	n	Mean tensile-strength (kg)	SE	n	Mean tensile-strength (kg)	SE	
2	5	5.65	1.19	4	5.1	1.43	> 0.1
4	4	7.5	1.84	4	10.9	3.00	> 0.1
6	6	19.2	2.33	5	26.8	2.33	< 0.05

added to the diet of half the animals in each group (1 g of inorganic P/100 g alfalfa). The inorganic phosphate was given as a neutral mixture of primary and secondary sodium phosphate. The groups of animals were killed two, four and six weeks after the osteotomy. The bones of half the control animals and half the phosphate-treated animals were used for the measurement of the tensile-strength at the osteotomy site by a modification of Falkenberg's method (2). Undecalcified sections of the fracture site of the remaining bones were stained according to Schenk (Goldner stain).

Table 1 shows the results of the measurements of the tensile strength of the bones. There was no histological difference between the controls and the phosphate-treated animals two weeks after the fracture. At four weeks the fracture area of the control animals showed the usual picture of subperiosteal desmal cartilaginous ossification

and trabecular bone, but a considerable amount of cartilage was still present. In the phosphate group, however, there was much more trabecular bone, and in three out of four animals there was no cartilage. In the other phosphate-treated animal there were a few small areas of cartilage. It is of interest that these histological differences were not associated with a significant difference in tensile-strength.

However, after six weeks, phosphate treatment significantly increased the tensile-strength at the fracture site (Table 1). The results of our study suggest that phosphate treatment accelerates the increase of the tensile-strength of a healing fracture and increases the rate of accumulation of trabecular bone in the callus.

REFERENCES

1. GOLDSMITH RS, WOODHOUSE Ch F, INGBAR SM and SEGAL D. *Lancet* i: 687, 1967.
2. FALKENBERG J. *Acta Orthop Scand* Suppl **50**, 1961.

EXPERIMENTAL PRODUCTION OF ARTHRITIS BY INTRA-ARTICULAR INJECTION OF VITAMIN A IN RABBITS

M. BONI, P. BERLANDA, L. LENZI and G. RAVERA

Orthopedic Clinic of the University of Pavia, Pavia, Italy

It has been suggested (1–3) that osteoarthritis, far from being a mechanical degenerative process, is to be interpreted as the result of

an active degradation of the matrix of the articular cartilage. In this paper we demonstrate that lysosomal enzymes are capable of

producing experimental arthritis in rabbits which is comparable to the naturally occurring disease.

Female New Zealand albino rabbits weighing about 3 kg were used. Three intra-articular injections of 100,000 IU vitamin A palmitate were given at three-day intervals into the right knee, while the left knee, injected with solvent only, was used as a control. The rabbits were sacrificed at regular intervals from three days to one year after the first injection. Macroscopic and microscopic studies and histochemical and biochemical analyses were performed on articular cartilage of the dissected specimens.

Results. In the treated knee, 30 to 40 days after the beginning of the experiment, the first macroscopic and microscopic lesions began to appear on the articular surface of the femurs, and consisted mainly of small cracks, fissures, fibrillation and superficial ulcers of the cartilage. These lesions worsened progressively and slowly became associated with proliferation of connective tissue, which can be interpreted as an attempt to repair the lesions and culminated in the formation of true osteophytes after eight to nine months; the entire process, including glucosamine and galactosamine variations, closely parallels naturally occurring osteoarthritis of the knee.

REFERENCES

1. CHRISMAN OD. *Clin Orthop* **64**: 77, 1969.
2. COLLINS DH and MCELLIGOTT TF. *Ann Rheum Dis* **19**: 318, 1960.
3. CRELIN ES and SOUTHWICK WO. *Yale J Biol Med* **33**: 243, 1960.

SERUM IONIZED CALCIUM IN A NORMAL POPULATION STUDIED WITH A CALCIUM ION-SENSITIVE ELECTRODE

F. LINDGÄRDE and O. ZETTERVALL

Department of Medicine, University of Lund and Malmö General Hospital, Malmö, Sweden

Ion exchange electrodes represent the first practical method for the measurement of calcium ion activity in biological fluids (1). We report here our experience on the use of a calcium ion-sensitive electrode (Orion Research Co.) for the study of serum ionized calcium in approximately 300 individuals.

A model 99-20 flow-through electrode system connected to a model 801 digital pH meter was used. The sample to be tested was pumped through the system at a rate of 50 µl/min using a 1 ml disposable plastic tuberculin syringe and a model 88-20 syringe pump. The electrode potential reached stability within 2 min and remained constant for several minutes thereafter. Therefore, mv readings were always done after 3 min. Known solutions of calcium chloride (1 to 2 mM/liter) in 0.150 M NaCl containing triethanolamine and trypsin were used for calibration of the system. Triethanolamine (15 µl, 1 M solution) and trypsin (BDH, 6 mg) were added to 10 ml of the Ca-NaCl solutions. The mv readings obtained with the 1 and 2 mM calcium chloride solutions were plotted on a mv-log(Ca^{++}) diagram and a straight line connecting the two points was used as a calibration curve. The difference between the electrode potentials given by the two standard solutions, and thus the slope of the calibration curve, were found to change insignificantly during a day's use of the electrode. With time, however, as the electrode membrane deteriorated, this potential difference decreased. When the potential difference decreased below 6.5 mv the membrane was changed. For measurement of unknown samples the following procedure was adopted. After a 20 to 30 min "warm-up" of the system, during which time the electrode stabilizes, the standard solutions were measured, after which the serum determinations were made. For the latter purpose, alternate samples of 1 mM standard solution and serum were pumped through the system until the readings for the standard solution differed by 0.2 mv or less. Finally, the 1 and 2 mM standard solutions were again measured. For each serum sample a new calibration curve was plotted, using the mv reading for the standard solution obtained in connection with the serum and the known slope of the calibration curve, i.e. the mean of the slopes of the standard curves obtained at the beginning and the end of the whole series of measurements.

The addition of triethanolamine and trypsin to the standard solution was used to increase reproducibility of the serum determinations. Without these additions mv readings for sera were often erratic. The presence of triethanolamine may, however, influence the calcium ion activity in the standard solution or alter the response of the electrodes.

Venous blood was obtained with minimal stasis and immediately transferred anaerobically to glass centrifuge tubes containing mineral oil. After the blood had clotted at room temperature the tubes were centrifuged and serum was drawn into a tuberculin syringe which was then immediately connected to the electrode system.

For evaluation of the methodological error duplicate determinations of ionized calcium were carried out with 26 sera. The coefficient of variation was 1.6%.

The effect of storage was studied in several experiments. When sera were kept under oil at 4 C for 24 hr there was no appreciable change in calcium ion concentration. Storage for two or three days, however, affected the values, the calcium ion activity decreasing by about 2.5% of the initial value after three days. In contrast to this, serum could be kept frozen (–15 C) under oil for up to 10 days without change in ionized calcium. Prolonged freezing probably effects the value because of loss of CO_2 as indicated by an increase of serum pH. After restoring pH by re-equilibration of the samples with 5% CO_2 the original serum ion activity is again obtained. In this way constant calcium ion values have been obtained with sera stored for two months.

Three individuals were examined for possible diurnal or meal-related variations in serum ionized calcium. For this purpose five or six samples were obtained during 24 hr. The values were uninfluenced by meals, body position or the time of the day when the sample was taken. For each individual, no single value differed from the mean of the determinations by more than 2.9%.

The serum calcium ion activity and total serum calcium were determined in sera from 150 women and 147 men, aged 17 to 93 years. The majority of the subjects were healthy. Some patients with disease not obviously affecting calcium metabolism, such as hypertension and diabetes, were included, especially in the higher age groups. None of the subjects was hospitalized but some 40 individuals aged 75 and above were residents of an old-age home. For the women the mean value of ionized calcium was 1.24 and for the men 1.22 mM/liter; SD were 0.06 and 0.05 mM/liter, respectively, with a corresponding SE of 0.005 and 0.004 mM/liter. The means are different ("t" test, $P < 0.001$). In men there is a statistically significant decrease with age in serum ionized calcium whereas in women the decrease is smaller and of borderline significance. Thus linear correlation analysis of the male data gave r = –0.40, $P < 0.001$. For the female group r = –0.20, $0.02 < P < 0.05$. This finding in men was substantiated in a separate experiment, when sera from nine young males (mean age 22 years) were compared with sera from nine older men (mean age 55 years). The sera were sampled and then measured in random order on the same day. The calcium ion activity of the older group was significantly lower than that of the younger group (difference between means 0.07 mM/liter, "t" test of pair differences, $P < 0.01$). No significant difference was noted in a similar experiment with female sera.

The tendency to decrease with age was also noted for total serum calcium. Thus, $r = 0.39$, $P < 0.001$ when male serum calcium was correlated to age. Again the relationship was less obvious in women, $r = 0.18$, < 0.05 $P < 0.10$.

In both men and women ionized and total serum calcium are correlated with $r = 0.31$, $P < 0.001$ and $r = 0.43$, $P < 0.001$ for the respective sexes.

Comment. The technique for determination of serum calcium ion activity as outlined in this paper has given reproducible results with a low methodological error. The values reported above, obtained when using standard calcium solutions containing trypsin and triethanolamine for calibration purposes, may, however, differ from the "true" serum calcium ion values as obtained with standard solutions without these additions. In experiments, not reported in detail here, the presence of triethanolamine has been found to introduce a systematic error by increasing the level of measurement by approximately 10%. Correcting for this error in the calculation of the mean value of the calcium ion concentration in 297 "normal" serum samples, the figure obtained is 1.11 mM/liter. This is in close agreement with Moore's (1) result i.e. 1.136 mM/liter for mean normal serum ionized calcium as obtained with triethanolamine-free standard solutions.

The mean serum ionized calcium in women was slightly higher than that in men. This difference may be due to the slight but definite decrease with age in serum ionized calcium in men and the insignificant similar tendency in women. Such age dependency has not been found in some reported investigations (1, 2) in which there were fewer samples investigated than in the present study. The same workers found no statistically apparent co-variation of ionized and total serum calcium which, however, could be demonstrated in our material.

REFERENCES
1. MOORE EW. in: "Ion-selective electrodes." Gaithersburg, National Bureau of Standards, 1969, p 215.
2. HATTNER RS. *Clin Chim Acta* **28**: 67, 1970.

EFFECT OF TOTAL PARATHYROIDECTOMY AND UREMIA ON THE CHEMICAL COMPOSITION OF BONE, SKIN AND AORTA IN THE RAT

DANIEL S. BERNSTEIN, PETER PLETKA, ROBERT S. HATTNER,
CONSTANTINE L. HAMPERS and JOHN P. MERRILL

Department of Nutrition, Harvard School of Public Health and Department of Medicine, Peter Bent Brigham Hospital and Harvard Medical School, Boston, Massachusetts, USA

Chronic renal failure is frequently associated with osteodystrophy and metastatic calcifications affecting soft tissues and arteries, including the aorta. Subtotal or total parathyroidectomy (PTX) usually results in improvement of the skeletal abnormalities and resolution of metastatic calcifications, but arterial calcifications are usually unaffected.

Samples of rib, skin and aorta of eight groups of rats were analyzed for calcium, magnesium, phosphate and hydroxyproline. Four groups were made uremic by 5/6 nephrectomy (NX) and of these, two groups were sacrificed at three and six weeks. Blood urea nitrogen (BUN) levels attained were 101 ± 11 (mean $\pm$ SE) and 56 ± 4 mg/100 ml respectively. Of the remaining uremic groups, one group was subjected to PTX by excision at the same time as partial NX was performed, and sacrificed at six weeks; another group underwent PTX three weeks after the onset of uremia and was sacrificed three weeks later. BUN levels at sacrifice were 54 ± 4 and 58 ± 3 mg/100 ml respectively. Two other groups underwent PTX only and were sacrificed at three and six weeks. Control groups were also sacrificed at six weeks.

Table 1 indicates the results obtained in five of these groups. In the uremic non-PTX group (Group B) the composition of bone, apart from small decreases in phosphate, remained unaltered from that in the control group (Group A). However, the concentration of calcium decreased in skin and nearly doubled in the aorta. This occurred also in the three-week uremic non-PTX group (not shown in the Table) where the calcium was 9.85 ± 1.18 (SD) mg/g of fat free dry weight. The level of magnesium remained unchanged, but phosphate rose in the aorta in this group.

PTX, in the absence of uremia, was associated only with a fall in the hydroxyproline concentration in all three tissues (Group C).

PTX performed concurrently with partial NX prevented the decrease in hydroxyproline concentration in bone and skin, and to a lesser extent in the aorta (Group D). The most significant effect was the prevention of the aortic calcium increase and, to a lesser extent, the decrease in skin calcium.

PTX performed after the onset of uremia (Group E) also resulted in a fall of aortic calcium but had no effect on the composition of bone and skin.

It is concluded that uremia of moderate severity and duration, and associated with secondary hyperparathyroidism, does not result in any marked change in the composition of bone in the rat. It is associated with a fall in skin and an increase in aortic calcium. The increase in aortic calcium content in uremia can be prevented by PTX and, moreover, even when it occurs it can be reversed by PTX.

TABLE 1. *Mean calcium, phosphate, magnesium and hydroxyproline levels of bone and skin in uremic and parathyroidectomized rats*

Bone	Ca mg/g FFDW	PO₄ mg/g FFDW	Mg mg/g FFDW	HO-PR mg/g FFDW
Bone				
Control (n = 8),	259.6 (4.5)	130.5 (1.0)	5.57 (.08)	30.0 (1.0)
Uremia, 6 weeks (n = 7)	253.2 (6.1)	122.4 (2.1)	5.50 (.10)	28.8 (1.1)
PTX, 6 weeks (n = 7)	255.8 (7.5)	123.5 (2.8)	5.49 (.23)	25.85 (.97)
PTX and uremia, 6 weeks (n = 6)	253.2 (6.3)	124.5 (2.5)	5.80 (.19)	29.0 (1.5)
PTX, 3 weeks (n = 8),				
uremia, 6 weeks	239.9 (5.1)	125.5 (1.9)	5.98 (.15)	27.45 (.57)
Skin				
Control (n = 8)	2.77 (.24)	2.96 (.12)	.35 (.01)	74.2 (3.8)
Uremia, 6 weeks (n = 7)	0.82 (.03)	3.34 (.29)	.31 (.00)	73.0 (3.8)
PTX, 6 weeks (n = 7)	1.38 (.10)	3.39 (.12)	.32 (.01)	65.7 (3.7)
PTX and uremia, 6 weeks (n = 6)	1.14 (.08)	3.41 (.12)	.33 (.01)	70.8 (2.1)
PTX, 3 weeks (n = 8),				
nremia, 6 weeks	0.77 (.04)	3.66 (.21)	.40 (.01)	64.3 (1.3)
Aorta				
Control (n = 8)	5.57 (.60)	3.20 (.17)	1.13 (.08)	47.3 (.73)
Uremia, 6 weeks (n = 7)	10.90 (.78)	4.40 (.32)	0.78 (.06)	43.3 (1.9)
PTX, 6 weeks (n = 7)	6.37 (.45)	3.64 (.09)	1.10 (.06)	41.4 (1.8)
PTX and uremia, 6 weeks (n = 6)	2.67 (.37)	3.90 (.27)	0.72 (.05)	42.4 (2.6)
PTX, 3 weeks (n = 8),				
uremia, 6 weeks	3.31 (.20)	4.58 (.15)	.76 (.02)	37.62 (.75)

FFDW = fat free dry weight.
HO-PR = hydroxyproline.
Figures in parentheses indicate ±SE.

THE EFFECT OF CALCEMIC DISORDERS AND UREMIA ON THE MINERAL CONTENT OF SKIN

SHAUL G. MASSRY, JACK W. COBURN, DAVID L. HARTENBOWER, JAMES H. SHINABERGER, JOHN R. DePALMA, ELEANOR CHAPMAN, and CHARLES R. KLEEMAN

Cedars-Sinai Medical Research Institute and Departments of Medicine, Cedars-Sinai Medical Center, Wadsworth VA Hospital and UCLA School of Medicine, Los Angeles, California, USA

In disorders of calcium metabolism, calcium salts may be deposited in soft tissues before such deposits can be detected by X-ray. To determine whether chemical analysis of soft tissues might be useful in early recognition of abnormal calcium deposition, 194 small skin biopsies (100 to 200 mg) from 146 subjects were analyzed for content of water, calcium and magnesium. The samples were taken by elective biopsies or during various surgical procedures from normal subjects, patients with primary hyperparathyroidism or other hypercalcemic disorders, and from patients with advanced chronic renal failure, with or without evidence of clinically overt secondary hyperparathyroidism. The patients with renal disease included those managed without dialysis and others maintained by

TABLE 1. *Water, calcium and magnesium content of skin in patients with disordered calcium metabolism*

	No.	% water	Calcium	Magnesium
			mg/kg dry weight	
1. Normal subjects	17	68.7 ± .98	323 ± 13	164 ± 10
2. Primary hyperparathyroidism	28	68.2 ± .59	574 ± 24	198 ± 11
3. Other hypercalcemic disorders	8			
a) malignant disorders	5	69.2 ± 1.0	595 ± 19	135 ± 16
b) post-renal transplant	3	69.7 ± 1.7	731 ± 41	196 ± 21
4. Nondialyzed uremic patients	34			
a) with overt secondary hyperparathyroidism	14	67.8 ± 1.7	557 ± 41	235 ± 13
b) without overt secondary hyperparathyroidism	20	68.6 ± .93	350 ± 22	202 ± 18
5. Dialyzed uremic patients	55			
a) with overt secondary hyperparathyroidism	17	68.8 ± 1.5	488 ± 29	242 ± 22
b) without overt secondary hyperparathyroidism	38	68.4 ± .47	394 ± 12	184 ± 10

Values are presented as mean ± SE.

regular hemodialysis for two to 50 months. The biopsies were obtained by a simple incision of the dermis, either from the forearm, abdominal wall or the neck. The site from which the biopsy was taken did not appear to affect the mineral content of the skin. The syndrome of clinically overt secondary hyperparathyroidism in uremia has been described previously (1). Almost all uremic patients with this syndrome have radiographic evidence of hyperparathyroidism.

The mean values for the water, calcium and magnesium content of the skin from all these patients are presented in Table 1. Patients with primary hyperparathyroidism and those with other hypercalcemic disorders had a significantly higher calcium content in their skin than normals ($P < 0.01$). Uremic patients with clinically overt secondary hyperparathyroidism, whether treated with hemodialysis or not, had amounts of calcium in their skin which were significantly higher than normal values ($P < 0.01$). In the absence of the syndrome of clinically overt secondary hyperparathyroidism, calcium content of the skin was usually within the normal range (Fig. 1). The calcium content of the skin in patients with renal failure did not correlate with the level of serum calcium, the product of blood

concentration of calcium and phosphorus, or with the duration of hemodialysis.

In 10 uremic patients with overt secondary hyperparathyroidism, the calcium content of the skin was evaluated before and one to 10 months after subtotal parathyroidectomy. Calcium content of the skin fell by 119 ± 34

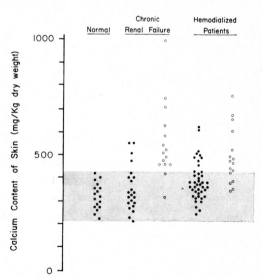

FIG. 1. Calcium content of skin in normal subjects and uremic patients. The squares represent individual values for normal subjects. The shaded area represents the mean ± 2 SD for the normal values.
O, with secondary hyperparathyroidism;
●, without secondary hyperparathyroidism.

183

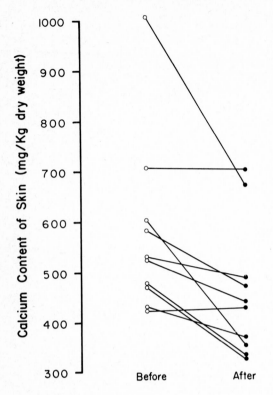

FIG. 2. Effect of subtotal parathyroidectomy on calcium content of skin in 10 uremic patients with clinically overt secondary hyperparathyroidism.

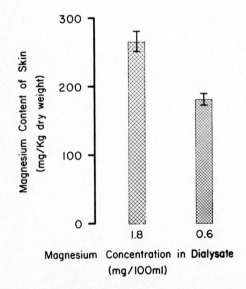

FIG. 3. Effect of the level of magnesium concentration in the dialysate on the magnesium content of the skin in patients undergoing regular hemodialysis.

mg/kg dry weight. There was considerable variation in the decrease of calcium in the skin from the different patients, and the skin calcium failed to change in two patients (Fig. 2).

When patients without evidence of clinically overt secondary hyperparathyroidism were treated with hemodialysis, using dialysate containing 8.0 mg of calcium per 100 ml for two to 12 months, there was a significant increase in the calcium content of their skin, from 355 ± 11 to 510 ± 61 mg/kg dry weight ($P < 0.01$). However, radiographic evidence of soft tissue calcification did not appear in these patients during this period of time.

The magnesium content of the skin in patients undergoing maintenance hemodialysis is also affected by the concentration of magnesium in the dialysate. In Fig. 3, the mean values of the magnesium content of skin are compared in two populations of patients treated with hemodialysis for periods of two months to five years with dialysates containing magnesium in concentrations of 1.8 and 0.6 mg/100 ml. Although there was an overlap between the individual values, the skin content of magnesium of the two groups is significantly different ($P < 0.01$).

These studies indicate that 1) patients with primary hyperparathyroidism and uremic patients with clinically overt secondary hyperparathyroidism have higher values of calcium in their skin than normal subjects. High calcium in skin may aid in the diagnosis of equivocal cases of primary hyperparathyroidism and may offer another criterion for the recognition of the syndrome of clinically overt secondary hyperparathyroidism in uremia; 2) calcium analysis of the skin may allow early detection of soft tissue calcification; 3) subtotal parathyroidectomy in uremic patients is associated with a decrease in the magnitude of calcium deposits in soft tissues; 4) dialysis with a dialysate containing high calcium concentration may produce or aggravate soft tissue calcification; and 5) in patients maintained with hemodialysis, the level of magnesium content of the skin depends on the concentration of magnesium in the bath.

REFERENCE

1. MASSRY SG, COBURN JW and POPOVTZER MM. *Arch Intern Med* **124**: 431, 1969.

HISTOMORPHOMETRIC STUDIES OF BONE IN PATIENTS ON CHRONIC HEMODIALYSIS

F. KUHLENCORDT, H.-P. KRUSE and C. LOZANO-TONKIN

Universitäts-Krankenhaus Eppendorf, Hamburg, Germany

There is no uniform agreement about the frequency of generalized bone changes in patients undergoing chronic hemodialysis treatment. This may be due to different factors, such as the period of the chronic renal insufficiency before the beginning of dialysis, the type of dialysis, as well as the methods by which evidence of bone disease is assessed. We have studied the type, frequency and course of the osteopathy in our cases.

Iliac crest biopsies of the patients in our chronic hemodialysis program were examined. The histomorphometric methods which were used are described elsewhere (1). In undecalcified bone sections the percentage of neutral surfaces, osteoid, activated osteoblasts, resorption lacunae and polynuclear osteoclasts on the endosteal surfaces, as well as the medium breadth of osteoid seams, were estimated. Formation and resorption of the bone were ascertained by quantitative microradiography, and the volumetric density of the spongy bone was determined.

In all cases significant bone changes were found; a pathological high resorption rate seen on microradiography was the main finding, and was assumed to be an expression of regulatory hyperparathyroidism. Bone formation was mostly in the normal range or slightly higher. The bone mass usually indicated a condition of osteopenia. A direct connection between serum calcium level and the seriousness of the bone disease could not be proved. Histologically there was no disturbance of bone mineralization. Vitamin D treatment was out of the question because the calcium phosphorus product was too high.

Supported by the Deutsche Forschungsgemeinschaft.

REFERENCE

1. KUHLENCORDT F, BAUDITZ W, LOZANO-TONKIN C, KRUSE H-P, AUGUSTIN H-J, REHPENNING W and BARTELHEIMER H. *Klin Wschr* (in press).

THE EFFECT OF HYDROCHLOROTHIAZIDE ADMINISTRATION ON SERUM AND URINARY CALCIUM IN NORMAL, HYPOPARATHYROID AND HYPERPARATHYROID SUBJECTS

STUDIES ON MECHANISMS

ARNOLD S. BRICKMAN, JACK W. COBURN, MARCELO H. KOPPEL,
MONROE PEACOCK and SHAUL G. MASSRY

Medical Service, Wadsworth VA Hospital and Departments of Medicine, Cedars-Sinai Medical Center and UCLA School of Medicine, Los Angeles, California and Endocrine Unit, Massachusetts General Hospital, Boston, Massachusetts, USA

In normal humans, thiazide diuretics have been reported to produce either no change in serum calcium or an increase of less than 1.0 mg/100 ml. A larger increment in serum calcium has been noted in patients with primary and secondary hyperparathyroidism. These differences could be due to variation in dosage or duration of drug administration or both. It has been suggested that thiazides may stimulate the parathyroid glands, enhance the action of parathyroid hormone (PTH), or act directly on bone. In contrast to other diuretics, chronic thiazide administration produces hypocalciuria, which has been attributed to enhanced renal reabsorption of calcium secondary to volume depletion; alternatively, thiazides could augment calcium reabsorption by enhancing PTH action on the nephron.

The present study was undertaken to evaluate the mechanisms responsible for changes in serum and urinary calcium produced by thiazide administration. After three to four control days, hydrochlorothiazide, 200 mg/day, was given for four days to normal, hyperparathyroid and vitamin D-treated hypoparathyroid subjects. Blood and 24-hr urine samples were collected twice daily during the control and thiazide-treatment days and for four to six days thereafter. Measurements included Na, Ca, Mg, P and creatinine in blood, and urine and serum immunoreactive PTH.

The mean values and ranges of serum calcium for the three groups of subjects are shown in Table 1 and the data for urinary calcium and sodium are presented in Table 2.

There was a significant increase in serum calcium during thiazide treatment in all three groups, and serum calcium returned to control levels by three to five days after the drug

TABLE 1. *Effect of hydrochlorothiazide on serum calcium*

	Serum calcium mg/100 ml before, during and after thiazide administration		
	Before	During (Days 3 to 4)	After (3 to 5 days)
Normal	9.57 ± .10	10.19 ± .07	9.55 ± .11
n = 11	(9.12 to 10.12)	(9.54 to 10.53)	(8.83 to 10.01)
Hyperparathyroid	11.23 ± .28	11.91 ± .22	11.18 ± .28
n = 11	(9.74 to 13.03)	(11.00 to 13.40)	(9.85 to 12.94)
Hypoparathyroid	8.86 ± .19	9.42 ± .21	8.91 ± .13
n = 6	(8.21 to 9.60)	(8.89 to 10.03)	(8.41 to 9.32)

Values are means ± SE. Figures in parentheses are range.

186

TABLE 2. *Effect of hydrochlorothiazide on urine sodium and calcium*

Urinary sodium	No.	Control mEq/day	Thiazides (% change from control)	
			Day 1	Days 3 and 4
Normal	10	166 ± 12	+133 ± 11	–22 ± 5
Hyperparathyroid	10	140 ± 18	+162 ± 42	+ 4 ± 19
Hypoparathyroid	5	155 ± 16	+ 88 ± 31	+28 ± 20
Urinary calcium		*mg/day*	*% change from control*	
Normal	10	231 ± 35	–11 ± 11	–52 ± 7
Hyperparathyroid	10	305 ± 44	– 7 ± 12	–61 ± 7
Hypoparathyroid	5	307 ± 104	– 6 ± 9	+ 7 ± 6

Values are means ± SE.

was discontinued. Mean increases (±SE) were similar in the three groups (normals, 0.62 ± 0.09 mg/100 ml, hyperparathyroids, 0.69 ± 0.15; and hypoparathyroids, 0.56 ± 0.10). Two "normocalcemic" hyperparathyroid patients became overtly hypercalcemic during thiazide administration. Plasma PTH levels, measured in all serum samples in several patients, did not change. Serum phosphorus levels increased in all three groups while serum magnesium failed to show a consistent change.

Urinary sodium rose substantially on the first day of thiazide administration in all subjects but urinary calcium did not change. On days 3 and 4 of drug administration, urinary sodium fell to or below control levels, and urinary calcium decreased in normal and hyperparathyroid patients but remained unchanged in the hypoparathyroid patients (hypoparathyroid vs. both normal and hyperparathyroid, $P < 0.001$). Thiazides often caused a fall in GFR, but because of the rise in serum calcium, filtered calcium was unchanged in two of three studies. Urinary phosphorus excretion increased in most studies throughout the days of thiazide administration.

These observations indicate: 1) acute thiazide administration produces similar increases in serum calcium and phosphorus in normal, hyper- and hypoparathyroid subjects, 2) stimulation of PTH release is not responsible for this phenomenon; 3) thiazides fail to cause hypocalciuria in hypoparathyroid subjects despite sodium losses and volume depletion. These data suggest that acute thiazide administration may produce increases in serum calcium and phosphorus by a direct action on the skeleton, although it is also possible that thiazides produce this effect by potentiating the action of factors which augment bone resorption (e.g. PTH, vitamin D). Furthermore, these studies suggest a dependence of the hypocalciuric effect of thiazides on the presence of parathyroid hormone.

187

DIALYSIS BONE DISEASE

E. RITZ, B. KREMPIEN, H. KUHN and F. HEUCK

Medizinische Universitätsklinik and Pathologisches Institut der Universität Heidelberg, Heidelberg and Katharinenhospital, Stuttgart, German Federal Repubiic

Two hundred and fifty patients from 16 German hemodialysis centers are currently being studied in an investigation on dialysis bone disease. Preliminary data of the study are already available.

Our patients are subjected to a standard clinical examination; predialysis serum chemistry and parathyroid hormone (PTH) levels are measured; X-rays of the entire skeleton are taken and evaluated by one examiner; slit lamp examination of the cornea is performed; calcium content of the skeleton is studied by the densitometric procedure of Heuck; iliac crest biopsies have so far been obtained from 130 patients.

The frequency of clinical signs of bone disease was as follows: bone pain 16%; spontaneous fractures 1%; loss of height 1%; pseudogout 22%; extraosseous calcifications (nonvascular) 18%; red eye syndrome 11.9%. Pseudogout, red eye syndrome and extraosseous calcifications were associated with bone disease, whereas vascular calcifications were found in long-term hemodialysis patients without clinically significant bone disease. There were marked differences in the incidence of clinical bone disease (ranging from 3 to 29%) between different dialysis centers. On the whole the incidence of clinical bone disease in different centers correlated well with the average degree of rehabilitation achieved. However, rapidly progressing hyperparathyroidism occurred in some well dialyzed patients in the course of treatment. Parathyroidectomy has so far been necessary in nine of the 250 patients.

The few predialysis serum PTH levels sofar determined correlated well with the severity of histological evidence of hyperparathyroidism; the highest values were found in patients with clinical and roentgenological signs of osteitis fibrosa. Roentgenological (12% of all patients) and histological signs of hyperparathyroidism did not correlate very well, since severe histological changes were found to be associated with inconspicuous roentgenological signs. The sign most frequently encountered was acro-osteolysis of the lateral aspect of the clavicle with enlargement of the acromio-clavicular articulation (80% of all patients with positive X-ray signs); next came coarse bone structure and subperiosteal resorption zones of the radial aspect of the phalanges (60%); ground glass appearance of the skull, subperiosteal resorption of the medial aspect of the tibia, sclerosis of vertebral bodies and enlargement of the ileosacral articulation were uncommon, each being found in less than 20% of cases. Loosers zones were found in only one patient.

None of the 80 bone specimens studied so far showed normal bone. The most prominent change encountered was increase of osteoid, the amount of which correlated with the total duration of uremia. There was no decrease and possibly even an increase of osteoid after several years of dialysis (up to five years). Micromorphometric measurements and microradiographic studies are currently being carried out in decalcified sections.

In the above series, dialysis bone disease seems to be an advanced stage of classical uremic bone disease. Bony changes specific for dialysis, such as osteoporosis, were not encountered.

HOMEOSTATIC RESPONSE TO ABRUPT CHANGES IN PLASMA CALCIUM LEVEL IN CHRONIC RENAL FAILURE

MICHAEL KAYE, S. SAGAR, G. F. COHEN, J. T. POTTS Jr. and T. MURRAY

Division of Nephrology, Department of Medicine, Montreal General Hospital, Montreal, Canada, and Endocrine Unit, Massachusetts General Hospital, Boston, Massachusetts, USA

Patients stabilized on a chronic hemodialysis program were studied. They were using Kiil dialyzers with the dialysate running at 0.5 liter/min and discarded after a single pass through the kidney. Abrupt alterations in plasma calcium were induced by exposure to a dialysate calcium of either 0.2 mg/100 ml (instead of the normally used 6 mg/100 ml) to produce hypocalcemia, or one of 11 mg/100 ml to produce hypercalcemia. In each study the low calcium dialysate was used initially until the plasma calcium fell by 2 mg/100 ml, whereupon the high calcium dialysate was used. The plasma calcium was allowed to rise during the following 2 to 4 hr to 12 mg/100 ml when the low calcium containing dialysate was again started and the fall in plasma calcium to the previous level followed.

Nineteen studies have been carried out. In each, uptake or loss of calcium was calculated by the arteriovenous difference across the dialyzer, blood flow rate and hematocrit. Sampling was every 5 to 10 min. Ionized calcium (Orion electrode) was shown to parallel total calcium. Immunoassayable parathyroid hormone levels were stable until the plasma calcium was elevated, after which they fell but did not become unmeasurable.

Analysis of the rate of change of plasma calcium in relation to the calcium transferred either in or out of the body was carried out using the following formula:

$$\frac{\text{mg of calcium transferred to effect a change in plasma caicium of 1 mg/100 ml}}{\text{body wt in kg}}$$

This corrects for variables such as blood flow rate through the dialyzer, hematocrit and body size and indicates the calcium required to be added or removed from the body to change the plasma calcium by a unit quantity. Using this concept the mean results ($\pm$ SE) were 4.2 ± 0.5 from the patient's normal baseline plasma calcium level to the peak of hypercalcemia, and 1.9 ± 0.3 from the peak to return to the baseline ($P < 0.001$). Similarly from the nadir of hypocalcemia to the baseline was 2.2 ± 0.2, as compared with 4.2 ± 0.5 to hypercalcemia ($P < 0.001$). The finding that more calcium has to be infused to elevate the plasma calcium above normal, as compared with the amount necessary to bring the plasma calcium to normal, suggests that endogenous calcitonin secretion is attempting to minimize the rise in plasma calcium. In support of this was the observation that the most marked changes were seen in patients with active secondary hyperparathyroidism who presumably had the most marked resorption rates. Increased responsiveness to calcitonin would be expected under these circumstances.

CALCIUM ABSORPTION AND EXCRETION IN THE GUT IN CHRONIC RENAL FAILURE

M. REINER, A. NADARAJAH, N.J.Y. WOODHOUSE, V. NUNZIATA, L. SEVITT and G.F. JOPLIN

Royal Postgraduate Medical School and Department of Medicine, Hammersmith Hospital, London, England

Calcium metabolism was investigated in 18 patients with chronic renal failure: eight had chronic pyelonephritis, four chronic glomerulonephritis, four polycystic disease of the kidneys, one rheumatoid arthritis and amyloid, and one primary hyperparathyroidism with renal calculi and secondary renal failure.

The following parameters were measured: a) serum calcium, phosphorus, alkaline phosphatase, electrolytes and renal function; b) urinary calcium and phosphorus excretion; c) Ca^{47} kinetics: Ca^{47} 24 hr space, Ca pool size, bone formation rate (accretion), endogenous fecal calcium; d) Ca^{45} fractional true absorption with a double isotope test using i.v. injected Ca^{47} and concurrently orally administered Ca^{45}; e) iliac crest biopsy for quantitative histological analysis (eight patients); f) external calcium balance: net absorption, balance and bone resorption rate (five patients).

Four patients became hypercalcemic in the course of their disease and autonomous parathyroid hyperplasia (tertiary hyperparathyroidism) was diagnosed.

Results. The data presented in detail are those concerned with calcium absorption and calcium excretion into the gut. With the exception of one case with primary hyperparathyroidism and four cases of tertiary hyperparathyroidism, all the patients showed true absorption values at the lower end of the normal range, but 75% had an abnormally raised endogenous fecal calcium loss. No correlation was found between the intestinal calcium transport defect and the severity of the renal failure.

The existing discrepancy in the literature between net absorption data and values for true absorption of calcium in chronic renal failure can be explained by our findings of a high endogenous fecal loss. The five patients who were simultaneously studied by an external balance and isotope methods illustrate this aspect of the disease. Although their true absorption was in the normal range, their net absorption was abnormally low, putting them in negative calcium balance.

EXPERIMENTAL RENAL OSTEOPATHY

B. KREMPIEN and E. RITZ

Pathologisches Institut and Medizinische Klinik, Universität Heidelberg, German Federal Republic

We studied 100 or 250 g male Wistar rats at various intervals after five-sixths nephrectomy, bilateral nephrectomy or ligature of ureters. Controls (Co) were sham operated; food intake was kept identical by pair feeding. Parathyroidectomy (PTX) was done by thermocoagulation.

After five-sixths nephrectomy (U) we found

narrowing of the epiphyseal line, increase of osteoid in the metaphysis and diaphysis, replacement of osteoblasts by fusiform cells and increase of osteoclasts. Uremia of three weeks duration did not cause osteitis fibrosa in spite of marked hyperplasia of parathyroids (PTH-resistance). Nephrectomy caused no increase of osteoid in PTX animals. The bony changes could not be reproduced by increasing serum urea levels (3,000 mg/100 ml urea in drinking water) and acidosis (NH_4Cl) and did not disappear after peritoneal dialysis. Histological changes were accompanied by marked biochemical alterations in metaphyseal preparations. Lactic acid: U, $26.8 \pm 1.7 \times 10^{-9}$ M/mg wet wt per 3 hr; Co, 20.1 ± 2.8; $P \langle 0.02$. Glucose uptake: U, 6.55 ± 0.65; Co, 4.58 ± 0.49 ($P \langle 0.01$). Pentose cycle: U, $21.2 \pm 2.6\%$; Co, $17.1 \pm 6.6\%$ (not significant). Glucose decarboxylation: U, 0.54 ± 0.07; Co, 0.26 ± 0.05 ($P \langle 0.02$). After PTX only a decrease of glucose decarboxylation was demonstrable: U, 0.688 ± 0.07; Co, 0.414 ± 0.46 ($P \langle 0.02$).

Ca kinetics were studied in our model of uremia with Ca^{47}. Data were analyzed according to Aubert and Milhaud. Bone accretion rates and exchangeable pools were diminished after nephrectomy both in PTX and non-PTX animals. Exchengeable pool: U, 27.6 ± 4.0 mg; Co, 31.2 ± 1.7. vo^+: U, 34.2 ± 3.6 mg/day; Co, 42.5 ± 2.5.

The rate of bone mineralization (linear apposition in diaphysis of tibia), measured with tetracycline and alizarin red S (nontoxic doses), was markedly diminished after nephrectomy in uremic animals as compared to sham-operated controls. Co, before sham operation 16.7 ± 2.9 μ/three days; after sham operation 16.5 ± 3.1. U before nephrectomy 16.8 ± 2.3; after nephrectomy 13.1 ± 1.4 ($P \langle 0.001$). After PTX the difference was no longer significant.

Autoradiographic studies with Ca^{45} pointed to a diminished rate of bone formation and remodeling in animals at various ages with uremia of short duration. Removal of label from the primary calcification zone in the epiphyseal plate and incorporation of label into metaphyseal spongiosa and periosteal apposition of label was reduced. In animals prelabeled four weeks before nephrectomy, the deeply buried former line of apposition persisted unchanged. After long-term uremia the rate of incorporation of label into metaphyseal spongiosa and the rate of periosteal and endosteal apposition of label were clearly increased, although still lower than in controls.

The defect of mineralization could be overcome by vitamin D and 25-hydroxycholecalciferol. The zone of primary calcification (line test) increased and osteoid in the metaphysis decreased at all dose levels (0.1 to 1,000 IU), both with vitamin D and 25-hydroxycholecalciferol, in fasting uremic rachitic rats. The response to vitamin D was significantly diminished when compared with rachitic controls (vitamin D resistance). The effect of vitamin D on bone was independent of its promoting effect on intestinal Ca absorption (fasting animals, Ca administration intraperitoneally).

Synthesis of bone matrix was evaluated by autoradiography and by incubation of metaphyseal chips *in vitro* (H^3-glycine, $S^{35} O_4$). Incorporation of H^3-glycine into "cell fraction" (CF) and trichloroacetic acid precipitate (TCA) as well as into alkali insoluble collagen (AIC) was diminished in animals five days after nephrectomy. Co: CF, 33.95 ± 2.48, 10 to 12 M/mg decalcified defatted dry bone; AIC, 0.158 ± 0.009. U: CF, 24.39 ± 0.68; AIC, 0.091 ± 0.013 ($P \langle 0.02$). After PTX, incorporation of H^3-glycine into AIC was still diminished in uremic bone although there was no longer a difference for CF and TCA. PTX, 0.095 ± 0.016; PTX-U, 0.066 ± 0.018 ($P \langle 0.05$). These results agree well with autoradiographic evidence for diminished labeling of newly formed osteoid in uremic

191

animals both with and without PTX.

Specific activity of acid mucopolysaccharides (a-MPS) in metaphyseal preparations after 3 hr incubation *in vitro* was significantly diminished in uremic rats both with and without PTX. Co, 135 ± 9.3 count/min per mg decalcified defatted dry bone; U: 90.6 ± 6.64 ($P < 0.05$). PTX, 18.7 ± 1.55; PTX-U, 12.95 ± 1.55 ($P < 0.02$). By autoradiography, mean uptake of label per cell was clearly increased in uremia without PTX. Co, 6.4 ± 0.18 grains/cell area; U, 7.96 ± 0.1 ($P < 0.05$), but not after PTX. PTX, 7.81 ± 0.09; PTX-U, 6.83 ± 0.29 ($P < 0.10$).

The discrepancy of the *in vitro* and *in vivo* results may be due to the fact that serum S^{35} was higher in nephrectomized animals. In addition, the width of the epiphyseal plate was diminished in uremia. Co, 281 ± 48 μ; U, 212 ± 32 ($P < 0.05$). Extrusion of S^{35} label from cartilage cells was slow in uremic animals. Furthermore, in long-term experiments, removal of a-MPS from metaphyseal spongiosa was delayed after nephrectomy. No difference was detectable after PTX.

To summarize, in our experimental model nephrectomy caused bone disease with alteration of cell metabolism and with histological changes characteristic of osteomalacia and hyperparathyroidism. Various parameters of mineralization and the rate of matrix formation were diminished. Vitamin D resistance and PTH resistance can be shown in our model.

THE ROLE OF FLUORIDE IN CALCIFIED TISSUE

EQUILIBRIUM DEPOSITION OF FLUORIDE*

I. ZIPKIN

School of Dentistry, University of California at San Francisco, San Francisco, California, USA

Although a large number of factors affecting the deposition of fluoride in calcifying structures have been studied, only incidental attention has been paid to the effect of partial inanition. Such a regimen, provided no secondary sequelae obtained, would afford the opportunity to study the effect of a reduction in total bone apatite in a physiological system on the uptake of fluoride *in vivo*. If no change occurred in the ash content, presumably apatite, and in the major constituents of calcifying structures exposed to equal amounts of fluoride, it might be expected that the concentration of fluoride would be higher in the reduced bone mass, whereas the total fluoride deposited in selected hard tissues would be essentially similar. Such a finding would encourage the hypothesis that the apatite of bones and teeth could act as an ion-exchange medium *in vivo* as has already been demonstrated *in vitro* by Neuman et al. (1). A reduced bone mass may be produced by drastically altering the Ca/P ratio of the diet with a concomitant and significant change in the Ca/P ratio in the femurs and mandibles of rats receiving equal amounts of fluoride over a relatively short period of time (2). It might be expected that this unphysiological bone apatite would have a disturbed ion-exchange function and that a nonequilibrium situation would result.

In the present study, six pairs of litter-mated, weanling rats received equal amounts of fluoride in the drinking water for 28 weeks, and one rat of each pair received 60% of the food intake of its ad lib. fed mate. The molar teeth, mandibles, femurs and remaining carcass were analyzed for fluoride. All data were evaluated for differences of means by Fisher's t test for paired values.

The weight, diet and fluoride intakes of control and test rats are presented in Table 1.

It is apparent that body weight closely paralleled diet intake, indicating that no secondary sequelae occurred as a result of the reduced diet intake in the pair-fed rats.

Table 2 shows that the weight, ash and fluoride content of the molars were unaffected by partial starvation. The weight of the mandibles, femurs and carcass was markedly reduced in the starved rats, whereas the

TABLE 1. *Weight, diet and fluoride intake of control (C) and test (T) Rats*[a]

	C	T	T/C
Body weight[b] (g)	245.0±15.3	155.0±10.6	0.63
Diet intake (g)	1866 ±83.5	1120 ±41.8	0.60
F intake (mg)	30.6± 2.4	30.5± 2.0	1.00

[a] Six control rats received an adequate diet ad lib. for 28 weeks. Litter-mated test rats were restricted to 60% of intake of control rats on a paired basis.
[b] Final weight. Twenty-one-day-old rats at the start weighed 46 g.
Mean values ± SE.

* Work done at National Institute of Dental Research, National Institutes of Health, Bethesda, Md., USA.

193

TABLE 2. *Deposition of fluoride in bones and teeth of control (C) and partially starved pair-fed rats (T)*

		C	T	T/C
		Molars		
Weight	g	0.145 ± 0.005	0.155 ± 0.006	1.07 ± 0.04
Ash	%	78.7 ± 0.91	78.8 ± 1.11	1.00 ± 0.02
F	%	0.057 ± 0.008	0.063 ± 0.005	1.10 ± 0.13
Total F	mg	0.083 ± 0.012	0.098 ± 0.009	1.18 ± 0.14
		Mandibles		
Weight	g	0.454 ± 0.016	0.370 ± 0.031	0.82 ± 0.08
Ash	%	72.5 ± 0.38	72.4 ± 1.02	1.00 ± 0.02
F	%	0.077 ± 0.009	0.095 ± 0.006	1.23 ± 0.22
Total F	mg	0.348 ± 0.040	0.346 ± 0.021	0.99 ± 0.14
		Femurs		
Weight	g	0.750 ± 0.029	0.490 ± 0.045	0.65 ± 0.05[a]
Ash	%	69.5 ± 0.61	69.7 ± 0.38	1.00 ± 0.02
F	%	0.070 ± 0.005	0.099 ± 0.007	1.40 ± 0.15[b]
Total F	mg	0.525 ± 0.041	0.479 ± 0.047	0.91 ± 0.01
		Carcass[c]		
Weight	g	7.95 ± 0.27	5.71 ± 0.44	0.72 ± 0.03[a]
F	%	0.081 ± 0.007	0.121 ± 0.008	1.49 ± 0.10[a]
Total F	mg	6.42 ± 0.42	6.86 ± 0.65	1.07 ± 0.09

[a] $P < 0.01$; [b] $P < 0.05$. For all other comparisons, $P > 0.05$.
[c] Data expressed on an ash basis. All other data given on a dry, fat-free basis.
Mean values ± SE.

ash % was unchanged. The % of fluoride was approximately 25 to 50% higher in the smaller bones and carcass, but the total fluoride deposited was the same in every case ($P > 0.05$) in this long-term study of 28 weeks. These data are compatible with the hypothesis that, *in vivo*, bone apatite may serve as an ion-exchange medium of sufficient capacity, even in the starved rat with an 18 to 35% reduction in total bone mass to retain the fluoride to which it is exposed. In this study, approximately 25% of the fluoride intake was retained by the rat, with presumably about 95% being retained by the skeleton and teeth. The similar ash values of the bones of normal and starved rats would indicate that no striking chemical alteration occurred in their apatitic structure.

Other *in vivo* data on the physiological handling of fluoride by bone would also support the physicochemical ion replacement concept as playing a major role in deposition and mobilization of fluoride. For example, it has been well established that fluoride continues to accumulate in bone long after the major constituents, Ca and P, reach a steady state, and eventually reaches a plateau in deposition. No change in the calcium and phosphorus concentrations in bone is seen after long-term exposure to fluoride, indicating that these ions do not participate in the ion competition and exchange as already demonstrated in *in vitro* studies. In addition, some 85 to 90% of the fluoride deposited in bone is retained following cessation of fluoride administration, indicating that it may be electrovalently bound and can be replaced only by other ions which could be more tightly held. The small amount of released fluoride may be secondarily adsorbed and held by looser than ionic charges.

In previously published short-term studies of six-week duration, the smaller bones of the rachitic rat contained a significantly higher concentration of fluoride than those of the pair-fed rat on an adequate diet ($P < 0.001$), but the total fluoride was significantly less ($P < 0.001$); it thus appears that the capacity of the bone to act as an ion-exchange medium is exhausted due to the reduced bone mass of apatite and to the alteration in bone calcium and phosphorus (Ca/P, $P < 0.001$). In contrast, the ad lib. fed rats receiving an adequate diet contained a somewhat smaller concentration of fluoride than the bones of the pair-fed rats, again receiving similar amounts of fluoride, but showed the same amount of total fluoride deposited, indicating normally functioning bone apatite. No significant changes were seen in the Ca and P concentrations of the bones of the pair-fed and ad lib. fed rats. Diet intake for the rachitic, pair-fed and ad lib. fed rats was 4.6, 4.4 and 8.3 g/day, respectively.

These studies support the hypothesis that fluoride *in vivo* follows, in the main, the physicochemical principles of ion-exchange in its deposition and mobilization. The equilibrium or homeostatic deposition of fluoride in bone may serve as a simple marker for determining the physiological state of bone.

REFERENCES

1. NEUMAN WF, NEUMAN MW, MAIN ER, O'LEARY J and SMITH FA. *J Biol Chem* **187**: 658, 1950.
2. ZIPKIN I, LIKINS RC and McCLURE FJ. *J Nutr* **67**: 59, 1959.

EFFECT OF FLUORIDE ON THE LIPID METABOLISM OF RAT BONE

I. WOLINSKY and K. GUGGENHEIM

Department of Nutrition, Hebrew University–Hadassah Medical School, Jerusalem, Israel

The direct participation of lipids in the process of bone mineralization has recently been proposed (1). In the preliminary studies reported here, the alteration of bone lipid metabolism by fluoride, an agent having an effect on bone crystal structure (2), was investigated.

Weanling white male rats were maintained on laboratory chow and distilled water for two weeks. The water of experimental animals was supplemented with 200 ppm F^-. After decapitation, metaphyseal and diaphyseal bone of the femora and tibiae from each animal was isolated and incubated in Krebs-Ringer phosphate buffer, pH 7.4, fortified with 10 mM glucose and containing 2.0 μc (0.035 μmole) l-C^{14}-acetate, for 3 hr at 37 C under an air atmosphere. Lipid isolation and fractionation were done as previously described (3).

Administration of F^- to experimental animals over the two-week period had no effect on the water, ash, calcium, phosphorus, protein and deoxyribose levels in the bone. However, in the experimental animals there were significant decreases in body weight gain and in the citric acid content of the bone. Furthermore, the lipid [Triglyceride (TG) plus phospholipid (PL)] content of fluoride-bone decreased sharply: 22 control animals, 1.84 ± 0.19; 21 experimental animals, 0.96 ± 0.09 mg/100 mg of fresh bone (mean $\pm$ SE).

The decreased lipid content of fluoride-bone was accompanied by a marked reduction in the incorporation of labeled acetate into lipid fractions (Table 1). 1.63 nmole of acetate/100 mg fresh bone were incorporated into the TG plus PL of control bone, whereas less than 1/7 of that amount (0.22 nmole) was incorporated into the lipids of bone, from rats receiving F^-. In control bone, 86% (1.40 nmole) of the acetate label was found in the TG fraction while in fluoride-bone only 59%

TABLE 1. *Incorporation of 1-C14-acetate into the lipid fractions of control and fluoride-bone*

	Control	Fluoride
	(nmole acetate/100 mg fresh bone)	
TG	1.40 ± 0.07	0.13 ± 0.007
TG fatty acid	0.91 ± 0.04	0.06 ± 0.004
	(65)	(46)
PL	0.23 ± 0.02	0.09 ± 0.003
PL fatty acid	0.13 ± 0.007	0.03 ± 0.007
	(57)	(33)

TG = triglyceride, PL = phospholipid.
Values are expressed as means ±SE of seven or eight animals. Figures in parentheses are the percentages of the incorporated substrate which appear in the fatty acid portion of the lipid molecule.

(0.13 nmole) of the incorporated acetate was found in the TG fraction. A higher percentage of acetate was incorporated into the TG and PL fatty acid portions of control bone than in the corresponding fractions of fluoride-bone.

These experiments indicate that there is a significant decrease in and alteration of the pattern of lipid synthesis from acetate in the bone of rats given F^-. Studies on the incorporation of other lipid precursors and the tissue specificity of the effects observed above are currently in progress.

REFERENCES
1. WUTHIER RE. *J Lipid Res* **9**: 68, 1968.
2. POSNER AS, EANES ED, HARPER RA and ZIPKIN I. *Arch Oral Biol* **8**: 549, 1963.
3. WOLINSKY I and GUGGENHEIM K. *Calcif Tissue Res* **6**: 113, 1970.

FLUORIDE AND OSTEOPOROSIS FROM PARALYSIS

LEON SINGER and W. D. ARMSTRONG

Department of Biochemistry, University of Minnesota, Minneapolis, Minnesota, USA

Studies designed to distinguish between the possible effects of skeletal fluoride concentration, bone resorption and bone formation in a limb paralyzed by severing the nerves of the brachial plexus on one side have been carried out in rats.

Male weanling rats were supplied food (0.5% Ca) of low fluoride content (0.5 ppm) labeled uniformly with Ca^{45} and distilled water (low fluoride group), or water containing 25 ppm F (high fluoride group). After 45 days on the respective regimens, representative animals of each group were: a) sacrificed, b) maintained for an additional three or six weeks on the low fluoride diet without radiocalcium and distilled water, or c) subjected to section of the nerves of the right brachial plexus and maintained for an additional three or six weeks on the nonradioactive diet and distilled water.

Hypertrophy did not occur in the humeri of the unoperated limbs of experimental animals as a consequence of increased body weight being placed on the functioning limb. The weights of the humeri of the right limbs of the operated animals were lower than those of the left limbs.

Both humeri of the operated animals of the low fluoride group showed an increase in weight of bone ash. It is interesting to note that the left humeri of the operated animals of the distilled water group, at three weeks and at six weeks after the surgical procedure, gained nearly as much mineral as did the humeri of the unoperated control animals. The operated right humeri of the group that received 25 ppm F in water gained very little mineral in the first three weeks. At six weeks, however, the ash weights of both the right and left humeri of this group had increased over those of the three-week period.

With the paralyzed limbs there was a progressive increase in humeral length reflecting growth in this parameter. There was no growth in width of the shaft at its midpoint or in width of the proximal epiphyseal area of the humeri. There were no differences in the measurements of length of the humeri of the operated and unoperated limbs of the same animals. The volumes of the bones were apparently identical, or nearly so, but there was obvious differences in bone density.

Since the animals were fed a diet labeled with Ca^{45} only during the first 45 days of the study, the amount of Ca in the bone that was derived, prior to the surgical procedure, from the diet during the preoperative period could be determined. A significant loss of radioactivity, or loss of the bone salt deposited during the early part of the study, occurred in the operated limbs by three and six weeks but not in the unoperated limbs. At three weeks, it was only in the low fluoride group that a significant difference existed between the bones of the two limbs of the operated animals. However, at six weeks, the humeri of the nonparalyzed limbs of the operated animals, in both groups, were significantly greater in amount of labeled bone retained than were the humeri of the operated limbs.

From the specific activities of the calcium of the humeri and the percent of bone apatite formed from the radioactive diet and still present at the experimental periods, it is obvious that the fractions of labeled bone or calcium in comparable bones (operated and unoperated limbs within a group) are similar. Significant differences were found in the amount of calcium derived from the pre-experimental diet (radioactive) in the two bones of all surgically treated animals at six weeks and even at three weeks in the low fluoride group. The findings can be accounted for only by resorption in the bone of the denervated limb being increased over that of the unoperated limb in the same animals, and further by formation of new bone in the operated limb occurring at a reduced rate. The results support the concept of a reduced ratio of formation of bone in the operated limb. In the distilled water group (low fluoride), there was an increase of 515 mg of bone ash in the left humeri at six weeks, as compared to the amount present in the bones of the "0" week animals, and there was an increase of only 276 mg of bone ash in the right limb of those animals over the same period.

The results of the study indicate that there was little effect of the skeletal fluoride load on the development of this form of bone atrophy.

THE EFFECT OF SODIUM FLUORIDE AND SODIUM MONOFLUOROPHOSPHATE ON THE MECHANICAL PROPERTIES OF NORMAL AND OSTEOPOROTIC RAT BONE

D. NORDENBERG, A. SIMKIN, I. GEDALIA and G. ROBIN

Laboratory of Oral Chemistry and Fluoride Research, Hebrew University–Hadassah School of Dental Medicine and Department of Orthopedics, Hadassah University Hospital and Hebrew University–Hadassah Medical School, Jerusalem, Israel

The purpose of this investigation was to evaluate the influence of fluoride administration as NaF and Na_2PO_3F on the mechanical properties of immobilized rat bones. Seventy-

TABLE 1. *Tensile strength, breaking strain and breaking energy absorption capacity of rat tibia specimens (compact bone)*

	Group 1 Ordinary diet	Group 2 50 ppm F as NaF	Group 3 50 ppm F as Na_2PO_3F
Tensile strength, kg/mm²			
Mobile tibiae	14.82 (8) ±1.68	13.92 (10) ±1.73	15.27 (11) ±1.38
Immobile tibiae	13.15 (12)[a] ±2.0	14.69 (11) ±2.13	14.18 (8) ±2.41
Breaking strain, %			
Mobile tibiae	0.93 (8)[b] ±0.19	0.74 (10) ±0.14	0.76 (9) ±0.15
Immobile tibiae	0.75 (10) ±0.11	0.83 (11) ±0.21	0.76 (8) ±0.19
Breaking energy absorption capacity, kg/mm³			
Mobile tibiae	0.078 (8)[c] ±0.02	0.058 (10) ±0.01	0.064 (9) ±0.02
Immobile tibiae	0.055 (10) ±0.01	0.068 (11) ±0.02	0.061 (8) ±0.02

Figures in parentheses indicate number of rats.
Mean values are given ±SD.
[a] Significantly lower than in mobile tibiae of rats on ordinary diet ($P < 0.05$).
[b] Significantly higher than in mobile tibiae-NaF group ($P < 0.025$), Na_2PO_3F group ($P < 0.05$) and immobile tibiae-ordinary diet group ($P < 0.025$).
[c] Significantly higher than mobile tibiae-NaF group ($P < 0.025$) and immobile tibiae-ordinary diet group ($P < 0.025$).

five 30-day-old male rats were divided into three groups of 25 each.

Group 1 received tap water as drinking water (about 0.5 ppm F); group 2 received drinking water containing 50 ppm F as NaF; and group 3 received drinking water containing 50 ppm F as Na_2PO_3F.

The rats in groups 2 and 3 were provided with F drinking water prior to immobilization of the tibiae in order to incorporate F into their bones. After four weeks, immobilization was initiated in the right tibia in 15 of the rats in each group by applying acryl resin as a fixed cylinder on the right limb (1, 2). Eight weeks after the experiment started all the rats were sacrificed, and the right tibiae were removed and kept moist in sealed containers in a deep freeze (–25 C). A small bone segment was removed from the distal border of each tibia and examined for ash content. Miniature specimens of compact bone were prepared by machine cutting and manual grinding on silico-carbide paper from the plane anterior surface of the tibia. During preparation, the specimens were cooled under a spray of Ringer's solution at 3 to 5 C. The final dimensions of each specimen were: length, 10 mm; and cross section at the center approximately 0.5×0.3 mm. Two holes were drilled in each specimen as a holding device. The dimensions of each specimen were measured either with a micrometer or using a microscope with a calibrated meshed eyepiece and an accuracy of 0.01 mm. Each specimen was tested for correction as to shape, surface texture and centricity of the holes relative to the neck under a microscope with $\times 100$ magnification. The prepared specimens were stored before mechanical testing in cold Ringer's solution. For measurements of breaking strain and energy absorbing capacity, the specimens were mounted on an apparatus designed by one of us (3). Special care was taken to center the specimens carefully since an uneven stress distribution could cause a bending moment in addition to the axial force. Tension load was exerted with small steel balls, weighing 0.25 g each, added by an accurate feeding mechanism, at a constant rate, until fracture took place. Elongation of the specimen was determined by repeatedly photographing it under increasing load and measuring the elongation changes between two selected points on the film with an accuracy of 1 μ. Each distance was measured 10 times and the average taken as the mean distance. The average error in the elongation measurements was ±2%.

In accordance with reports in the literature (4), no significant differences were observed between the mean ash contents of the mobile and immobile small tibia segments of the normal and fluoride-treated rats. Tensile strength, breaking strain and breaking energy absorption capacity were decreased in the immobile tibiae of the rats on a normal diet. These findings suggest that changes in strength of bone may not necessarily be related to its ash content or only to thinning of the cortex in osteoporotic bone, but may also be related to internal structural changes (5).

Fluoride administration, as NaF, decreased the breaking strain and breaking energy absorption capacity in the mobile tibiae of the normal rats (Table 1). The tensile strength was not significantly influenced. Fluoride administration, as Na_2PO_3F, decreased only the breaking strain in the mobile tibiae of normal rats. The significance ($P < 0.05$) was less accentuated than that in the NaF-treated group ($P < 0.025$). Breaking energy absorption capacity and tensile strength were not significantly influenced. The diminished mechanical

bone strength of the fluoride-treated rats is not consistent with the view of other investigators who administered similar F dosages; however their determinations were carried out on whole bone units (5, 6). The deterioration in the mechanical quality of the fluorotic bones may be due to the delay in the onset of mineralization in the newly formed bone followed by increased fluoride administration (7). The reason for the differences in bone strength, both among the NaF and Na_2PO_3F treated rats, is not clear. It may possibly be related to differences in the chemical bone composition reported in previous investigations (1, 8).

Fluoride administration as NaF or Na_2PO_3F did not significantly affect the mechanical properties of the immobile tibiae as compared to the mobile tibiae of the rats on the respective fluoride-diets. It may be concluded that fluoride administration seems to affect the mechanical properties of normal and osteoporotic bone in different ways.

This paper is part of the thesis submitted by D. Nordenberg in partial fulfilment of the requirements for the degree of D.M.D.

The authors are indebted to Harold C. Hodge, University of Rochester-School of Medicine and Dentistry, Rochester, N.Y. for suggesting this investigation.

REFERENCES

1. GEDALIA I, HODGE HC, ANAISE J, WHITE WE and MENCZEL J. *Calcif Tissue Res* 5: 146, 1970.
2. ANAISE J and SELA J. *J Dent Res* (in press).
3. SIMKIN A. M.Sc. thesis, Technion, Haifa, 1970.
4. KLEIN L, KANEFIELD DG and HEIPLE KG. *Calcif Tissue Res* 2: 20, 1968.
5. RICH C and FEIST E. in: "Fluoride in medicine." Berne, Huber Verlag, 1970, p 70.
6. BEARY DF. *Anat Rec* 164: 305, 1969.
7. BAYLINK D, WERGEDAHL J, STAUFFER M and RICH C. in: "Fluoride in medicine." Berne, Huber Verlag, 1970, p 37.
8. ERICSSON Y. *Caries Res* 1: 144, 1967.

199

LYSOSOMAL ENZYMES IN CARTILAGE AND
NEW BONE IN RACHITIC CHICKS

E. HAVIVI

Department of Nutrition, Hebrew University–Hadassah Medical School, Jerusalem, Israel

The rachitic state is characterized in growing animals by an accumulation of cartilage matrix which fails to mineralize (1). The removal of the organic matrix of the epiphyseal cartilage is a general feature of calcification. The participation of lysosomal enzymes able to hydrolyze collagen, protein and mucopolysaccharides has been postulated (2).

The purpose of this paper is to report on the enzyme activity of different regions of the cartilage and new bone and the action of lysosomal glycosidases on the removal of organic matrix in the ossification process.

Methods. Day-old white Leghorn chicks were kept in a chicken brooder over a 28-day period. They were divided into three groups as follows: group 1, on a control diet (3); group 2, on a rachitogenic diet identical to the control diet, vitamin D being omitted; group 3, on the control diet limited in

amount to that consumed by the rachitic chicks.

The chicks were killed by decapitation, bones were carefully cleaned and the resting and ossifying cartilage and new bone were taken from the proximal end of the tibia. The tissue samples were pooled and lysosomes separated (4, 5). The following enzymes were examined β-*glucosidase* (EC.3.2.1.21) (4), α- and β-*galactosidases* (EC. 3.2.1.22 and 3.2.1.23) (6), β-*glucuronidase* (EC. 3.2.1.31) (4), *N-acetyl-β-glucoaminidase* (EC. 3.2.1.29) (4), *hyaluronidase* (EC. 3.2.1.35) (7) and *cathepsin* (EC. 3.4.4.23) (8).

Results and discussion. The results show that the activities of all enzymes tested were several times higher in the ossifying cartilage and new bone regions than they were in the resting zone (Table 1). Pair-feeding did not bring about any statistically significant change

TABLE 1. *Effect of rickets on lysosomal enzymes*

Enzyme	Control			Rachitic		
	Resting Cartilage	Ossifying Cartilage	New bone	Resting Cartilage	Ossifying Cartilage	New bone
α-D-glucosidase	17 ± 0.9	68 ± 7.0	141 ± 12.7	13 ± 1.8	46 ± 3.3	87 ± 10.0
β-D-glucosidase	27 ± 4.1	71 ± 5.8	135 ± 12.1	39 ± 5.3	52 ± 3.6	92 ± 8.9
α-D-galactosidase	12 ± 0.9	53 ± 7.2	146 ± 11.0	15 ± 1.1	50 ± 5.8	75 ± 9.1
β-D-galactosidase	10 ± 1.5	48 ± 6.7	140 ± 16.4	6 ± 1.2	23 ± 5.0	65 ± 7.5
β-D-glucoronidase	14 ± 1.0	48 ± 2.9	140 ± 12.8	8 ± 1.1	26 ± 3.3	68 ± 10.0
Hyaluronidase	7 ± 0.9	87 ± 16.3	40 ± 2.7	8.6 ± 1.1	31 ± 12.4	27 ± 2.0
N-acetyl-β-glucoaminidase	50 ± 6.1	76 ± 8.5	162 ± 11.6	101 ± 12.1	119 ± 7.9	144 ± 9.8
Cathepsin D	14 ± 3.1	430 ± 31.3	104 ± 8.3	11 ± 1.3	141 ± 15.1	56 ± 6.7

Average values of six experiments each consisting of pooled material from 20 chicks. Enzyme units are nmole/mg protein per hr ± SD.

of enzyme activity compared with the control.

During the development of vitamin D deficiency the activities of most lysosomal enzymes were reduced relative to those of the control animals. An exception to this trend was the increased activity of N-acetyl-β-glucoaminidase in resting and ossifying cartilage of deficient chicks. Cathepsin activity was examined not only at pH 3.7 but also in homogenates of cartilage and bone at pH 8.0. Such preparations, when derived from rachitic chicks, had a proteolytic activity of 25% of controls.

It is possible that the reasons for the thickness and the increase in wet weight, DNA, glycogen store and protein content (9) of cartilage in vitamin D deficient animals are related to the increased production of organic compounds (10) on the one hand and the lack of lysosomal activity on the other, which does not reduce the amount of organic matter. Furthermore, these factors may also be responsible for the incompleteness of the mineralization in vitamin D deficient epiphyses.

REFERENCES

1. Park EA. *Bull NY Acad Med* **15**: 495, 1939.
2. McLean FC and Urist MC. "Bone, an introduction to the physiology of skeletal tissue." Chicago, University of Chicago Press, 1961.
3. Havivi E and Wolf G. *J Nutr* **92**: 467, 1967.
4. Vaes G. *Biochem J* **97**: 380, 1965.
5. De Duve C, Pressman BC, Gianetto R, Wattiaux R and Appelman F. *Biochem J* **60**: 604, 1955.
6. Vann Hoof F and Hers HG. *Europ J Biochem* **7**: 34, 1968.
7. Partridge SM, Davis HF and Adair GS. *Biochem J* **79**: 15, 1961.
8. Anson ML. *J Gen Physiol* **20**: 565, 1937.
9. Meyer WL and Kunin AS. *Arch Biochem* **129**: 483, 1969.
10. Canas F, Brand JS, Newman WF and Terepka AR. *Amer J Physiol* **216**: 1092, 1969.

EFFECT OF CORTISONE ON VITAMIN D METABOLISM

K. SCHAEFER, D. VON HERRATH, H.-U. KOCH and A. OPITZ

Artificial Kidney Unit, Klinikum Steglitz, Berlin, German Federal Republic

Two recently published papers on the antagonistic influence of cortisone and vitamin D on calcium metabolism are of special interest. Avioli et al. (1) 1968 have claimed in investigations on humans that prednisone influences the metabolism of vitamin D_3 in three ways: firstly that it accelerates the turnover, secondly that it diminishes the concentration of peak IV, which Blunt et al. (2) have identified as an active metabolite of vitamin D_3 (25-hydroxycholecalciferol) and thirdly that cortisone induces the formation of peak IVa, an inactive metabolite not previously described in humans. On the other hand, the results of Kimberg (3) show that rats predosed with cortisone produce more calcium binding protein in their intestinal mucosae than control animals. Nevertheless, the intestinal transport of calcium in the cortisone group was reduced. Provided that one accepts that 25-hydroxycholecalciferol is important for the formation of this protein—even if it only acted as a precursor of peak V, 25-hydroxycholecalciferol would still be important (4)—it is reasonable to assume that the cortisone animals have produced more 25-hydroxycholecalciferol.

Methods. Sprague-Dawley rats (average weight 100 g), kept on a normal diet, were divided into two groups, A and B. Five mg of hydrocortisone were then administered orally to each rat of group A. After eight days all the animals received an intracardiac injection of 0.25 µc 1,2-H^3-vitamin D_3. Forty-eight hr later the rats were killed, blood was obtained and the various organs removed. Mawer and Backhouse's technique (5) was used to prepare the serum and the organs. The resulting chloroform extracts were chromatographed on silicic acid columns, using increasing proportions of ether in hexane and methanol in ether as eluants. The eluted fractions were monitored for radioactivity by liquid scintillation counting.

Results and Conclusions. Our results clearly show that the metabolism of tritiated vitamin D_3 is affected by hydrocortisone. A reduced concentration of peak III (unaltered vitamin D_3) was found in the serum and all the investigated organs—intestinal mucosa, bone and liver, whereas the concentrations of peak IV (25-hydroxycholecalciferol) and peak V were significantly higher. In contrast to Avioli's results (1), we did not find any change in the quality of peak IV; in particular

we could not detect any increase of inactive components of this metabolite. Our finding that hydrocortisone obviously increases the concentration of the active vitamin D_3 metabolites, peak IV and peak V, would not only support Kimberg's data (3), but also suggest that the higher concentration of the mentioned peaks could be interpreted as biological adaptation in order to overcome the cortisone-induced reduction of the intestinal calcium absorption.

Supported by the Deutsche Forschungsgemeinschaft.

REFERENCES

1. AVIOLI LV, BIRGE SJ and LEE LW. *J Clin Endocr* **28**: 1341, 1968.
2. BLUNT JW, DELUCA HF and SCHNOES HK. *Biochemistry* **7**: 3317, 1968.
3. KIMBERG DV. *New Eng J Med* **280**: 1396, 1969.
4. SUDA T, DELUCA, HF, SCHNOES H K, PONCHON G, TANAKA Y and HOLICK MF. *Biochemistry* **9**: 2917, 1970.
5. MAWER EB and BACKHOUSE J. *Biochem J* **112**: 255, 1969.

EFFECT OF AGE AND VITAMIN D DEFICIENCY ON THE UPTAKE OF ALKALINE EARTH METALS BY RAT BONE

Y. DUPUIS and J. GAMBIER

Laboratoire des Facteurs de l'Ossification, Paris, France

The study of Sr^{85} fixation by bone in rats receiving a normal calcium diet, with adequate amounts of vitamin D, is a good index of calcium retention. The younger the animals the more marked the retention and fixation of alkaline earth metals. This is not, however, the case in vitamin D deficient animals. In effect, the lower retention of calcium, determined by classical balance studies, did not enable us to predict the higher uptake of Sr^{85} by bone observed recently (1). From the age of two and one-half months, the uptake of Sr^{85} by bone is greater in the vitamin D deficient rat than in the animals receiving vitamin D. The difference increases with age,

the deficient animals fixing at least five times more radioactive Sr^{85} than the vitamin D treated animals (2). The vitamin D deficient animals have a prolonged and marked hypocalcemia, as well as hyperplasia of the parathyroid glands and often considerable bone deformations.

By way of compensation, this particular fixation property in an animal with a negative calcium balance requires increased bone resorption as apparently indicated by an increased hydroxyprolinuria (3). The study of various parameters influencing calcium utilization may help clarify the problem.

Methods. Wistar male rats were used in

TABLE 1. *Mean values of the various parameters ($\pm$ SE)*

Age (months)	Serum (mg Ca/liter)	Pool (mg Ca/day)	Δ (mg Ca/day)	V_o^+ (mg Ca/day)	V_o^- (mg Ca/day)	Sr^{85a} per femur
Control						
4	68.5 ± 0.67	46.8 ± 3.5	6.8 ± 0.1	27.1 ± 5.05	20.3 ± 3	93 ± 4.97
5	57 ± 1	44 ± 5.34	5.1 ± 0.9	30 ± 1.5	24.9 ± 2.1	71 ± 4.45
13	73 ± 1.45	76 ± 17.5	4.4 ± 1.07	59 ± 7.5	54.6 ± 7.7	77.6 ± 6.9
16	61 ± 3.5	102 ± 25	3 ± 0.96	56.4 ± 14.7	53.4 ± 15.4	67.4 ± 5.6
Vitamin D						
4	107 ± 1	61 ± 7.67	10.5 ± 0.6	39.5 ± 2.9	29 ± 3.1	42.4 ± 1.46
5	101 ± 1.3	57 ± 2.6	8 ± 1.3	33.5 ± 2.05	25.5 ± 2.8	28 ± 2.3
13	97 ± 2	46 ± 3	8 ± 2.25	23 ± 3.05	15 ± 5.3	17.3 ± 2.8
16	94 ± 0.3	33.4 ± 2.37	4.5 ± 1.4	12.6 ± 1	8.1 ± 1.3	13.6 ± 1.5

[a] Femur radioactivity in parts per thousand of the injected Sr^{85} dose. The findings are roughly the same for the tibia, scapula and axis but definitely less for the parietal bone, except in the control group animals at 5 months.

Δ = calcium balance.

V_o^+ = mass of fixed calcium in the bone.

V_o^- = mass of free calcium in the bone.

this study. They were separated into two groups—those of the control group receiving a balanced diet containing 0.6 % calcium, with a Ca/P ratio of 1.2. As described previously (4) this diet lacked vitamin D. This diet, with added calciferol, was given to each animal in the vitamin D group at a level of 5 IU per day.

The experiment lasted 16 months. Six animals from each group were killed at 4, 5, 13 and 16 months, respectively, after having been studied according to the method of Aubert and Milhaud, using Sr^{85} (5). Bone samples from the tibia, femur, scapula, axis and parietal bone were removed and cleaned, and their radioactivity was measured.

Results. Throughout the experiment, the control animals showed hypocalcemia (Table 1). The striking feature is the relationship of the three main parameters: the pool and the mass of fixed calcium in the bone (V_o^+) and the mass of free calcium in the bone (V_o^-) decreased with increasing age in the vitamin D group while they increased with age in the controls. Similar inverse variations were observed in connection with the ability to retain Sr^{85}.

In general, the pool, V_o^+ and V_o^- values show an increase with age in the control group. For example, in this group the pool values ranged between 40 and 52 mg/day in the four-month-old animals and between 96 and 168 mg/day in the 16-month-old animals. The values were different in the vitamin D group where they ranged between 53 and 68 mg/day, and between 30 and 41 mg/day, respectively.

The data from control group rats seem to indicate morphological differences; the data from the group whose pools and V_o^+ are raised were also those showing the most marked bone deformations.

It has been demonstrated using Ca^{47} that the use of Sr^{85} provides a good indication of the functional nature in the two groups of animals. Thus, using the two isotopes, we can confirm certain variations in V_o^+ values and in radio-element fixation in bone.

Discussion. Sr^{85} fixation clearly shows functional differences between the two groups of rats studied. In those rats receiving the vitamin D diet a strong reduction of bone fixation with age is observed. However, in animals on a vitamin D deficient diet, there is a very steep immediate rise in fixation which persists. The V_o^+ decreases with age in a manner similar to Sr^{85} fixation for rats given vitamin D. But this does not apply to the animals on the vitamin D deficient diet; in the young ones with low Vo$^+$ values, the lower vitamin D values do not correspond to the degree of Sr^{85} retention. On the other hand, in the mature control rats there is good agreement between high Vo$^+$ values and Sr^{85} fixation.

Studies are now in progress to determine the significance of this disagreement between a low Vo$^+$ and a significant Sr^{85} retention in young vitamin D deficient rats. Nevertheless, it seems more likely that the exchanges are increased (those which delay a high Vo$^+$ value) in addition to an ability to fix Sr^{85} as is indicated by a high hydroxyprolinuria (3).

Other studies are also in progress to establish the relationship between the functions in the deficient animals which, when they mature, show all the signs of an elevated alkaline earth exchange and among them are a number which also show significant bone deformation.

REFERENCES

1. Dupuis Y. *CR Acad Sci* [D] (*Paris*) **267**: 2181, 1968.
2. Dupuis Y and Gambier J. *CR Acad Sci* [D] (*Paris*) **269**: 1997, 1969.
3. Dupuis Y and Digaud A. *J Physiol* (*Paris*) (in press).
4. Dupuis Y. *CR Acad Sci* [D] (*Paris*) **251**: 2587, 1960.
5. Aubert JP and Milhaud G. *Biochim Biophys Acta* **39**: 122, 1960.

VITAMIN D METABOLISM IN EXPERIMENTAL UREMIA

D. VON HERRATH, H.-U. KOCH, A. OPITZ and K. SCHAEFER

Artificial Kidney Unit, Klinikum Steglitz der F.U., Berlin, German Federal Republic

In the last five years it has been established that vitamin D$_3$ (cholecalciferol) needs to be metabolized into active forms in order to yield its biologic effects (1). One active metabolite was identified as 25-hydroxycholecalciferol (2) but in recent publications a more polar metabolite, introduced as peak V (3), peak IVb (4) and peak P (5) was claimed to possess even higher biological activity as far as the intestinal transport of calcium is concerned. The role of vitamin D and its metabolic fate in uremic bone disease is not yet fully understood. Since the results published on this subject are contradictory (6–8) we have carried out more investigations in this field with special regard to the long-term metabolism of vitamin D in experimental uremia.

Methods. Wistar rats (average weight 150 g), kept on a normal diet, were divided into two groups, A and B. The animals of group A were subjected to a five/sixths nephrectomy. Three weeks later, when the urea in the plasma of this group had reached constant levels of 74.1 $\pm$ 14.2 mg/100 ml (group B 37.0 $\pm$ 7.8 mg/100 ml; $P < 0.001$) the animals of both groups received an intacardiac injection of 0.11 µc 1,2-H^3-vitamin D dissolved in 0.1 ml of Intralipid$^{®}$. Three, seven, 10, 14 and 21 days later the rats were decapitated, blood was collected and liver, bone, muscle and intestinal mucosa were removed. Mawer and Backhouse's (9) technique was used to prepare the serum and the organs. The resulting chloroform extracts were chromatographed on silicic acid columns using increasing proportions of ether in hexane and methanol in ether as eluants. The eluted fractions were monitored for radioactivity by liquid scintillation counting.

Results and conclusions. In contrast to results of others (6, 10) we found no difference in the metabolism of tritiated vitamin D between normal and uremic rats. At all periods the distribution of unaltered vitamin D_3 and its metabolites (25-hydroxycholecalciferol, peak V, peak VI, peak VII) was similar for both groups. In particular, there was no accelerated turn-over in uremia. These identical results were obtained not only in the serum but also in all the organs investigated. In addition, the incorporated total radioactivity did not show any difference between the two groups.

An interesting finding was that we were not able to demonstrate very high concentrations of peak V in the intestinal mucosa and bone in either group A or group B.

Studies are now in progress to see whether or not different labeling, for example C^{14}-vitamin D_3, or different vitamin status may play a role. However, our results suggest that a disorder in vitamin D metabolism is not responsible for the development of the so-called vitamin D resistance in azotemic osteodystrophy.

Supported by the Deutsche Forschungsgemeinschaft.

REFERENCES

1. LUND J and DeLuca HF. *J Lipid Res* **7**: 739, 1966.
2. BLUNT JW, DeLuca HF and Schnoes HK. *Biochemistry* **7**: 3317, 1968.
3. MAWER EB, LUMB GA and Stanbury SW. *Nature (London)* **222**: 482, 1969.
4. MYRTLE JF, HAUSSLER MR and NORMAN AW. *J Biol Chem* **245**: 1190, 1970.
5. LAWSON DEM, WILSON PW and KODICECK E. *Biochem J* **115**: 269, 1969.
6. AVIOLI LV, BIRGE S, LEE SW and SLATOPOLSKY E. *J Clin Invest* **47**: 2239, 1968.
7. BAERG RD, KIMBERG DV and GERSHON E. *J Clin Invest* **49**: 1288, 1970.
8. VON HERRATH D, OPITZ A, KOCH H-U, KNOOP H and SCHAEFER K. *Klin Wschr* (in press).
9. MAWER EB and BACKHOUSE J. *Biochem J* **112**: 255, 1969.
10. AVIOLI LV, BIRGE SJ and SLATOPOLSKY E. *Arch Intern Med (Chicago)* **124**: 451, 1969.

THERAPEUTIC STUDIES IN VITAMIN D REFRACTORY RICKETS

REPORT OF FOUR CASES

P. LAPATSANIS, K. ATHANASIADOU-DANELATOU and J. KARPOUZAS

Paediatric Clinic of Athens University and Institute of Child Health, Athens Greece

Hypophosphatemic vitamin D refractory rickets is a rare disease which can be beneficially treated by very large doses of vitamin D. There is, however, a risk of nephrotoxic effects during the course of this treatment. This report discusses the clinical, radiological and biochemical findings in four children suffering from vitamin D refractory rickets, who were treated orally with vitamin D and sodium phosphate (PO_4), in order to assess the therapeutic and toxic effects of long-term treatment with vitamin D.

The findings in our four cases are given in Tables 1 and 2, and compared with those in previously reported cases.

Evidence of a good response to the treatment was the increase in the children's height (Cases 1 and 3) and some decrease in knee distance. Radiological improvement was noticed in two of the four patients (Cases 1 and 3). The daily dosage of vitamin D was rather small in comparison to that reported in the literature (26,000 IU in Cases 1 and 3, and 35,000 IU in Cases 2 and 4).

Sodium phosphate was given to two patients from the beginning of treatment,

TABLE 1. *Clinical and radiological findings at the beginning of and during treatment*

| | Height (percentile) | | X-ray findings | | Treatment | | | |
| | | | | | Vitamin D supplement IU daily | | PO⁴ mg/day (as inorganic P) | |
Case	Before treatment	After treatment	Before treatment	After treatment	Dose	Duration (months)	Dose	Duration (months)
1	25	50	+	Almost healed	26,000	9	900	9
2	< 3	< 3	+	+	26,000	6	900	6
3	$< 3^a$	3	$+^a$	Improved	26,000	6	900	6
4	10	10	+	+	26,000	9	900	5
48 patients in the literature (1–7)	Short stature	Improved	+	Improved	30,000 to 100,000		Given in 13 of the 48 patients	

a In (Case 3) 60,000 IU of vitamin D supplement were administered daily for twelve months prior to the beginning of the present treatment.

TABLE 2. *Biochemical findings at the beginning of and during treatment*

| | Serum alkaline phosphatase (King-Armstrong units) | | Aminoaciduria column chromatography (mg/kg per day) | | Ca balance | | P balance | |
Case	Before treatment	After treatment	Before treatment	After treatment	Before treatment	After treatment	Before treatment	After treatment
1	22	25 (1)	9	3.8	+	+	—	+
2	22	28 (4)	6.5	5.5	—	—	—	—
3	20	27 (1)	Not done		—	+	—	+
4	16	26 (3)	7.2	5.7	—	—	—	—
48 patients in the literature (1–7)	A variable increase in 3 patients		Not reported		—	+	—	+

Numbers in parentheses correspond to the interval period in months.

and to the other two patients, four and 12 months, respectively, after the start of vitamin D.

The beneficial effect of sodium phosphate in the treatment of rickets has recently been reported. No improvement was found for twelve months in the third child who received 60,000 IU daily of only vitamin D. The addition of PO_4 resulted in a marked improvement even when only 26,000 IU of vitamin D were given daily. No increase in serum phosphorus was seen.

A small increase of the serum alkaline phosphatase was noticed after the commencement of treatment in our patients (Table 2). Smith and Dick (7) had noticed a similar increase in a patient with nutritional rickets. This finding can be considered a good sign of therapeutic response. A mild aminoaciduria was detected in only two patients on paper chromatography. On column chromatography, a definite amino-aciduria was found in three patients (Cases 1, 2 and 4), and in one child (Case 1) the aminoaciduria decreased to normal limits when marked clinical, biochemical and radiological improvement

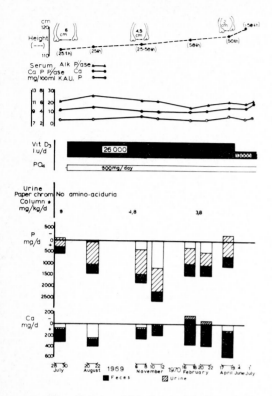

FIG. 1. The clinical and biochemical findings during the course of the treatment in one patient (case 1).

appeared (Table 2). Absence of, or mild, aminoaciduria has been reported in this type of rickets.

Calcium and phosphorus balances became positive or markedly improved in two patients (Cases 1 and 3), who showed clinical and radiological improvement. Patients 2 and 4, in whom neither clinical nor radiological improvement was noticed, continued with constant negative balances (Table 2).

In Case 1 the change of calcium and phosphorus balances from positive to negative during the six months of treatment led us to suspect hypervitaminosis D, a suspicion supported by the fact that there was radiological improvement, that the serum alkaline phosphatase was normal and that the serum calcium rose to just over 10 mg/100 ml (Fig. 1). Jackson (2) reported negative calcium balance with calciuria, followed by a positive calcium balance with increase of serum calcium after the administration of a very large daily dosage of vitamin D in a normal adult. The same author reported that in the normal adult, a large dosage of vitamin D produces an increased excretion of phosphorus in the urine. Therefore the repeated calcium and phosphorus balances seem to give useful information concerning: 1) the progress of the disease, 2) the necessary daily dose of vitamin D, and 3) an early evidence of hypervitaminosis D. Dent and Harris (8) pointed out that the resistance to vitamin D influences only the therapeutic effect of the vitamin D and not its toxic effects. Our last observation must be confirmed in other cases. It is a very important issue in the treatment of patients with vitamin D refractory rickets.

Finally, from this number of patients it is obvious that the necessary daily dosage of vitamin D varies in individual cases and needs careful follow-up to prevent, as far as possible, the toxic effects of vitamin D.

REFERENCES

1. FANCONI G. *Advances Pediat* **12**: 314, 1962.
2. JACKSON WPU. *Symp in Commemoration of 60th Anniversary of Nutricia, 1961*, p 49.
3. MENKING M and SOTOS JF. *J Pediat* **75**: 1001, 1969.
4. MONCRIEFF MW and CHANCE GW. *Arch Dis Child* **44**: 571, 1969.
5. ROSE GA. *Brit Med J* **2**: 857, 1964.
6. SAVILLE PD, NASSIM JR, STEVENSON FH, MULLIGAN L and CAREY M. *Clin Sci* **14**: 489, 1955.
7. SMITH R and DICK M. *Clin Sci* **35**: 575, 1968.
8. DENT CE and HARRIS H. *J Bone Joint Surg* **38**B: 204, 1956.

TRANSPLACENTAL EFFECTS OF CORTISONE AND VITAMIN D$_2$ ON THE OSTEOGENESIS AND OSSIFICATION OF FETAL LONG BONES IN RATS

A. ORNOY

Department of Embryology and Teratology, Tel Aviv University Medical School,
Government Hospital, Tel-Hashomer, Israel

High doses of corticosteroids are known to induce several bone changes. Among the most prominent are increased bone resorption and demineralization causing osteoporosis, slowing down or cessation of bone growth, and changes in the ground substance of cartilage and bone (1–3). In growing rats with balanced dietary intake of calcium and phosphorus, dense bone is formed in the metaphysis consisting of chondrocytes, unresorbed mineralized cartilage matrix and superinduced lamellar bone (4, 5).

Cortisone is known to affect fetal development, causing anomalies (especially cleft palate) in certain strains of mice (6) and in rats (7, 8). High doses of vitamin D$_2$ have also been found to affect fetal growth and osteogenesis (9). On the other hand, corticosteroids have certain effects which are antagonistic to those of hypervitaminosis D (10). The purpose of the present investigation was to study the transplacental effect of maternal hypercortisonism and hypervitaminosis D$_2$ on fetal osteogenesis and ossification of long bones.

Materials and methods. Thirty-six pregnant female albino rats (Charles River strain), weighing 200 to 250 g, were divided into six groups of six rats each. Two groups received, daily, 5 or 10 mg cortisone acetate dissolved in 0.5 ml normal saline (NS) by intramuscular injection. Two other groups received the same amounts of cortisone acetate, for the same period, concomitantly with 20,000 IU of vitamin D$_2$ dissolved in 0.5 ml olive oil. The vitamin D was administered daily by intragastric intubation. Two further groups served

as controls, one receiving vitamin D$_2$ alone and the other 0.5 ml olive oil per os concomitantly with 0.5 ml NS intramuscularly. All animals were treated daily from the ninth to the 21st day of gestation, and were sacrificed on the morning of the 22nd day.

Fetal long bones were removed, fixed in acetone or Bouin's solution and embedded in paraffin. Longitudinal sections were stained with hematoxylin and eosin, azan, aldehyde fuchsin, periodic acid schiff (PAS) alcian blue, von Kossa's stain for calcium salts, and Gomori's stain for alkaline phosphatase (11).

Results. In control fetuses: The length of the diaphysis was equal to the length of the two epiphyses and the metaphyseal line was straight. Deposits of calcium salts and secretion of alkaline phosphatase were prominent in the layer of calcifying cartilage in the epiphysis. In the metaphysis, the delicate bone trabeculae, which were PAS positive and stained blue with azan or aldehyde fuchsin, had central cartilaginous cores which stained blue with alcian blue and purple with basic fuchsin. In the diaphysis most trabeculae were thin and had no central cartilaginous cores. In the longitudinal sections, 10 to 15 osteoclasts were seen, mainly in the diaphysis.

In experimental fetuses: Hypervitaminosis D$_2$ induced only minor changes in the bones. The zone of hypertrophic and calcifying cartilage in the epiphysis was narrowed. Bone trabeculae were normal except for slightly increased osteoclastic activity.

In most of the cortisone treated rats, the cartilaginous cells and ground substance in the

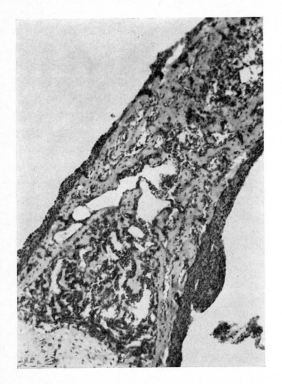

FIG. 1. Femur of experimental fetus, 22nd day of gestation. The mother received 10 mg of cortisone acetate daily during pregnancy. Note abundant wide bone trabeculae within diaphysis, and numerous preosteoblasts and osteoblasts Hematoxylin and eosin. ×52.

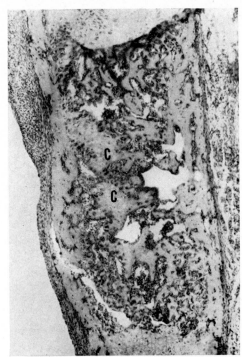

FIG. 2. Tibia of experimental fetus, 22nd day of gestation. The mother was treated with 20,000 IU of vitamin D_2 and 10 mg of cortisone acetate daily during pregnancy. Note cartilage cells (C) within the trabeculae. Hematoxylin and eosin. × 56.

epiphysis were altered. Most of the cartilage lost its typical staining properties and the width of the maturing and calcifying cartilage was reduced. However the cells secreted alkaline phosphatase and calcium salt deposits were present between them. With 10 mg cortisone, or cortisone plus vitamin D_2, the bone shaft was also shortened. The metaphyseal line was straight but normal metaphyses were practically lacking. Diaphyseal bone trabeculae had wide cores of calcified cartilage, intensely PAS positive, but staining red with azan stain. Only a thin peripheral layer of the trabeculae stained the normal blue with azan, even in trabeculae that were of membranous origin. The same trabeculae also stained red with aldehyde fuchsin. Sometimes groups of

hypertrophic cartilage cells were found in the diaphysis surrounded by a thin layer of calcified bone. Bone marrow cavities were obliterated by the persistence and fusion of bone trabeculae (Fig. 1, 2). A very large number of preosteoblasts were found, especially around bone trabeculae (Fig. 3). In the longitudinal sections, 20 to 30 osteoclasts were also found in the lacunae around bone trabeculae, near the metaphyseal lines and also near those trabeculae which surrounded the cartilage cells inside (Fig. 3). The addition of vitamin D_2 aggravated the bone changes caused by cortisone acetate. The hypertrophic and calcifying cartilage cell layer was still thinner. Little calcium was detected in this zone, and alkaline phosphatase was not se-

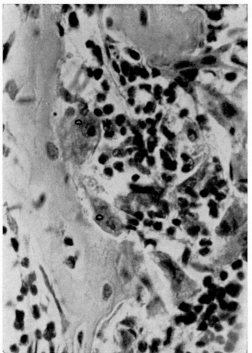

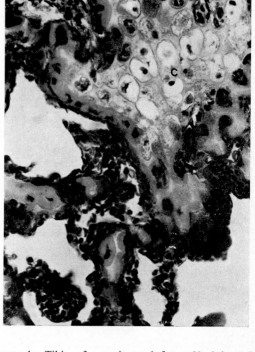

FIG. 3. Tibia of experimental fetus, 22nd day of gestation. The mother received 20,000 IU of vitamin D_2 and 5 mg of cortisone acetate daily during pregnancy. Note abundant osteoclasts (O) around bone trabeculae. Hematoxylin and eosin × 300.

FIG. 4. Tibia of experimental fetus, 22nd day of gestation. The mother received 20,000 IU of vitamin D_2 and 10 mg of cortisone acetate during pregnancy. Note abundant preosteoblasts, osteoblasts and cartilage cells (C). Hematoxylin and eosin × 200.

creted. Groups of hypertrophic cartilage cells within the diaphysis were more numerous and osteoclasts increased to 30 to 50 in the longitudinal sections of the bones (Fig. 4). As can be seen from the microscopic findings, cortisone acetate, especially in the higher doses, caused changes in the cartilage and bone ground substance, and impaired endochondral and membranous ossification. The addition of vitamin D_2 potentiated the effects of cortisone on bone, and increased osteoclastic activity.

Discussion. The observed transplacental effect of cortisone on fetal osteogenesis was similar to its effects on bone of growing rats (1, 4, 5). However, in these experiments the number of preosteoblasts and osteoblasts was not increased. On the contrary, by utilizing

tritiated thymidine, Simmons et al. (12) found that cortisone reduced the number of metaphyseal preosteoblasts and osteoblasts. It seems that embryonic bone reacts to the deleterious effects of cortisone by an attempt at compensation and self-repair, as evidenced by the increased number of bone-forming and bone-destroying elements. This may be explained by the generally increased ability for self-repair that exists in various embryonic tissues (13).

Concerning the increased number of osteoclasts, it may be that the altered bone matrix cannot be destroyed by the normal osteolytic process and so there is a compensatory increase in the number of osteoclasts. It is known that one way of measuring the activity of osteolasts is their ability to produce and release lysosomal proteolytic enzymes (14). Glucocorticosteroids are known to decrease the release of these enzymes by stabilizing lysosomal membranes (15), thus decreasing osteoclastic activity.

In previous studies, only daily doses of 40,000 IU of vitamin D_2 administered during pregnancy induced severe structural alterations of fetal bones (9). Thus it was expected that 20,000 units would cause only minor alterations. However concomitant administration of vitamin D_2 and cortisone acetate potentiated the deleterious effects of each substance. Placental alterations in rats were induced either by prednisolone (16) or vitamin D_2 (17). Thus prior placental damage by both substances may allow passage of larger amounts of vitamin D_2 or cortisone or both, causing even greater damage to fetal bones than with either substance alone.

Our results seem to indicate that cortisone and vitamin D_2 act independently on fetal bone, rather than competitively. It seems that the further increase in the number of osteoclasts induced in fetal bone by hypervitaminosis D_2, especially when administered concomitantly with cortisone, may be related to the bone demineralizing action of the vitamin.

REFERENCES

1. STOREY E. *Clin Orthop* **30**: 197, 1963.
2. BERNICK S and ERSHOFF BH. *Endocrinology* **72**: 231, 1963.
3. BERNSTEIN E. *Acta Pharmacol (Kobenhavn)* **26**: 413, 1968.
4. FOLLIS RH JR. *Proc Soc Exp Biol Med* **76**: 722, 1951.
5. HULTH A and OLERUD S. *Brit J Exp Path* **44**: 491, 1963.
6. EVANS HJ and CLINGEN G. *Anat Rec* **205**: 624, 1953.
7. CSABA G, TORA I and FISHER J. *Acta Paediat* **8**: 217, 1967.
8. HANSON CG and ANGERVALL L. *Acta Endocr (Kobenhavn)* **53**: 547, 1960.
9. ORNOY A, NEBEL L and MENCZEL J. *Arch Path (Chicago)* **87**: 563, 1969.
10. CRUICKSHANK EM and KODICECK E. *J Endocr* **63**: 57, 1958.
11. LILLIE RD. "Histopathologic technic and practical histochemistry," 3rd edn. New York, McGraw-Hill Book Co., 1965, Chap 14, 15.
12. SIMMONS DJ and KUNNIN AS. *Clin Orthop* **55**: 201, 1967.
13. WILLIS RA. "The borderland of embryology and pathology," 2nd edn. London, Butterworths, 1962, Chap 4, 6, 13.
14. VAES, G. *Exp Cell Res* **39**: 470, 1965.
15. DINGLE JT, FELL HB and LUCY JA. *Biochem J* **98**: 173, 1966.
16. BLACKBURN WR, KAPLAN HS and MCKAY DG. *Amer J Obstet Gynec* **92**: 234, 1965.
17. POTVLIEGE PR. *Arch Path* **73**: 371, 1962.

AUTHOR INDEX